DETROIT PUBLIC LIBRARY

3 5674 00988377 9

D1172750

On Stage For Teen-Agers

ON STAGE
for
TEEN-AGERS

*An Anthology of Non-Royalty
One-Act Comedies*

By

HELEN LOUISE MILLER

Boston

PLAYS, INC.

Publishers

J808.2 M618o
C.12

COPYRIGHT 1948

BY HELEN LOUISE MILLER

Reprinted, 1960
Reprinted, 1967

NO ROYALTY NEED BE PAID BY SCHOOLS, CLUBS, OR
SIMILAR AMATEUR GROUPS FOR STAGE PERFORMANCES
OF THESE PLAYS. APPLICATIONS FOR PROFESSIONAL
OR RADIO USE SHOULD BE ADDRESSED TO THE AUTHOR
IN CARE OF PLAYS, INC., 8 ARLINGTON STREET,
BOSTON 16, MASS.

PRINTED IN THE UNITED STATES OF AMERICA

FEB '79
CL

FOREWORD

The plays in this collection are the result of years of working, on stage and off, with teen-age boys and girls. Many of the plots and a great deal of the dialogue have been supplied, unconsciously, by the boys and girls themselves—which accounts, in part, for the popularity they have enjoyed with high school actors and high school audiences. The parts have been created with a view to easy type-casting and every effort has been made to render them comprehensible to the young actors and actresses who portray them. In the general comedies the leading characters are the kind of people most teen-timers long to be. Their adventures, problems and reactions are within the realm of actual teen-age experience. Although the characters and situations are based on adolescent traits and foibles peculiar to this age, these qualities have not been over-emphasized or exaggerated. No adolescent character is ever made to appear mawkish, abnormally awkward, shy or unconvincingly ludicrous.

The holiday plays, especially those commemorating historical holidays, are written for modern stage settings to overcome the difficulties of casting and costuming that arise in representing historical figures.

Appearing originally in the monthly issues of PLAYS, *The Drama Magazine For Young People,* all of the plays in this collection have been produced on stage by teen-agers in schools, recreation centres, clubs and churches throughout the country. Their success can be measured, not only from the standpoint of audience appeal, but also from a production angle. When boys and girls like and understand the roles assigned to them, memorization and rehearsals cease to be drudgery, and production becomes a pleasure for all concerned. One of the surest tests of a play is with the cast itself. If the actors can still enjoy the situations and find amusement in the lines, after hours of rehearsal, the play has more than a fair chance with the audience.

It is with the hope that directors, actors and audiences will find ON STAGE FOR TEEN-AGERS a source of pleasurable and profitable entertainment, that these plays have been assembled in book form.

Helen Louise Miller

CONTENTS

General Comedies

Holiday Comedies

On Stage For Teen-Agers

PARTY LINE

Characters

MR. AND MRS. FAIRCHILD
JUNIOR FAIRCHILD
KITTY FAIRCHILD
SCOTTY FAIRCHILD
POLLY KEEFER
REPAIR MAN

SCENE: *The living room of the Fairchild home.*

TIME: *The present.*

PARTY LINE

SETTING: *The living room of the* FAIRCHILD *home.*

AT RISE: *A victrola is playing a waltz.* KITTY, *the youngest Fairchild daughter, is dancing around the living room with an imaginary partner. Her eyes are half closed in an expression of bliss, and she holds her head to one side as if resting her cheek on her partner's shoulder.*

KITTY (*To her invisible partner*): Oh, Melvin, you dance divinely. Fred Astaire could learn plenty from you. Really, it's so easy to follow you that it's just like floating on a cloud. (*Laughing softly*)Oh, you're teasing me! I'm not such a wonderful dancer. It's just that I adore dancing with a tall man, and you're exactly the right height. (*Pause*) Oh, thank you. I'm so glad you like my dress. It's really nothing at all but it's the best I could find in town. You know our local shops are so limited in their selections! It's a problem to get something really smart. But I was lucky to get blue. Everybody says blue is my color.

JUNIOR (*Entering in time to hear the last of* KITTY's *monologue*): For Pete's sake! What goes on?

KITTY (*Whirling around in surprise*): Junior Fairchild! What are you doing home so early? Get out of here, and fast!

JUNIOR: Like fun! What are you doing anyhow? (*Peering about the room*) And who's in here with you — Kilroy?

KITTY: Don't be silly. There's no one here.

JUNIOR: Don't tell me you were dishing out that line to yourself.

3

KITTY: Oh, you wouldn't understand. I was just sort of — sort of rehearsing for Saturday night.

JUNIOR: Are you in another play?

KITTY: No.

JUNIOR: Then why the rehearsal? I don't get it.

KITTY: I told you you wouldn't understand. There's a dance at the Junior Country Club.

JUNIOR: Oho! Comes the dawn! Now I catch a glimmer. Who's your date?

KITTY: I'm not telling!

JUNIOR: As if I didn't know! It's good old Melvin.

KITTY: Oh, Junior! Do you really think he might? Honestly, do you?

JUNIOR: Gosh, how do I know? Hasn't he asked you yet?

KITTY: Oh, that's it. Most of the girls are getting their own dates, but I'm simply petrified to call him.

JUNIOR: What's to be scared of? He'll either say yes or no.

KITTY: But you see, Melvin's sort of a personality up at school. And, well, I might as well admit it, I just don't have the nerve to call him.

JUNIOR: Nerve! First time I ever knew you to be short on nerve. That was always your long suit.

KITTY: I know, but honest, Junior, this time I'm sunk.

JUNIOR: Why?

KITTY: I don't know what to say.

JUNIOR (*In disgust*): Just call him up and ask him.

KITTY: I know, but every time I start for the phone, my throat closes up and I break out in goose bumps. I don't know how to begin.

JUNIOR: Just say — "How's about a date for Saturday night, Chum?"

KITTY: Heavens, Junior! That's too blunt. I could never say that. What would he think of me?

JUNIOR: He'd probably catch on to the fact that you want to go to this dance.

KITTY: Oh, dear, can't you see I must be more subtle? I must have some clever approach, and then just the right build-up, so he'll catch on and invite me before I have to break down and ask him.

JUNIOR: I give up! I thought that's what you wanted...to ask him to this dance.

KITTY: I do, but...Oh, Junior, couldn't you be a sweet lamb and ask him for me?

JUNIOR: Me? Heck no! Why should I ask him?

KITTY: Because you know each other and he'd probably go if he knew you were going, too.

JUNIOR: But I'm not.

KITTY: Oh, yes, you are.

JUNIOR: Oh, no, I'm not.

KITTY: You are!

JUNIOR: I'm not!

KITTY: You are so! Polly Keefer is on your trail, and you know Polly always gets her man.

JUNIOR: Not this man! Huh-Uh! Not your Uncle Junior! I'm too cagey a bird to be caught by that scrawny little scarecrow. When I go dancing, it's gotta be with somebody strictly G.I.

KITTY: G.I.? What's that?

JUNIOR: *Glamorous Issue,* which Polly Keefer very definitely is not!

KITTY: Very well, Master Mind. Let's see you get out of it! Remember, she's been doing your library references for weeks now.

JUNIOR: Oh, sure, but...

KITTY: And what about that speech she wrote for you when you were running for Safety Commissioner?

JUNIOR: Oh, well, that was different.

KITTY: Sure. And so is the Athletic Association Ticket Drive that's starting next week. That will be different too without Polly selling tickets for your team.

JUNIOR: Hey, wait a minute! Is this blackmail?

KITTY: Not exactly, but Polly Keefer is the champion ticket salesman in school. You can't win the ticket contest without her.

JUNIOR: Gee, whiz! Do you think she'd quit just because...

KITTY: I do. If you turn Polly down on this dance, she'll turn you down so flat on that ticket drive that you'll never know what hit you.

JUNIOR: Holy smokes! Why this is serious! What'll I do? Polly's a swell kid at ticket sales but when it comes to dancing, she has two left feet.

KITTY: You should care about two left feet when you can't even tell a waltz from a rhumba.

JUNIOR: But I care plenty about this. Look here, Kitty, you'll have to help me out of this.

KITTY: Who? Me? What could I do?

JUNIOR: Well, tell her I'm all tied up. Tell her I'm busy. Tell her I'm a terrible dancer. Say I'm absolute poison.

KITTY: You can tell her all that yourself when she calls you, which she is going to do this evening.

JUNIOR: Aw, Kitty, have a heart. You know me on the phone. I get all tongue-tied. (*Phone rings*) Oh, Boy! I bet that's Polly. Answer it, Kitty, please, and if it's for me, tell her I just left for Kalamazoo.

KITTY: You do your own fibbing. I have enough on my conscience as it is.

JUNIOR: Oh, be a sport, Sis. Get rid of her. Make up some sort of excuse. After all, blood is thicker than water.

KITTY (*As phone rings again*): One good turn deserves another, Junior.

JUNIOR: Why must you stand there and quibble at a time like this?

KITTY: Will you call Melvin for me?

JUNIOR: O.K. You win. I'll even hop over to his house and try to land him for you; but for Pete's sake, answer that phone. (*Exit*)

KITTY (*At phone*): Hello...Hello...Hello. Well, that's funny. There's nobody on the line. Oh, well, I guess whoever it was will call again. Maybe it wasn't Polly after all. Poor Junior! He's shaking in his shoes at the idea of taking her to the party. Here's hoping he fixes everything up with Melvin. (*Puts on record and starts dancing again*) Melvin is such an unusual name...so different...so distinguished. Mel...vin. ...I love to say it! It sounds like a song. (MR. FAIRCHILD *enters.*)

MR. FAIRCHILD: What in the world are you doing, Kitty? Turn that thing off.

KITTY (*Startled*): Heavens, Dad! You scared the life out of me.

MR. FAIRCHILD: Where's your mother?

MRS. FAIRCHILD (*Entering*): Here I am, dear. What's on your mind?

MR. FAIRCHILD (*Pulling two tickets out of his pocket*): This ...two tickets for the Club dance on Saturday night. How about a date, Mrs. F.?

Mrs. Fairchild: Why, Bill, how wonderful! We haven't gone dancing for ages. And the Club dance is such a swanky affair. I'm delighted!

Mr. Fairchild: I thought you would be, and I'm sort of tickled myself.

Kitty: Saturday night? I thought that was the Arnolds' bridge party.

Mrs. Fairchild: Oh, my goodness! You're right! Bill, we can't go!

Mr. Fairchild: Nonsense. Those tickets set me back plenty. Of course we'll go.

Mrs. Fairchild: But the Arnolds!

Mr. Fairchild: The heck with the Arnolds! You and I are going places on Saturday night.

Mrs. Fairchild: But I promised...or half promised. Mary is going to call me this evening.

Mr. Fairchild: Then tell her the deal is off. Your husband has other plans.

Kitty: Try the old headache line or the unexpected company.

Mrs. Fairchild: Kitty, you know I don't approve of telephone lies.

Kitty: I know, but, gee whiz, this is an emergency!

Mr. Fairchild: You're a girl after my own heart, Kitty. You and your mother cook up some kind of story. I'm going to take a bath. Oh, and by the way, if Jack Higgins calls, I'm out. That bird has been trying to sell me insurance for a week, but so far I've managed to keep one jump ahead of him. (*Exits.*)

Mrs. Fairchild: If Mary Arnold does call, Kitty, it might be just as well if she didn't find me in. I hate these long drawn out arguments and falsehoods. If she doesn't get me tonight, she'll probably ask someone else.

KITTY: My goodness! I might as well be a switchboard operator in this house. If the phone rings, Junior's gone to Kalamazoo, you're out, and Dad hasn't come home yet.

MRS. FAIRCHILD: It is silly, isn't it? But — (SCOTTY *bursts into the room on a run and bumps into her mother at the door*) Heavens, Scotty! Look where you're going! You almost knocked me down!

SCOTTY: Sorry, but I've run all the way home! Were there any calls for me?

KITTY: Nope, not a one.

SCOTTY: Oh, thank goodness! Mother, I'm in the most awful mess! Two boys asked me to the Junior Country Club Dance on Saturday, and before I knew it, I had accepted both of them!

MRS. FAIRCHILD: Scotty! What an awful thing to do!

KITTY: Don't tell me you're walking out on poor, loyal, long-suffering Wayne Crawford?

SCOTTY: Of course not! But we had a fight, and I thought it would be smart to go with somebody else for a change. So when the other guy asked me, I said yes. But then Wayne and I made up, and of course I have to go with him.

KITTY: So what are you going to tell your No. 1 Dope?

SCOTTY: I've already called him, but thank goodness he wasn't home; so I just left the message with his mother.

MRS. FAIRCHILD: These poor mothers! What excuse did you give?

SCOTTY: None! I didn't have to. But heaven help me when he gets home! He'll be calling me for an explanation.

KITTY: Of which you are fresh out.

SCOTTY: Well, natch! I can't very well tell him I've given him the brush-off for Wayne. So, Kitty, dear, if he calls just tell him —

KITTY: Sure, I know. Just tell him you've gone South for the winter. This family has too much social life, if you ask me.

SCOTTY: Oh, well, Kitty, you'll understand how it is when you get a little older.

KITTY: Older! Listen, you, I'm old enough now to be the trouble shooter for this whole family. You're all scared to answer the phone. (*Phone rings.*)

SCOTTY: There he is! Kitty, do your stuff! Say I'm not in!

MRS. FAIRCHILD: Oh, dear, if that's Mary Arnold I just don't know what to tell her at this late date!

MR. FAIRCHILD (*Off stage*): If that's Higgins, tell him he has the wrong number!

KITTY: It's a good thing you have me around here to do all the dirty work. (*At phone*) Hello! Fairchild residence. Hello! (JUNIOR *bursts in.*)

JUNIOR: Hey, be careful what you say if that call's for me!

KITTY (*Almost dropping the phone*): Oh, Junior, see what you made me do! Hello! Hello! Now the connection is broken, and we don't know who called.

MRS. FAIRCHILD: Maybe it's just as well. Come on, Scotty, I want you to help me look over my clothes. Your father and I are stepping out Saturday night.

KITTY: If the Arnolds don't get you first!

SCOTTY (*As she and* MOTHER *exit*): I'm counting on you, Kitty. You can always think of something to say.

KITTY: Oh, Junior, how did you make out? Was Melvin at home?

JUNIOR: Yes, he was there, and I have him all wrapped up in cellophane for Saturday night.

KITTY: Oh, Junior, you're wonderful! How did you do it?

JUNIOR: Oh, it was easy. He seemed tickled to death.

KITTY: He did! Oh, Junior, I could hug you! I hope you didn't make me sound too anxious!

JUNIOR: Not at all. I was very tactful about the whole thing. He said he'd call you this evening and find out all the details.

KITTY: Oh, boy! That's simply super-duper! Junior, you're a swell fixer! Oh, it will be heavenly to go to the dance with Melvin! Do you think his dad will let him have the car?

JUNIOR: Car? What car? The Martins don't even have a car!

KITTY (*Stunned*): Martins! Martins! What do they have to do with it?

JUNIOR: Well, you know as well as I do that Mr. Martin rides to work with Pop every morning.

KITTY: Junior Fairchild! You don't mean to tell me you asked that little Pipsqueak Martin to go to that dance!

JUNIOR: Pipsqueak! What a nickname for Melvin!

KITTY: Oh, no! This couldn't happen to me!

JUNIOR: What's all the uproar? *I only did what you asked me. I've got Melvin Martin lined up as your Saturday night date.

KITTY: Oh, Junior! How could you? I despise Melvin Martin! He's nothing but a sawed-off, little hammered-down runt! How could you make such a mistake! It was Melvin Thomas I wanted. (*Starts to cry*) Now you've ruined my whole life! Absolutely ruined it! I wouldn't be caught dead with old Pipsqueak Martin!

JUNIOR: Well, gee whiz! How was I supposed to know it was Melvin Thomas! (*Laughs*) Gosh! That's a funny one!

KITTY (*Still crying*): Funny! There's nothing funny about it! It's terrible! Perfectly terrible! Didn't I tell you Melvin was a personality?

JUNIOR: Well, so's Pip — er — I mean Melvin Martin!

KITTY: He's no personality! He's a character! Oh, dear, I

wish I was dead! And I *would* die rather than go with that horrid little boy!

JUNIOR: But you'll have to go now. I've already hooked him.

KITTY: Then you can unhook him! And right now! I'm not going, and that's flat! (*Phone*)

JUNIOR: Oh, boy! That'll be Melvin!

KITTY: Then let it ring!

JUNIOR: We can't do that. Go ahead and answer it!

KITTY: Not on your life! You got me into this, and you can just get me out of it. Answer it yourself! (*Phone rings insistently.*)

JUNIOR: But what if it's Polly?

KITTY: You're good at thinking up answers. Think fast and answer that phone.

JUNIOR: Oh, all right! (*Loses nerve*) But gosh! I don't know what to say!

KITTY: "Hello" will do for a start!

JUNIOR: O.K.! Here goes! (*Grabs phone and yells*) Hello! (*Pause*) Too late! They hung up.

SCOTTY: Was that for me?

JUNIOR: I don't know. They hung up.

SCOTTY: With two of you right here in this room, it seems to me you could answer the phone.

JUNIOR: Yeah! But she won't answer it!

SCOTTY: Then what's wrong with you? You're no cripple!

MRS. FAIRCHILD (*Enters*): I thought I heard the phone.

SCOTTY: You did, but these two dopes just let it ring.

MRS. FAIRCHILD: Oh, dear, I bet it was Mary Arnold.

SCOTTY: It could have been Wayne. (*Phone*)

MRS. FAIRCHILD: Answer it, somebody!

JUNIOR: Not me! Whoever it is will just mean more trouble.

SCOTTY: You're the closest, Kitty, you answer it.

KITTY: Not for a hundred dollars! As sure as I touch it it will be Pipsqueak Martin.

MRS. FAIRCHILD: Really, this is ridiculous! All of us afraid to answer the phone! Very well! I'll answer it myself! (*Starts to phone*) It might be important.

KITTY, SCOTTY, JUNIOR: If it's for me, I'm not in!

MRS. FAIRCHILD: Oh, dear, I wish I weren't "in" either. (*Phone*)

MR. FAIRCHILD (*Entering in bathrobe*): Can't somebody answer that confounded phone?

MRS. FAIRCHILD (*Relieved to hand him the phone*): Here, dear, it's probably for you!

MR. FAIRCHILD (*Takes it and then suddenly hands it back*): On second thought *you'd* better answer it. I don't want to get tied up with Jack Higgins tonight.

MRS. FAIRCHILD: This is disgraceful! We're all acting like children!

SCOTTY: I believe it's stopped ringing now.

JUNIOR: Boy, that's a relief!

KITTY (*Still sniffling*): Yeah, a relief till next time, and then it'll start all over again.

MRS. FAIRCHILD: Why, Kitty, you've been crying! What's the matter?

KITTY: It's Junior! He — (*A fresh burst of tears*) Oh, it's too awful to talk about!

MRS. FAIRCHILD: Junior, have you been teasing Kitty?

JUNIOR: Teasing her? Gosh, no! I was just getting her a date for Saturday night.

KITTY: And he got that awful little Pipsqueak Martin who doesn't come up to my shoulder.

SCOTTY: How horrible! Junior, you're a little beast! No wonder Kitty is upset!

JUNIOR (*Tearing his hair*) : This is what I get for trying to be helpful.

KITTY : And that awful little Pipsqueak Martin is going to call me any minute. Oh, dear! I'd rather die than go with him. (*Phone rings. Everybody jumps and looks accusingly at the nearest person.*)

JUNIOR : I think I'll go upstairs. (*Starts to exit.*)

MR. FAIRCHILD (*Firmly*) : Junior, you come right back here. If you got your sister into this jam, you'll have to get her out.

JUNIOR : But, gee whiz, Pop! It might be for me! You haven't heard my side of the story! (*Phone*)

MR. FAIRCHILD : There's time for that later. Right now, Duty is calling with a loud insistent ring.

JUNIOR : Oh, have a heart, Dad! That might be Polly!

SCOTTY : We might as well get it over with. Go ahead and answer it.

JUNIOR : Oh, all right... (*At phone*) Hello...Hello...This is the Fairchild residence...Who?...What?...What's that? (*Hanging up*) Aw, shucks! This phone is crazy. Whoever it was, hung up.

MR. FAIRCHILD : They'll probably call back in a few minutes and in the meantime, perhaps we can straighten this out. Just what have you done to reduce Kitty to this tearful state?

JUNIOR : I went out to get her a date and got my wires crossed.

MRS. FAIRCHILD : Explain it, Junior. Just what did you do?

JUNIOR : Well, I invited Melvin Martin instead of Melvin Thomas and that's what kicked up all the ruckus!

SCOTTY : Melvin Thomas! Melvin Thomas! Kitty, my poor, dear, sweet little sister! Is it Melvin Thomas that's causing all this heartbreak?

KITTY : Yes! I think he's marvelous and I've been trying for days to get up my nerve to ask him to our Club Dance.

SCOTTY: Well...it just goes to show you that one girl's dish is another girl's poison. Melvin Thomas happens to be my Number One Discard. If you still want him, I bet I can fix it!

KITTY: Do I want him! Oh, Scotty, lead me to him.

SCOTTY: Just let me at that phone and I'll have everything fixed in three minutes. I'll even lend you my last year's formal, if you'd like to wear it!

KITTY: Oh, Scotty, you're the most wonderful sister in the world! Do you really think he'll go with me?

SCOTTY: Sure he will, and he'll like it too. After all, Kitty, we Fairchild sisters have to stick together!

JUNIOR: Well, I'll be jiggered!

SCOTTY: (*At phone*): I'll dial him right now. (*Works at phone during following conversation.*)

MR. FAIRCHILD: Well, Junior, that seems to let you out of a very nasty jam, doesn't it?

JUNIOR: Yeah, she sure had me going there for a while.

MRS. FAIRCHILD: I only wish my problem would smooth itself out like that.

MR. FAIRCHILD: Great Heavens! Are you still stewing about the Arnolds and their bridge party? Just tell them we've made other plans.

MRS. FAIRCHILD: But, Jim, Mary Arnold would never forgive us. A bridge party is sacred to her.

JUNIOR: Oh Boy! Oh Boy! Oh Boy! This'll kill you, Moms, but I knew there was something I was supposed to tell you. I thought of it in bed last night and doggoned if it hadn't slipped my mind by morning.

MR. FAIRCHILD: Now what have you forgotten?

JUNIOR: It's about the Arnolds. I met Mrs. Arnold yesterday

after school and she told me to be sure to tell Mother that her bridge party was called off.

MRS. FAIRCHILD: Oh, Junior, that's wonderful!

MR. FAIRCHILD: See, what did I tell you? You were just making a mountain out of a molehill.

SCOTTY (*At phone*): Oh, dear, the line's busy! I do think a party line is the most aggravating thing in the world. (*Doorbell*)

MR. FAIRCHILD: I'll go. I seem to be the only one in the house with gumption enough to answer a bell when it rings.

MRS. FAIRCHILD: Not in your bathrobe, Jim! I'll go. (*Exit.*)

KITTY: Try again, Scotty. Maybe the line isn't busy any longer.

SCOTTY: I have a better idea. Run get your coat and we'll just amble down to the Nook for a soda. Maybe the boys'll be in there, and I can fix everything even better than on the phone.

KITTY: Oh, that'll be great.

SCOTTY: And wear my hat. It makes you look older.

KITTY: Gee, thanks. You come along and see if I get it on at that sophisticated angle.

SCOTTY: All right. And listen, Kitty, if this works out, we can all go together in Wayne's car...that is, if he can get it.

MRS. FAIRCHILD (*Entering with* POLLY): It's Polly Keefer, children. She just dropped in for a few minutes.

JUNIOR: If you'll excuse me, I'll take a look at the furnace.

MR. FAIRCHILD: Never mind, Junior, I fixed it right after I came home. You won't need to do anything to it till bedtime. Sit down, Polly.

POLLY: Oh, I can't stay a minute. I...er...that...is...I just stopped in to ask a question.

JUNIOR: By golly, Mother, I forgot to stop at the store for those lemons. Seeing Polly just reminded me...er...that is... I'd better get them.

MRS. FAIRCHILD: Never mind, dear. I got oranges instead. I think we can manage without them. But as you were saying, Polly, you wanted to ask a question?

POLLY: Well, yes, er...that is...are all of you going to the dance on Saturday night?

SCOTTY and KITTY: Yes, we are.

POLLY: Well, I wondered, if you'd care if we'd join you?

KITTY: Who?

POLLY: My date and I.

JUNIOR: Gee, do you have a date?

POLLY: Yes, you see...well, I *was* going to ask somebody else (*Looks at* JUNIOR *who shuffles around in embarrassment*) but at the last minute I decided to ask Melvin Martin!

KITTY: Melvin Martin!

POLLY: Yes, and it was the funniest thing! When I first asked him he stammered around about having some sort of date with you! Imagine! But I soon straightened him out on that score, and we're going together. I just thought you might have room for us.

KITTY: Oh, sure, sure! That'll be all right, won't it, Scotty?

SCOTTY: Why, yes, I guess so....Sure, we'll pick you up about eight, Polly.

POLLY: Gee, thanks a lot. That's swell. Well, I must be going. So long, everybody.

ALL: So long, Polly.

JUNIOR: Oh, Brother! Am I relieved!

MR. FAIRCHILD: So that was the other side of the story, was it, Son?

JUNIOR: That was it. Now I won't have a chill every time the phone rings.

KITTY: Nor I.

SCOTTY: Nor I.

MRS. FAIRCHILD: I must admit I'll be more comfortable myself. (*Doorbell*)

MR. FAIRCHILD: Now the only person that could possibly be would be Jack Higgins. (*Starts to go out.*) You can just tell him I've gone to bed with a bad cold.

JUNIOR: Gee whiz, Dad, don't start that all over again. From now on, I'm going to answer all the phones and doorbells in the house. I'll get it.

KITTY: We were silly, weren't we? All of us scared to answer the phone.

MRS. FAIRCHILD: It's easy to talk now that the danger is over

JUNIOR (*At door*): Sure, sure, come right in, but we hadn't noticed anything wrong. (TELEPHONE REPAIR MAN *enters carrying a box of tools.*)

REPAIR MAN: We've just had several reports that this phone is out of order.

ALL: What?

REPAIR MAN: We'll soon find out. The operator has been testing all afternoon, but nobody answers.

JUNIOR: Can you beat it?

MR. FAIRCHILD: Well, er ... it was mighty kind of you to look into the matter so quickly.

MRS. FAIRCHILD: I always say ... there's nothing like a telephone.

REPAIR MAN (*At phone. Dials and says*): Trouble Operator, please call 4 ... 6 ... 7 ... 8 ... 1. (*Hangs up*) We'll soon see if it is O.K. (*Phone rings.*) Very well, Operator. Everything seems to be satisfactory here. (*To* FAIRCHILDS) That does it.

MRS. FAIRCHILD: Thanks ever so much.

MR. FAIRCHILD: Mighty fine service you have here.

REPAIR MAN: We try to do our best, but the way some of these dumb clucks use a telephone sometimes get you down. (*All laugh in a self-conscious way.*)

MR. FAIRCHILD: Yes, I can imagine. Well, good day, sir.

REPAIR MAN: So long. Just report any further trouble and we'll fix you up.

MR. FAIRCHILD: Thank you.

MRS. FAIRCHILD: I'll show you out. (*Exit.*)

KITTY: Well, blow me down!

SCOTTY: This takes the cake!

MR. FAIRCHILD: It just goes to show you ... (*Phone rings. All make a wild dash for it, insisting "I'll get it!" "That must be for me!" "I'll answer." "Give it to me." "I'll take it.' as the curtain closes.*)

THE END

PRODUCTION NOTES

PARTY LINE

Characters: 3 male; 4 female.

Playing Time: 30 minutes.

Costumes: Everyday modern dress. **Mr.** Fairchild wears a bathrobe in his second entrance.

Properties: Two tickets, a box of tools.

Setting: A modern American living room, comfortably furnished. A small table holding a victrola and records stands against back wall. A small telephone table with telephone on it stands against right wall.

Lighting: None required.

PIN-UP PALS

Characters

SANDY, *President of the Pin-Up Pals.*
RAE, *Secretary.*
MARTHA, *an objector.*
JAN
KAREN } *candidates for membership.*
OTHER MEMBERS

SCENE: *The club room of the Pin-Up Pals.*

TIME: *The present.*

PIN-UP PALS

SETTING: *The club room of the Pin-Up Pals, an organization of teen-agers, in the throes of hero worship. The room is decorated with large pictures of male screen and radio stars, the most prominent of which are Frank Sinatra and Van Johnson, holding the place of honor over the Speaker's table. These two pictures, identical in size, are decorated with sprays of evergreen.*

AT RISE: SANDY BLAKE *is adjusting the sprigs of green on the picture, and* RAE KING *is pasting a picture in a large scrapbook on the Speaker's table.*

SANDY: Oh, dear, this vine keeps slipping down over Frankie's left eye and gives him the most rakish look.

RAE: I was supposed to bring flowers for the decorations, but Sis threw her corsage away last night, and I couldn't get a single one. Dale won't send her flowers again until Saturday night, so I was out of luck.

SANDY: Mother thinks it's silly to decorate the boys this way, but I think it's cute.

RAE: So do I. But greens look like the aftermath of Christmas. I wish we could have had real flowers.

SANDY: Helen Davis suggested paper ones, but I said it would be sacrilege to use anything phony for Frankie and Van.

RAE: I'll say! Oh, Sandy, aren't they magnificent!

SANDY: And how! Gee, Rae, wouldn't it be super if we could go to New York or Chicago or Hollywood or somewhere

where we could see somebody like Frankie or Van or Danny Kaye in person?

RAE: Oh my, just to think of it gives me butterflies in my stomach! I honestly think I'd fold up and die if I saw Gregory Peck, or Guy Madison, or Dick Haymes in person!

SANDY: Ruth Dixon has a cousin who sat at the very next table to Joseph Cotten one time at a night club in New York. Some of his cigarette ashes actually fell on her dress when he got up to dance!

RAE: Wasn't that marvelous!

SANDY: Ruth told all about it one night at club meeting. You know she has Joe for her Pin-Up.

RAE: Yeah, I know. I was going to take him for my Pin-Up Pal, but she got him first. Anyhow, I like Bill Williams better. He's younger and has more personality. Don't you think so?

SANDY: Sure. I think he's positively dynamic! How's our Club Scrapbook coming along?

RAE: I have it up to date. Sally Brooks has one hundred and seventy-nine pictures of Danny Kaye including some when he was a baby. She's mad about him.

SANDY: I wonder who'll be the Pin-Up Men this month.

RAE: They'll never beat last month's crop. Glenn Ford, Phil Harris and Alan Ladd all in one evening.

SANDY: That was a Dream Night for sure! And Frannie Bowman read her personal letter from Robert Hutton.

RAE: I'm glad I was a charter member. It's getting so hard to choose a Pin-Up Pal now. All the good ones are taken.

SANDY: Yes, it's awful. I just wonder what Karen and Jan have decided. They don't know many movie stars.

RAE: Oh, they go to the movies all the time because it helps them with their English.

SANDY: I think they're marvelous. Gee, I've spoken English all my life and yet I only got a C on my report card!

RAE: I guess those girls have had it pretty rough. But they were lucky to get out of Austria. I heard both their parents died in concentration camps, but they don't talk about anything that happened over there.

SANDY: Wasn't it wonderful that they had an American uncle to take them in? (*Three girls enter*—MARTHA MERRILL. SALLY BROOKS *and* RUTH DIXON.)

ALL: Hy'a, kids! How's everything?

RAE: Swell. We're all set for the meeting.

SALLY: Oh, Frankie and Van look darling! I love the decorations.

SANDY: Thanks. I had a time with them.

RUTH: We came early so we could help. What's to do?

RAE: You can arrange the chairs, if you like.

RUTH and SALLY: O.K. Let's go. (*They begin to arrange folding chairs as for a meeting.*)

MARTHA: Who are the new members for tonight, Rae? I missed the last meeting.

RAE: Karen and Jan Bernstein.

MARTHA: Not those two Eager Beavers!

SANDY: Why not? They're crazy to join!

MARTHA: Crazy is right! What in the world do we want with those two museum pieces in our club? All they do is study and they're positively weird in some of the get-ups they wear to school.

RAE: Maybe we look a bit weird to them at times. That new hat of yours is enough to startle some people.

MARTHA: Don't get personal, Rae. After all, I am only interested in the welfare of the club. You forget that some of the nicest girls in town belong. How do you think their parents will feel if we start taking in riffraff?

SANDY: Who says they're riffraff?

MARTHA: Well, for heaven's sake! Look where they live! And who is their uncle anyhow?

RAE: Mr. Bernstein.

MARTHA: Natch! But where does he work? What does he do? He's janitor and handy man down at the Pine Street School.

SANDY: So what? What does that have to do with Jan and Karen joining the club? We don't have any rules about the professions of our aunts and uncles.

MARTHA: That's not the point. You know as well as I do that those girls are foreigners. Refugees! Ugh ... they might not even be clean.

RAE: Martha Merrill, you make me sick. They're as clean as you are!

MARTHA: Well, I like that!

SANDY: And they're just as good as any of us—so there!

RUTH: What's all the argument?

SALLY: Sounds like a hair-pulling match! What's up?

MARTHA: Did you girls know Karen and Jan Bernstein are joining the club tonight?

SALLY and RUTH: Sure. So what?

MARTHA: So that let's me out. If I have to associate with **girls** like that, I'm leaving!

SALLY: Oh, Martha, don't be silly. Karen and Jan are nice kids, and they're dying to do all the things the rest of us do.

RUTH: And why shouldn't they? My goodness, Martha, I had no idea you were such a snob.

MARTHA: I'm not a snob! I'm just particular about the company I keep! I've never run around with people from the South End and I don't expect to start now.

SANDY: Then why don't you go home and stay there?

MARTHA: I will and now.

RAE: Girls, girls! Let's all calm down! There's really nothing to fight about. Martha, why don't you be a sport just for this evening at least and stay through the meeting. It won't kill you to be nice to them for just one evening, will it?

MARTHA: Well, no ... but it's the principle of the thing I object to. I think our club should be strictly an exclusive organization.

RUTH: Well, let's fight it out later. It's almost eight and here come some of the gang. (*Several more girls enter and exchange greetings.*)

SALLY: Come on, Martha, sit over here by me and I'll show you my latest pictures of Danny Kaye.

MARTHA: All you think about is Danny Kaye. Don't you ever get sick of him?

SALLY: Heavens, no! I simply adore him. (*More girls arrive. There are exclamations of pleasure at sight of the decorated pictures. As girls take their places they open their pocketbooks and produce pictures of screen and radio stars and exchange them with each other. Some have movie books and radio guides which they share with each other. There is a lot of laughing and talking, during which you hear squeals of admiration and such phrases as..."Isn't he perfect?" "I'm mad about him!" "He's just out of this world!" After a few minutes,* SANDY, *the President, raps for order.*)

SANDY: The meeting will please come to order. (*Girls quiet down.*) We will have the reading of the minutes by the Secretary.

RAE: The January meeting of the Pin-Up Pal Club was held in our regular club room with an attendance of seventeen members. The new Pin-Ups were Glenn Ford presented by Maud Elliot, Phil Harris presented by Grace Lewis and Alan Ladd presented by Joan Cummings. These three girls were accepted as new members in good standing and their Pin-Up Pal pictures were added to the Club Collection. Frannie Bowman read a personal letter from her Pin-Up Pal, Robert Hutton, in which he promised to send her his latest portrait autographed with a personal message. It was decided that hereafter the large photos of the club Patrons, Frankie and Van, should always be decorated with fresh flowers or with vines for our club meetings, as a token of our everlasting esteem and affection. A new rule was also passed that no new members may be taken into the club unless their Pin-Up Pals and Pictures are unanimously accepted by the members present. After the business session the meeting was adjourned for a social hour of dancing and light refreshments served by the social committee. These minutes are respectfully submitted by your secretary, Rae King.

SANDY: Are there any omissions or corrections? (*Silence*) If not, the minutes stand approved as read. Is there any old business?

MARTHA: Since I was absent last week, I should like to ask a question about the new rule governing the acceptance of new members?

SANDY: You have the floor.

MARTHA (*She stands up.*): Do I understand that even after the club has approved a candidate for membership, she can still be disqualified if her chosen Pin-Up Pal does not meet with the approval of the group?

SANDY: That is correct.

MARTHA: That's all I wanted to know. Thank you. (*She sits down.*)

RUTH: But, Martha, you wouldn't be so mean as to ...

SANDY (*Rapping for order*): The meeting will please come to order. This evening we are to take in two new members,

Karen and Jan Bernstein, but since they have not yet arrived, we will postpone that part of the meeting until later. Is there any new business?

SUSAN: Madame President, as Chairman of the Craft Committee I would like to report that we are learning how to make lampshades. As soon as we have our samples ready we will mount any girl's Pin-Up Pal on an oiled paper shade. We're ready to take orders at the close of this meeting. We're selling them for fifty cents apiece and will turn the money over to the general treasury.

SANDY: That's wonderful, Susan, and I'm sure all the girls will want to order. Let's give Susan and her committee a round of applause for their good work. (*Applause*)

BETTY: Madame President, I have a proposal to put before the club. The other day I got the most wonderful idea for changing the name.

SANDY: But there has never been any question of changing our name, Betty. Right from the beginning when we decided to start a Fan Club, we agreed on the name "Pin-Up Pals."

BETTY: That's what gave me the idea. The initials of Pin-Up Pals, P...U...P spells *pup*. I think it would be cute to call ourselves "the pups." (*Babble of voices pro and con.*)

MARTHA: Madame President, I object. It would be most undignified.

GRACE: Madame President, I think it would be much more clever and original than just "Pin-Up Pals."

RUTH: Madame President, I think such a drastic change should be given serious thought.

SANDY: I'm inclined to agree with you, Ruth. I'll appoint Betty and Susan as a committee to interview every club member and get her reaction before next meeting. And now we are ready for a report from our Corresponding Secretary, Eunice Halleck.

Eunice: Madame President, I have the honor to report that during the past month our club has sent out seventy-nine fan letters, and received sixty-two answers, forty-five of which contained photographs which I have turned over to the Scrapbook Chairman.

Sandy: A very fine report, Eunice. (*Applause*)

Eunice: I also received a letter from a Fan Club in Los Angeles, called the "Sinatroops." They sent us a copy of their club bulletin, and their constitution and by-laws. If you would like to see them, they are also with the Scrapbook material.

Sandy: That was swell, Eunice. It's nice to keep in touch with other Fan Clubs and learn how they do things. Are there any other reports?

Grace: Madame President, I had a letter from my girl friend who used to live next door to us in Cleveland. She lives in New York now and belongs to a fan club called the "Sinatra-bugs." She told me that last week she and her gang waited three hours outside the Waldorf to see Frankie. (*Chorus of Oh's and Ah's*)

Girl: Did she really see him?

Grace: Yes, she finally saw him just as he was getting into a taxi and she says he has the most beautiful back of the head she ever saw. (*Sighs of admiration*) She promised she'd write and tell me every time she sees anybody really famous.

Sandy: Thanks a lot, Grace. I hope your friend keeps us in mind when anything exciting happens. It is now time for us to be installing our new members, but so far Karen and Jan have not arrived. I wonder what can be keeping them.

Martha: Madame President, since they think so little of the privilege of joining the Pin-Up Pals that they can't even get here on time, I move that...

RUTH: Oh, shut up, Martha. Give them a chance. You know they work after school.

MARTHA: It's a little late for an afterschool job.

RUTH: Well, they work after supper, too. They both help out at the corner grocery store, and I guess they had to work late tonight.

MARTHA: If they have to work, they shouldn't join organizations that take up so much of their time.

SANDY (*Pounding with her gavel*): Girls! This is entirely out of order. Jan and Karen were approved as candidates at our last meeting and I am sure they will be here to propose their Pin-Up Pals and to present their pictures.

MARTHA: Madame President, I might as well speak before the whole club. I disapprove of taking in these two foreigners. We have nothing in common with them, and I, for one, intend to see to it that we keep this club up to its former standards.

SANDY: There's no point in discussing this now, Martha. We voted these girls in at our last meeting. It's all sealed and settled.

MARTHA: Oh, no, it's not. You just heard our Secretary read the regulation that says no member can be admitted unless her Pin-Up Pal is approved by the group. Well, I'm telling you now, you'll have one loud dissenting voice. Mine. (*Sits down.*)

SANDY: I do hope the rest of you girls will not let Martha's prejudices influence you. Jan and Karen are nice kids. They can't help it if they're not quite like the rest of us and I think... (*As* KAREN *and* JAN *enter,* RAE *pulls* SANDY *by the skirt and directs her attention to the newcomers. They are shabbily dressed, but beaming with pleasure. They each carry a large picture wrapped in newspaper.*) Good evening, girls. We were beginning to worry about you.

JAN: Excuse, please. We work late tonight.

KAREN: We run all the way. Almost we got lost. I make the wrong turning.

SANDY: Just sit down and we will proceed with the business in our usual manner. (*Girls are seated*) Our Secretary will read your Recommendations.

RAE: Jan Bernstein and Karen Bernstein have been recommended for membership in the Newville Pin-Up Pal Club. Upon your presentation of an acceptable Pin-Up Pal to be added to our collection of Heroes and World Famous Celebrities you will be sworn into membership.

SANDY: Have you each chosen your Pin-Up Pal?

BOTH: Yes.

SANDY: And are you sure that you have chosen someone who is not already represented here?

BOTH: Yes.

SANDY: Then you may bring your pictures to the front of the room and make your presentation speeches. (*Girls move to Speaker's table carrying their pictures.*)

JAN: Begging your ladies' pardons, I would please to speak for myself and sister. She loses her English when she is frightened.

SANDY: Go right ahead and don't be nervous.

JAN: It is a great honor to join American Club. We try to live up to it in our small way. When we choose our Picture Pals, Karen and I, we think and think. We see the fine young men in the cinema. We hear the singing lovers on the radio. But still we wait. We think and think. It is so important. Last night we talk to Uncle Nathan. We explain our great need. We tell him how our Pin-Up Pal must be great, how he must be famous; how he must be loved by all people, the rich and poor and great and small. And my Uncle Nate, he knows what to do. He makes up our mind. Uncle Nate has job at school building. He takes care of all the throwing-outs. He

saves many fine things from the throwing-outs...and he
saves our Pin-Up Pals.

KAREN (*Suddenly finding her voice*) : He brings home these
pictures when teacher puts up baby pictures for kindergarten
and now they are ours...our Pin-Up Pals for keeps. (*Un-
wrapping pictures*) I present for my Pin-Up Pal...George
Washington, the Father of His Country.

JANE: And I choose for my Pin-Up Pal, Mr. Abraham Lincoln,
the sixteenth President of the United States. (*There is
silence at first, followed by a hubbub of talking.*)

SANDY: But, girls, you don't understand. Your Pin-Up Pal
must be a celebrity.

JAN: My Uncle Nate says they are the most celebrated celebrities in these United States.

KAREN: First in War, First in Peace, and First in the Hearts
of his countrymen.

SANDY: Oh, dear! How can I make you understand? A Pin-
Up Pal is somebody you positively worship.

JAN: Americans do not worship their country's heroes?

SANDY: Oh, yes, of course, they do...but...

KAREN: These others—(*Pointing to the pictures around the
room*) Are they better celebrities?

SANDY: Mercy, no. Everybody knows that George Washington
and Abraham Lincoln are the greatest National Heroes of all
time...but...

JAN (*Looking pleased*) : So says my Uncle Nate. He says
every American school child loves these men. They make
great Pin-Up Pals for Karen and me.

SANDY: Oh, dear! I thought you understood about this club.
It's just a club for fun. We put up these pictures because they
are our dream men, our heroes...

KAREN: For us, the men who give us this so beautiful a country,
they are our dream men.

JAN : So short a time we live in this country. So many things we learn to love. In Austria, we had a Pin-Up Man too. Everywhere — in school, in church, on the streets, in the houses — you see the same Pin-Up Man...a hateful little man with a cruel mouth and a little moustache. Here you have many pictures in your houses. If you do not like them after a while, you tear them up and throw them away. That is what you can do in a free country. You can take your choice. We make our choice...Mr. Abe and Mr. George.

SANDY: It's just no use. They won't do. They're out of place here.

KAREN: Out of place? How could George Washington not have a place in America?

SANDY: Oh, you just don't understand. Rae, can't you help me get the idea across to them?

RAE: Maybe they are putting a new idea across to us, Sandy.

SANDY: You mean you think we should accept their Pin-Up Pals?

RAE: How could we, as Americans, refuse them? (*Rises*) Girls, we've heard a lot of talk here tonight about keeping our club exclusive, and about what kind of people should be admitted. Martha, you were one of the chief agitators. I ask you now, do you have any fault to find with the Pin-Up Pals Jan and Karen have selected?

MARTHA: When you put it that way, no. But just the same...

RAE: Just the same, maybe it would be a pretty good idea for us to have some other fans besides movie stars and radio singers. Maybe it isn't such a bad idea for us Teen-Timers to admire some real heroes for a change.

GRACE: You're right, Rae. I'm with you.

RAE: We bobby sockers get a lot of publicity about our fan clubs and fan mail and swoonology, and I guess some of it does sound pretty silly to grown-ups. But we're not quite so stupid that we fail to recognize real Americanism when we see it. I move that the Pin-Up Pals presented by Jan and Karen be accepted and added to our Hall of Fame. All in favor...say "aye." (*Loud chorus of ayes.*)

SANDY: Congratulations, girls. That means you are full-fledged Pin-Up Pals.

JAN: Oh, thank you. Thank you.

KAREN: Uncle Nate said our Pin-Ups would be tops.

SANDY: That's an idea. Girls, what do you say we give America's greatest Pin-Ups the place of honor? (*Girls all stand and yell "Aye! Aye." They then applaud as* RAE *and* SANDY *take down the pictures of Van Johnson and Frank Sinatra and put up Washington and Lincoln. They stand the Johnson and Sinatra pictures on the stage propped against the table.*) Well girls, we've lived to see Frankie and Van step down in favor of two other Pin-Ups who will always be America's choice. (*Applause*)

MARTHA (*Coming forward*): Ever since I joined this club, Frankie has been my Pin-Up Pal, but I guess tonight I forgot about one of his favorite songs. I have it on a record and I play it so often I know the words by heart...but...well... I guess they didn't mean very much until tonight. Anyhow... you all know how The Voice sings "The House I Live In." (*She sings the first verse of the song*) I guess I was forgetting about that song when I was blowing my top awhile back...so thanks, Jan and Karen, for reminding me that your Pin-Up Pals had exactly the same idea. And if you don't mind my saying so, it's going to be my idea from now on. Welcome to the Pin-Up Pals, girls, and let me be the first to congratulate you. (*Applause as curtain falls on tableau of girls shaking hands.*)

THE END

PRODUCTION NOTES

PIN-UP PALS

Characters: 5 female; female extras.

Playing Time: 30 minutes.

Costumes: Everyday modern dress. Karen and Jan are rather shabbily dressed.

Properties: Sprigs of green, large scrapbook, paste, pictures of screen and radio stars, movie magazines, radio guides, gavel, large pictures of George Washington and Abraham Lincoln each wrapped separately in newspapers.

Setting: The club room. The room is decorated with large pictures of male screen and radio stars. Large pictures of Frank Sinatra and Van Johnson are above the speaker's table which is at one side. These pictures are decorated with sprays of evergreen. Some folding chairs stand against a wall.

Lighting: None required.

WHAT'S COOKIN'?

Characters

MRS. MORGAN
MRS. VANE ⎫
MRS. HALE ⎰ *Judges for the Meatless Menu Contest.*
JOSEPHINE ARMSTRONG ⎫
NANCY HASTINGS ⎰ *Junior High School waitresses.*
FRANK ARMSTRONG, *an athletic cook.*
TED HAYNES, *Frank's friend.*
DR. ANDREWS, *Principal of Hamilton Junior High.*
COACH MURDOCK
A PHOTOGRAPHER
CONTESTANTS *in the Meatless Menu Contest.*

SCENE: *The cafeteria of the Hamilton Junior High School.*

TIME: *The present.*

WHAT'S COOKIN'?

SETTING: *The cafeteria of the Hamilton Junior High School.*

AT RISE: *The P.T.A. Health and Nutrition Committee are seated at the central table. They are being served by* NANCY *and* JO, *Junior High School waitresses. The ladies are thoughtfully chewing bites of Peanutburger au Gratin. Each face wears a faraway look. Pause.*

MRS. MORGAN: Peanutburgers au Gratin! Very tasty. Very tasty, indeed, I should say.

MRS. VANE: Needs a mite more salt, I think. Yes, just a pinch would do the trick.

MRS. HALE: Terribly rich. Good, understand, but terribly rich.

MRS. MORGAN: Ummmmm. Yes, I daresay it is. But after all, this recipe for a meat substitute involves a rare combination— peanuts and cheese.

MRS. HALE: Almost *too* rare, if you ask me. I can feel pounds settling down on me with every bite.

MRS. VANE: I certainly think we should put Peanutburgers au Gratin on our final list. After all, even without enough salt, they were far more appetizing than Lincoln-Leftovers or Meatless Mulligan.

MRS. HALE: Oh, by all means. (*Consulting memorandum*) I have it listed here as grade A. In fact, I think it stands a good chance for first prize. But we must be getting on. How many more recipes must we taste?

NANCY: Just two, Mrs. Hale. Graham Cracker Meatloaf and Yankee Doodle Goulash.

Mrs. Morgan: My goodness, these children surely are original when it comes to names. Graham Cracker Meatloaf! Well, bring that one on and get me another glass of water. I might need it to wash this one down. (Nancy *goes to get water.*)

Mrs. Vane: That name doesn't appeal to me one bit. Graham Cracker Loaf would have been much better. In a contest for meat substitutes, I think it wiser not to mention the word meat at all. The power of suggestion is so strong.

Jo (*Setting down plates*): Here it is, ladies, right out of the oven. Entry number 24. (Nancy *brings extra glasses of water.*)

Mrs. Hale (*Sniffing*): Smells pretty good, doesn't it? Well, here goes. (*Pause while ladies all taste Graham Cracker Meatloaf. While the ladies are tasting,* Jo *and* Nancy *exchange anxious glances.*)

Nancy: Is it all right?

Jo: What does it taste like?

Mrs. Morgan: It's hard to say. Sort of a cross between shredded wheat and caramel popcorn. (*Reaches for glass of water.*) I move we strike this one off the list.

Mrs. Vane (*Coughing*): I second the motion. It's as dry as punk, and has no taste at all.

Mrs. Hale: I must admit it smelled better than it tasted. I wonder how it would be with ketchup.

Mrs. Vane (*Shuddering*): Perish the thought! Leave well enough alone, Alice, and let's try the next one. What did you say it was, child?

Nancy: Yankee Doodle Goulash. How does that sound?

Mrs. Morgan: It sounds truly alarming to me. What's in it?

Mrs. Vane: That's an unfair question, Harriet. We should be able to tell when we taste it. (*Girls go out for plates of Goulash, taking the other plates with them.*)

Mrs. Hale: For my part everything is beginning to taste alike.

Whose idea was this contest in the first place?

MRS. MORGAN: Mine, if you must know, Alice. And I still think it is a fine cause. Getting these young girls to take an interest in preparing nutritious meals without the use of meat is certainly worth while.

MRS. HALE: I'm glad I have a strong stomach, although I must say most of these concoctions have been delicious. (*Jo and NANCY enter with Dish Number 25 — Yankee Doodle Goulash.*)

NANCY: And here is the best yet, Number 25, Yankee Doodle Goulash.

MRS. MORGAN: Somehow, I never quite trust these goulashes.

MRS. HALE: I share your doubts, Harriet, but this looks very tempting.

MRS. VANE: I agree with you. Well, here's hoping it's as good as it looks.

MRS. MORGAN (*Raising her fork*): One, two, three, all together — Taste! (*The ladies attack the twenty-fifth dish with gusto and apparently find it to their liking. There are sighs of contentment.*)

MRS. VANE: Ladies, I do believe we have found the prize-winner.

MRS. MORGAN: There's no doubt about it. That is the finest goulash I have ever eaten.

MRS. HALE: In fact, it's almost too good. I'm inclined to suspect that there is meat in it somewhere.

MRS. MORGAN: Nonsense! That is just good, rich broth flavored with tomato and cheese.

MRS. VANE: And there's macaroni in it too.

MRS. HALE: Maybe that is why it's called Yankee Doodle Goulash. Remember (*Singing*), "He stuck a feather in his hat and called it Macaroni!"

MRS. VANE: Very clever, very clever indeed. But it's really the chestnuts that give the dish its fine flavor.

MRS. MORGAN: Not entirely, my dear. I think there is a trace of nutmeg in the sauce that is responsible for that exotic tang.

MRS. VANE: Well, whatever it is, my vote goes for Yankee Doodle Goulash for first prize.

MRS. MORGAN: And mine, too. What do you say, Alice? Are you going to make it unanimous?

MRS. HALE: Well, if you are all perfectly certain that there isn't a shred of meat in it, I'll go along with the rest.

MRS. MORGAN: Of course there's no meat. The Recipe Committee.has checked them all, so we can let our palates decide. Personally, I think we have made an excellent choice. (*To* NANCY) Here, child, just try a mouthful of this goulash and tell me if you have ever tasted anything better.

MRS. VANE (*To* Jo): And you, try a bite of mine. (*Both girls taste and register admiration.*) Now isn't that simply divine? (*The girls nod happily, their mouths full.*)

MRS. HALE: Well that's that. Now who is to notify the prize-winners so we can have our official celebration?

NANCY: Jo and I will attend to it, Mrs. Hale. We'll call Dr. Andrews on the house phone and he'll ring the bell. That is the signal for all the contestants to report to the cafeteria.

Jo: You ladies will probably want to go upstairs and freshen up before you make the awards.

MRS. VANE: We certainly do. Will you send someone to tell us when to come back?

NANCY: We'll call you in plenty of time.

MRS. VANE: Thank you. We all look somewhat the worse for wear. (*The ladies depart. Left alone,* Jo *turns to* NANCY *in despair.*)

Jo: Nancy, what on earth am I going to do? Frank will positively kill me.

NANCY: I've seen that brother of yours pretty murderous at times, but what have you done to him now that you expect the worst?

Jo: I'll never tell you what made me do it, but I sent in Recipe Number 25, that Yankee Doodle thing, in his name.

NANCY: Do you mean to say that you made up a recipe and sent it in under your brother's name?

Jo: No, I didn't make it up. It's his own recipe all right, but we don't talk about it very much outside of the family circle, because it makes Frank so mad. His hobby is cooking. He gets out in the kitchen every chance he gets, and cooks up the unholiest concoctions you ever heard of. The funny part is, though, that they are always good.

NANCY: Will wonders never cease? Frank Armstrong, Captain of the Junior Tigers, Winner of the 9A Wrestling Matches, just a cook at heart.

Jo: I know. That is what makes it so funny. He'll be fit to be tied when he finds out. But when I read about the prize being offered in this contest, I just thought it was a good chance for Frank. I knew he had a good recipe, and I — well— I just sent it in.

NANCY: Why didn't you send it in under your name?

Jo: Oh, that wouldn't have been honest. I want Frank to have the prize and the glory as well.

NANCY: If I know Frank, he won't want any of the glory. Not in this contest. Jo, it will be a perfect scream. Coach Murdock is going to make the awards and poor old Frank — won't he be every color in the rainbow when Coach makes him a speech about being the best little home-maker in Hamilton High?

Jo: Oh, dear? It will be dreadful! Nancy, you must think of a way out. Frank and Ted will be coming in here any minute now. It's their day on cafeteria duty, and we'll have to break the news gently.

NANCY: I'll say gently, or he'll break your neck. Thank goodness, I'm not in your shoes, Jo Armstrong.

Jo (*Half crying*) : Oh, Nancy, be a good kid, and help me tell him. He has a soft spot in his heart for you anyhow, and maybe he won't be quite so mad if you tell him.

NANCY: I'll stand by and help pick up the pieces, but you'll have to tell him the glad tidings yourself. Sh! Here they come. Let's be busy straightening this place up. (*The girls bustle around the table as* FRANK *and* TED *enter. They are 9th grade boys.*)

FRANK: Hy'a, Poison Puss! Or shall I say, Poison Pusses? What does the Cafeteria give today for two starving men?

TED: I'm hungry enough to eat you two girls, uniforms and all. How about smuggling us a sandwich before the angry mob starts to stampede down here?

NANCY: Have you galoots forgotten that this is the day for the special P.T.A. Luncheon? The rest of us common people eat an hour later today. This lunch hour is just for the contestants in the Meatless Meal Contest, and the prize recipe will be announced and a $25 Bond awarded to some lucky genius of the kitchen.

FRANK: Yeah, and I bet the recipe won't be worth the paper it's written on.

NANCY (*With meaning*) : Oh, I'm sure this one will be perfectly elegant.

FRANK: Could be. Who won? Anybody I know?

Jo: How should we know? We're not the judges.

TED: Yes, but you were right here while the committee was making up its mind. Come on, tell us who won.

NANCY: I'll tell you *what* won, if that will do you any good. First prize goes to a fancy dish called Yankee Doodle Goulash.

TED: Gleeps! What is that?

NANCY (*With a look at* Jo) : I don't know exactly, but it has macaroni and cheese, and tomatoes, and peppers, and nutmeg, and chestnuts —

FRANK (*Surprised*): Chestnuts? Say that again. Did you say *chestnuts?*

JO: Now, listen to me, Frank, and control yourself. Please, please, don't get mad or holler at me, or hit me or anything till I tell you the whole story.

FRANK: What story? What is all this?

JO: It's about the chestnuts. I mean the recipe. You see it's really your recipe for Camp Casserole, only I gave it a fancy name on account of the macaroni and on account of how I thought it should have a patriotic title, so I thought up Yankee Doodle Goulash.

FRANK: Wait a minute. Wait a minute. What do you mean— *you* thought it should have a patriotic title, so *you* called it Yankee Doodle Goulash? Josephine Armstrong, what have you been up to? (FRANK *seizes* JO *by the shoulders and shakes her.*) What have you done with my recipe?

NANCY: Now don't yell, Frank, please don't yell. You'll have the whole faculty down here in a jiffy.

TED: And don't shake your sister's head clear off her shoulders. Give her a chance to answer.

JO: Oh, Frank, you'll probably never forgive me, but I entered your recipe in the contest and it won.

FRANK (*In a low tense voice*): Sister, or no sister — crime or no crime, I'll murder you for this.

TED: Easy, fellow, easy. This looks like something pretty nifty to me. I want to see what is going to happen next.

FRANK (JO *retreating around the table*): You're going to see a short play entitled, "Boy Beats Girl," and then I suppose I'll go to jail.

NANCY (*Catching hold of his arm*): Now, be sensible, Frank.

I'll admit it's pretty bad, but you have won a twenty-five dollar Bond.

TED: Sure, think of that, Cookie.

FRANK (*Wheeling on* TED): One more crack out of you, and there won't be enough left of you to bury. And if ever I hear you call me that name again, I'll skin you alive.

TED (*Innocently*): What name? Oh! You mean "Cookie"? (FRANK *rushes at him but* NANCY *gets between them.*)

NANCY: Honestly, you two act as if you don't have a grain of sense. Now if you just calm down, I think I can fix things up.

JO: Oh, Nancy, do you honestly think you could?

NANCY: I think so.

FRANK: You better think fast if you want that sister of mine to live.

NANCY: First, am I right in assuming you wouldn't refuse that Bond, Frank?

FRANK: Well, no — er yes. Why, of course, I'd take a Bond if anybody should hand it to me.

TED: The part he objects to is walking up in front of the dear ladies and sharing the limelight with a lot of silly giggling girls.

FRANK: Exactly. And furthermore I'm not going to do it. I'm leaving right now.

TED: Oh, no, you're not. You're going to stay here and collect your prize.

JO: At least stay long enough to hear Nancy's plan.

NANCY: Let me see the entry blank, Jo, the one you filled out when you entered Frank's recipe.

JO: I don't have it. The committee took all the blanks.

NANCY: Well just what did you put on the blank? What name did you use for the writer of the recipe?

JO: I've told you — I used Frank's name.

NANCY: But isn't Frank just a nickname? Isn't his real name Francis?

FRANK: Sure it is, but I never use it. Everybody knows me as Frank.

NANCY: That's just the point. Everybody knows you as Frank, but your real name is Francis. Now which did you use on the entry blank, Jo?

Jo: Francis. I put Francis J. Armstrong. I made it Francis because it seemed more legal to give his real name.

NANCY: Then all is not lost.

FRANK: I don't see what difference it makes. Frank or Francis —it's still me.

NANCY: Yes, but Francis can be either a boy's name or a girl's name depending on the spelling. And no one is ever quite sure which is which. In this case, everyone will be expecting a girl, so all you have to do is be a girl, receive the prize and then fade out of existence.

TED: Nancy, you're a genius.

FRANK: What do you mean — all I have to do is be a girl?

NANCY: Just dress up like one when you walk up to get the prize.

Jo: That's a heavenly idea. He can wear my reversible coat, and a pair of my wedgies I meant to take to the shoemaker. They are still in my locker. I'll get them in a jiffy. (*Jo runs off stage.*)

FRANK: I'll do no such thing, I tell you. Jo, you come back here. I won't have any part in this masquerade.

TED: Oh, yes you will. Don't you think your friends know what is best for you? You take Nancy's advice and we'll all rally around and help you out of this. Come on now, be a good sport. Roll up those trouser legs. With a loose coat on you and some glamour girl shoes, you'll be Miss America.

FRANK: Get out of here. I tell you I won't do it. I'll be the laughing stock of the school.

NANCY: Not if you listen to your Aunt Nancy and your Uncle Ted. Come on now. Let Ted work out on those trouser legs and I'll take over the make-up job.

FRANK: Make-up? You mean that gooey lipstick and rouge? None of that trash goes on me.

TED: Very well, stubborn. Have it your own way. But in five minutes that whole gang will be down here determined to hand you a prize. And what is worse, there will be photographers. Have you thought of that? Your picture in the paper with the recipe for Yankee Doodle Goulash right below it!

FRANK (*In agony*): Why does this have to happen to me? It will make me a criminal. I know it will.

NANCY: Then why don't you be a good boy and let us make you over? As Francis J. Armstrong, you'll win the prize and save your dignity.

FRANK: O.K. I give up. Go ahead. Do anything you like, but I warn you — one false move with that lipstick and the show's over. I quit.

NANCY: I'll be careful. Quick now, Ted. Hoist those bloomer legs to half mast, and I'll see what I can do with his school-girl complexion. (TED *and* NANCY *go to work on* FRANK. Jo *enters with the contents of her locker. She has managed to find a pair of wedgies, a skirt, and a triangular scarf.*)

Jo: Wasn't it lucky I wore this scarf today? We can use it to tie around Frank's head, peasant style. If we pull out a lock or two of hair around his face, he'll look as if he has a feather cut.

FRANK: My gosh! Now it's feathers! What next?

Jo: Next, I'd suggest this skirt. Luckily I am in this uniform so you are welcome to my second-best skirt, just cleaned and pressed last week. With your sweater, it won't look half bad.

(*The three conspirators help* FRANK *into the clothes and when he is in full regalia, the effect is not bad at all. The triangular peasant scarf is the crowning touch. If the make-up is carefully applied,* FRANK *should be a regular charmer.*)

TED (*Bowing low and using an affected accent*): May I have the honor of this dawnce, Lady Gwendolyn? (FRANK *aims a kick at* TED *but misses him.*)

NANCY: No rough-house, please. Let me see you walk across the room, Frank, as if you were going to get the prize. (FRANK *slouches carelessly across the room.*)

JO: That will never do. Get more swing into your walk.

TED: Like this. Let me show you. (*Does an absurd imitation of a model's walk.*)

JO: No, no, nothing like that. Oh, there's no time to give you any more coaching on how to behave. Your best bet is to keep quiet. Say as little as possible and smile as much as you can. Try the smile now — just once. Smile sweetly and drop your eyes, like this, as if you are too shy for anything when you get the Bond. Now you try. (FRANK *does a fair imitation.*)

FRANK: Is that O.K.?

TED: Well, it wouldn't fool me, but we'll hope the others are more gullible.

NANCY: Now, Jo, you skip upstairs and tell those judges it's time to come down here. I'll phone Dr. Andrews so he can ring the bell for the contestants. Frank, you go out in the hall and come in with the rest of the girls.

FRANK (*Indignantly*): Cut out that "rest-of-the-girls" stuff.

NANCY: Oh, don't quibble. You know what I mean.

JO: Just sort of hang around toward the end of the line and try to act natural.

TED: I'll hop out in the kitchen and see if I can lend a hand out there.

FRANK: Now listen you, I'll go through with this thing, but if anybody laughs or looks funny, or makes any wisecracks, you'll hear from me.

Jo: Honestly, Frank, we're trying to help you, and I don't see how anything can go wrong if you do your part. (*They all exit* — Jo *and* FRANK *left* — TED *and* NANCY *right.*)

NANCY (*As she goes off stage*) : I'll call Dr. Andrews and he'll ring the bell right away.

TED: I wouldn't miss this for a farm. (*Laughs all the way out. There is a brief pause. Then a bell rings. A second pause and* Jo *enters with the three* JUDGES.)

Jo: Everything is ready. Dr. Andrews and the Coach should be here in a minute. (*They all stand at center table.* NANCY *enters.*)

NANCY: Dr. Andrews says he'll be right down. He's bringing the Coach with him. Oh, here they are now. (COACH MURDOCK *and* DR. ANDREWS *enter.*)

DR. ANDREWS: Good morning, Ladies. I take it you have come to a decision.

MRS. MORGAN: Yes indeed, a unanimous decision. First prize goes to — (*Consults memorandum*) let me see — oh, yes, Francis J. Armstrong for Yankee Doodle Goulash.

MRS. VANE: I know you'll agree with us when you taste it.

DR. ANDREWS (*To the* COACH) : Francis Armstrong, Francis J. Armstrong? Can you place a girl by that name, Coach?

COACH: Can't say that I remember a girl by that name, Doctor, but then my business is with the other side of the house. I don't get to know many of the girls. Of course we have Frank Armstrong and his sister.

DR. ANDREWS: Oh, no, her name is Josephine. It must be another family. (*The contestants begin to mill into the room in groups of two's and three's.* FRANK *is among them, trying desperately to keep in the background.*)

DR. ANDREWS: Just make yourselves at home, girls. Scatter around and sit wherever you like. This is a very informal occasion, though I can imagine it is an exciting one for all of you. (*The girls go to places at various tables.* FRANK *slips into a chair at the extreme right of the room.*)

DR. ANDREWS (*To the* JUDGES): Will you be seated, Ladies? (*They sit at the center table;* DR. ANDREWS *and the* COACH *remain standing.* Jo *and* NANCY *stand looking on from the doorway.* TED's *head is stuck around the corner of the kitchen door.*) It certainly was a pleasure to me to learn that so many of you girls had voluntarily taken part in the Meatless Menu Contest sponsored by the P.T.A. The judges tell me that all of the recipes were good and that the winner is positively mouth-watering. I guess there is no one on our entire staff who is better able to appreciate the value of foods than Coach Murdock. He sees what good food means in the development of healthy, hardy young men, and so I've invited him to come down here today and say a few words of encouragement to all of you girls, who one of these days are going to have to cook for some man. May I present Coach Murdock? (*Applause.*)

COACH: Well, girls, I'm not going to make any speech. You all know the old saying that the road to a man's heart lies through his stomach, and if you want to get a man, feed him. I can't give you any better advice except to say, feed him well, and by well, I mean give him vitamins — the vitamins that are to be found in a well-balanced diet of meats, fruits, milk and fresh vegetables. And now, I'm going to have my picture taken with the winner of this contest. The photographer should be here any minute now, and as soon as the Chairman of the Judges has announced her decision, I'm going to have my picture taken eating a big serving of whatever it is that has won the prize. So now, let me present Mrs. Harriet

Morgan, who will announce the winning recipe. Mrs. Morgan. (*Applause.*)

MRS. MORGAN: Really, girls, it was quite a treat to taste all your lovely dishes. The other ladies and myself were quite at a loss as to how to decide on the best because they were all so good, until we tasted the very last one — Number 25. The name of it is Yankee Doodle Goulash, and the winner — I know you can hardly wait to hear the name. Well, I won't keep you in suspense another minute. The winner is Miss Francis Armstrong. (*Applause and people crane their necks to see who will answer to the name. At first* FRANK *does not rise.*)

MRS. MORGAN: Miss Francis Armstrong. Where is she? Come forward, Miss Armstrong, your prize is waiting for you. Ah! There she comes. Let's give her another round of applause. (*More applause as* FRANK *approaches the table.*)

COACH: Miss Armstrong, you have won honor and distinction for yourself as a creative cook, and at the same time have earned a substantial reward in the shape of a twenty-five dollar Bond which it is my pleasure to present you at this time. (*Hands Bond to* FRANK.)

FRANK: Thank you very much.

DR. ANDREWS (*Shaking hands*): And may I add my congratulations?

MRS. MORGAN: We are all very proud of you, my dear.

MRS. VANE: Perhaps you have some more of those wonderful recipes up your sleeve.

MRS. HALE: It is nice to meet a young girl who is interested in domestic problems. (PHOTOGRAPHER *enters with flashlight equipment.*)

PHOTOGRAPHER: I guess I'm just in time. Sorry, Dr. Andrews. I couldn't make it sooner. Held up in the office. But I'm anxious to get a shot of this Meatless Menu Award. Is this the lucky young lady?

DR. ANDREWS: Miss Francis J. Armstrong.

PHOTOGRAPHER: Pleased to meet you. Now, let's do a shot of the young lady and the judges. (*Arranges grouping.*) Here, Miss, you stand in the center holding your Bond and I want each of you ladies to pretend you are eating some of the — whatever it is that won the prize.

MRS. MORGAN: Yankee Doodle Goulash.

PHOTOGRAPHER (*Handing them each a plate*): Now let's see. Are we all set? (*Steps back for a final look.*) Everybody look this way, please. (*Just as he is ready for the flash,* MRS. MORGAN *gets an inspiration.*)

MRS. MORGAN: Oh, wait, wait! Just a minute, please. Let's give our little star a chance to fix her hair. Every girl wants to look her very best in a picture. You'll want to take this thing off. (*Before* FRANK *can stop her,* MRS. MORGAN *has whipped off the triangular scarf, thereby disclosing his haircut and his identity. There are gasps and giggles.*)

DR. ANDREWS: Why, Frank Armstrong! What is the meaning of this?

COACH: If I'm not a Chinese Grasshopper, it's Frank Armstrong.

MRS. MORGAN: If this is a joke, young man, it's a mighty poor one.

MRS. VANE: You certainly owe us an apology.

MRS. HALE: Just what are you trying to do?

COACH: Shouldn't we give the boy a chance to explain?

FRANK: There's really nothing to explain —

MRS. MORGAN: Oh, yes, there is. What are you doing in those clothes claiming a prize you didn't win?

JO (*Coming forward*): But he did win it, Mrs. Morgan. Oh, dear, it's all my fault. You see I sent in his recipe without his knowledge or consent.

TED: The poor guy was ashamed of claiming a prize in a girls' contest, so —

NANCY: I persuaded him to pose as a girl and accept the prize under the name of Francis instead of Frank.

JO: And that *is* his own name, so it's perfectly legal.

DR. ANDREWS: It all sounds pretty complicated to me. Is this a conspiracy?

JO: Nothing of the sort. Frank didn't know a thing about it until today. I knew he'd never let me send in his recipe if he knew about it.

COACH: Why not?

JO: Because he never wants to let anyone know he can cook. He thinks it's sissy. (*Laughter*)

DR. ANDREWS: Well, Frank, it looks as if this predicament is none of your making.

FRANK: It certainly isn't, Sir.

TED: And no real harm's been done after all.

COACH: Except to poor Frank's feelings.

FRANK: You mean I may keep the prize?

MRS. MORGAN: After all, there was nothing in the contest rules disqualifying boys.

MRS. HALE: Not a word.

MRS. VANE: I think it's very unusual to have a boy for the winner, and I heartily approve of it.

MRS. MORGAN: And we're sure it's his very own work.

JO: Everything but the name. I made that up.

COACH: Then I'd say Frank has won the prize fairly and squarely. (*Shakes hands.*) Congratulations all over again.

DR. ANDREWS: And mine, too. Your only mistake was to think that cooking is a sissy job. I must confess I can stir up a cake that might win a prize on its own merit. And I can bake what you young folks might call a "mean pie." (*Laughter and applause*)

PHOTOGRAPHER: Excuse me, sir, but what about my picture?

COACH: Ready any time now.

FRANK: But not in these duds.

COACH: I should say not. Get rid of that female finery and look like yourself.

MRS. MORGAN: And just to prove that the ladies in the house can be good sports about being defeated by a male cook, let's all sing the new version of "Yankee Doodle" that you'll find on the tables. (*While* FRANK *changes clothes the cast sings to the tune of "Yankee Doodle".*)

> "Father and I went out to eat
> With all the young and oldsters,
> And all the men and all the boys
> Were strong as granite boulders.
>
> "Yankee Doodle, keep it up,
> Keep your health foods handy.
> Vitamins will pep you up
> And keep you feeling dandy."

(*By the time the song has been sung twice,* FRANK *is ready for the picture. The* PHOTOGRAPHER *calls:* Ready, please. This way, everyone, *and snaps the picture.*)

COACH: And now it's all over but the cheering. What do you say, Folks, three big ones for Frank Armstrong, the Yankee Doodle Cook of Hamilton High — Ready — hip — hip. (*Curtains close on cast cheering for* FRANK *and his Yankee Doodle Goulash.*)

THE END

PRODUCTION NOTES

What's Cookin'

Characters: 5 male; 5 female; extras.

Playing time: 30 minutes.

Costumes: The judges are smartly dressed, wear hats, and red, white, and blue badges. Nancy and Jo may wear white dresses as uniforms. Frank and Ted are dressed in long trousers and sweaters. The other characters dress in everyday clothes.

Properties: Glasses of water; plates; dishes of various foods that judges must taste; forks; a pair of wedgies; a triangular scarf; a skirt; lipstick; flash camera; an envelope to represent the Bond.

Setting: This is a typical school cafeteria. There are long tables across the back of the stage. On the wall are signs — Salads, Soups, Desserts, etc. Down center there is a table set for three, attractively decorated with flags and flowers. On either side of the center table there are two or three ordinary tables and chairs.

Lighting: None required.

SNOOP'S SCOOP

Characters

SCRIBS FISHER, *Editor of THE DIVE BOMBER.*
SPIKE, *the Sports Editor.*
DAN, *a reporter.*
JULIE, *a reporter.*
WALT, *Advertising Manager.*
GEORGE, *a member of the staff.*
SNAPS, *a seventh-grade shutter-bug.*
SNOOP, *a seventh-grade news hound.*

SCENE: *The busy office of THE DIVE BOMBER.*

TIME: *The present.*

SNOOP'S SCOOP

SETTING: *The busy office of* THE DIVE BOMBER, *the official weekly publication of Emerson Junior High School.*

AT RISE: SCRIBS FISHER, *Editor-in-Chief, is seated at his desk, his feet propped higher than his head, as he studies the ceiling in deep thought. At a long table a boy and girl reporter are scribbling away, and at a typewriter, left stage, the Sports Editor is picking out an article. At another table the Business Manager is tearing his hair over a pile of ads. Each table bears a placard identifying the workers: Editor, Reporters, Sports Department, Advertising Department. The Editor suddenly swings his feet to the floor and smites his desk.*

SCRIBS: I have it! My new editorial—"What Price Glamour?" How's that?

SPIKE: From the looks of you, you probably know as much about glamour as I know about who is going to win Saturday's game.

DAN: What are you trying to do? Make this news sheet a Fashion Magazine or a Guide to Beauty?

SCRIBS: You fellows don't know much about psychology. I tell you this student body is glamour-conscious, and if we make the *Bomber* more glamorous, we'll get more subscribers, and our Business Manager will have fewer headaches.

DAN: Acorns to you, Scribs! Can you imagine the male population of this school rushing to get a copy of the *Dive Bomber* just because it contains a new article by Scribs Fisher on how to be glamorous?

59

JULIE: I'm siding with Scribs. Don't you boys forget our feminine subscribers count for something around here, and I happen to know you boys are mighty susceptible to glamour. Otherwise where'd I get some of these luscious little tidbits for my gossip column, like this, for instance?

"Can it be that one of Emerson's Athletes is risking his figure by eating too many ice cream sodas down at the Diamond Grille? Or is the pretty little blonde behind the counter the main attraction? How about it, Spike? Is it Sodas or Sadie?"

SPIKE (*Indignantly*): Hey, you can't print that. Why, that's label, that's what it is.

SCRIBS: Label? You mean libel. And it's not even libel, my good man. That's what you call the truth — the kind that hurts.

DAN: Remember, "Truth is stranger than fiction," and this is plenty strange, old boy.

SCRIBS: Maybe your Uncle Scribs ought to toddle down to the Diamond Grille some afternoon. Might learn something about glamour. How about it, Spike?

SPIKE: Aw, shut up. Julie, give me that paper. (*In reaching for JULIE's paper, he grabs another which he holds up out of her reach and reads aloud.*) Hey, give ear to this. If you thought that bunch of hooey was funny, you'll positively die laughing at this:

"Three guesses what is the latest hobby of the Editor of the *Dive Bomber*. Knitting. Well, maybe not exactly knitting, but it's close enough. At any rate, he holds the yarn while Susie Clairmont winds it into a big ball. Yes, sir, maybe he's taking lessons from John Alden, and Priscilla, but we'll let him speak for himself."

SCRIBS (*Jumping up and starting around the table in pursuit of* S<small>PIKE</small> *who still has the paper*) : Of all the bare-faced, unadulterated, made-up bosh! Give me that scandal sheet.

J<small>ULIE</small>: Give that to me. That goes in my column.

S<small>PIKE</small>: Ah me! Revenge is sweet! Julie, you have a great future if somebody doesn't strangle you the day after the *Bomber* comes out.

S<small>CRIBS</small>: That piece of sabotage gets into the paper over my dead body.

W<small>ALT</small> (*Who has taken no part in the general hilarity*) : There's going to be more than one dead body around here in a minute if you crazy coots don't settle down. Can't you see I'm working?

S<small>CRIBS</small>: You're right, Walt. This is a newspaper office — not a battlefield. I'll call it quits, Spike, if you lay that paper back on Julie's desk.

S<small>PIKE</small>: O.K. But if you permit that Sadie story to get into print, it'll be war to the finish.

W<small>ALT</small>: Can't you two forget your personal grievances for a minute? It might interest you to know that the *Dive Bomber* is in danger of crashing — financially, I mean. The whole back page is empty. Not a single ad — not even a teensy, winsy one.

S<small>CRIBS</small>: Ah, no. Your Uncle Scribs fixed that. I sent George Kelley down to see old Mr. Foose, and he's good for the whole page.

W<small>ALT</small>: Are you sure?

S<small>CRIBS</small>: We can't miss. Foose has money to burn. That's why he sells Automatic Heaters. What's a little ad in the *Bomber* to a guy with a million dollars?

J<small>ULIE</small>: But if he has all that money, why would he need to advertise? After all nobody in Junior High School is likely to buy an automatic heater.

D<small>AN</small>: It's easy to see you're no business woman, Julie. We kids take our papers home, don't we, and our parents read them.

SPIKE: Sure thing. That's just why I don't want that soda story in the paper.

DAN: They read the ads too and it's our parents who spend the money in this town.

JULIE: Yes, but I can't imagine an important man like Mr. Foose bothering with a paper the size of the *Bomber*.

SCRIBS: That's where your Uncle Scribs is a man of vision, my girl. Now, Walt, just relax. George should be popping in here any minute now with the bacon. (*Door opens and a seventh-grade boy and a girl enter. Both are breathless with excitement.* SNOOP, *the girl, is clutching a notebook.* SNAPS *has a camera.*)

SNOOP: Hey, Scribs, is it too late for a big article?

SCRIBS: It's always too late for one of your articles, Baby Face.

SNOOP: But honest, Scribs, this is sensational. It's a real scoop this time. Honest.

SNAPS: She's right, Scribs. It's a wow. No kidding. And I got some pictures.

SCRIBS (*Patiently*): How often have I told you kids that we cannot be bothered with you seventh-grade news hounds? What do you think this is — the Cradle Roll?

SNOOP: All right, Scribs, you'll be sorry if you turn this down. I tell you I got a hot story, and if you pass it up you'll never forgive yourself.

SNAPS: That's straight, Scribs. Honest.

SCRIBS: Well, what is this wonderful tale? Let's hear it.

SNOOP: No, sir. If I tell you what it is, you won't let me write it. You'll turn it over to some ninth-grader.

SCRIBS: Nope. If it's any good, you can write it. I promise.

SNAPS: And you will use my pictures?

SCRIBS: Maybe. If you didn't have your thumb over the lens. Come on now, Snoop. What is this wonderful yarn?

SNOOP: Well, if you promise to let me write it and be a regular reporter, I'll tell. (*In a stage whisper*) Somebody has been trying to blow up the library.

SCRIBS (*Feeling her forehead*): Snoop, you must have a fever. Are you sure you feel all right?

SNAPS: This is no joke, Scribs. This is the real dope.

DAN: Boy, if this is true, you've got a real story there, Scribs.

SCRIBS (*To* SNOOP): How do you know?

SNOOP: I heard 'em talking. They found dynamite in the library.

SPIKE: Dynamite! Boy, this should blow the school wide open.

SNOOP: It would have, if they hadn't discovered it in time.

SCRIBS: Not so fast. Who found what dynamite where, and who put it there?

SNOOP: Don't ask so many questions. I tell you I just came from the office where I heard Mr. Allison talking to police headquarters asking them to send two cops up right away.

SCRIBS (*Whistles*): Boy, this sounds like the real thing.

JULIE: I bet it's some kind of fifth column work.

SPIKE: The Trojan horse is within our gates.

SCRIBS: I bet you're right. Here, Snoop, you sit right down here and dash off a first draft of your story. Now remember to get your lead straight. *What, where, when* and *why*. The *who* we don't know yet, but I hope we'll find out soon. Snaps, what pictures did you get?

SNAPS: Three shots of the library and one of the librarian.

SCRIBS: Take your film out, and I'll rush it down to the lab right away. Zowie, this is the biggest story that ever broke.

DAN: Imagine anybody trying to pull something like that right here in Elmville.

SPIKE: We ought to call in the F.B.I.

WALT: I wouldn't be surprised if it was somebody right here in our own school.

SCRIBS: Pipe down, everybody, so Snoop can write. After all, we should give the kid a break. (GEORGE KELLEY *enters, whistling.*)

GEORGE: Howdy, folks.

SCRIBS: Sh! We have a big story here. We're trying to rush it through.

GEORGE: What's up?

SCRIBS: Tell you in a minute. I want to write a headline for this piece that'll knock 'em cold. Snoop, don't worry about your spelling. We'll fix that later.

SNOOP: O.K. *Dynamite* had me stumped right away.

GEORGE: Dynamite? Snoop! How did you get up here so fast? I was telling her a joke a few minutes ago, and she shot down the hall as if she had popped out of a cannon. Never even got to the end of my story.

SNOOP: Joke? What joke?

GEORGE: Why, about finding dynamite in the school library.

ALL: Joke? Was that a joke?

GEORGE: Sure, I was telling Snoop some guys just found dynamite in the library, and she ran off before she even asked me where, so I never got my punch line in.

SCRIBS: Then allow me to ask, where was the dynamite actually found?

GEORGE: In the dictionary, of course. (*Laughs heartily but alone.*)

SCRIBS: Eliza Jane Emory, otherwise known as Snoop, otherwise known as General Nuisance, —

SNOOP: Honest, Scribs, I thought it was a real story. I am just as surprised as you are.

SCRIBS: I thought you said you heard Mr. Allison sending for two policemen.

SNOOP: I did. Honest I did.

GEORGE: Sure she did. Mr. Allison just told me the Police

Department is sending up two cops to help direct traffic at noon and after school.

SNAPS: Go-g-gosh. I guess you won't need these pictures.

SCRIBS: Right. And we won't need you two baby reporters now or ever. Git! Scram! Vamoose! Exit!

SNOOP: Oh, please, Scribs. Don't chase us out. Please give us another chance.

SCRIBS: What for? Another chance to ruin us? Don't you realize what would have happened if we had printed that story? Fatal, final ruin.

WALT: The same ruin that is going to overtake us anyhow, if that irresistible Mr. Kelley doesn't bring in the ad from Mr. Foose. Instead of chasing these kids out of here, why not put them to work? I can use them at my desk folding subscription blanks. That kind of work doesn't take any brains.

SNAPS: Sure, Walt, we'll do it. Thanks.

SPIKE: And be thankful you don't have to face a firing squad.

SNOOP: I'd do anything just to get on this paper staff.

WALT: Well, then get to work and keep quiet.

SCRIBS: And keep out of my sight, if you know what's good for you.

DAN: Maybe I can get a story out of this financial crisis. "Crack up in *Dive Bomber.*"

SCRIBS: Don't try to turn Rumor into Humor or vice versa. This business of the back page is no laughing matter.

GEORGE: You said it. That man Foose knows the meaning of sales resistance.

WALT: Maybe you had a poor sales talk.

GEORGE: He didn't even listen to it. Just gave me the go-by in words of one syllable.

SCRIBS: Couldn't you sell him on the idea of the *Bomber* carrying his ad into hundreds of homes?

GEORGE: Not for two hundred dollars, I couldn't.

WALT: But that's only five dollars a week for forty issues.

DAN: He'd be a goose not to grab such a bargain.

GEORGE: Please understand once and for all, Mr. Foose is not a goose. If he is to be compared to any creature in the animal kingdom, let it be a moose.

JULIE: A moose? For mercy's sake, why?

GEORGE: Because he not only looks a bit like a moose, but he sounds like a moose and acts like a moose. You should have heard the way he bellowed at me when I asked him to take an ad. When I started my sales talk, he lowered his head and came charging across the room at me, for all the world like the old bull moose he has hanging on the wall above his desk.

SCRIBS: Hey, wait a minute. This must have done something to you. How could he have a moose over his desk?

GEORGE: Don't be so literal. It wasn't a whole moose — just the head and the branches. It's some sort of hunting trophy the old boy got in the north woods. But one thing is certain, my hunting days are over in that department. Mr. Alphonso J. Foose will never hear from this young whippersnapper again. "Whippersnapper" is his name for me — not mine.

SCRIBS: Gee willikins! We're sunk. There's no other man in town who could buy that back page. Couldn't you have made friends with the old moose, I mean Foose, and sold him an ad by sheer force of personality?

SPIKE: Couldn't you have appealed to his sporting blood?

GEORGE: I could not. He settled all that in the first round. He doesn't like boys to begin with; and has no use for Junior High School newspapers in the second place. He says they are: (a) a waste of time and (b) a public nuisance. Getting ads from honest citizens is a racket and he will be gosh-blinkety-blinked it he'll pay one red cent toward supporting a toy newspaper for a lot of little kids who want to play at newspaper writing.

WALT: Well, that leaves us two hundred dollars short of meeting our budget.

SPIKE: Two hundred simoleons.

SNAPS: Couldn't we sell more subscriptions to make up the difference?

SCRIBS: Quiet from the kindergarten! You two are to be seen and not heard.

SNOOP: Maybe I could talk to Mr. Foose. I'm not afraid of him.

SCRIBS: What do you think we are? A bunch of baby-killers? We're not going to toss you two innocent babes to the lions— even if that would be one way of getting rid of you.

JULIE: Maybe you didn't use the right psychology on the gentleman.

SPIKE (*With sarcasm*): I suppose you would try glamour.

JULIE: Well, it might work.

SCRIBS: Not a bad idea.

GEORGE: Not a chance. I tell you Mr. Foose has only one interest and one love besides his automatic heaters and that is the aforementioned moose he has hanging above his desk. When I started out, I happened to notice Old Antlers and I asked a question or two about him — just to get the conversation started, and for a second Old Stony Face began to thaw; but the minute I mentioned Ad he froze up solid.

JULIE: But there must be some way to break down that sales resistance. I once read a book on salesmanship that said you can sell anybody anything if you go about it in the right way.

GEORGE: The fellow who wrote that book had never met Mr. Foose and his moose.

SNOOP: Please, Scribs, let me try. Honest, I think I have a good angle. Let me go see him.

SCRIBS: Don't bother me; I'm busy.

SNOOP: But I know I could help.

SPIKE: Is there anything you seventh-graders think you can't do? You want to play football, you want to be in plays, you want to be on the newspaper staff, and now you want to tackle Foose and his moose.

DAN: Talking about fools rushing in where angels fear to tread.

SCRIBS: You two can do me a great favor by departing from this room before I count ten.

WALT: No, no — not before they fold all of those blanks.

SPIKE: What do you say we all go down to the Diamond Grille and drown our sorrows in ice cream sodas?

SCRIBS: For once, Spike, you have spoken words of wisdom. Come on, Julie. Maybe you can dig up some more items for your gossip column.

GEORGE: Maybe I could sell an ad to the Diamond Grille.

SCRIBS: They already have one, but we'll try for another. Is it safe to leave these two youngsters here without a nurse?

GEORGE: They'll be O.K. If we take the dictionary with us, they can't play with dynamite.

WALT: Be sure to get every one of those blanks folded by the time we get back.

SNAPS: O.K., Boss.

SNOOP: Please, Scribs, won't you let me try?

SCRIBS: The answer is *No*. And after today if you and that shutter-bug come fooling around this office, I'm going to tell your Home Room teacher to lock you up. (*All exit except* SNAPS *and* SNOOP.)

SNAPS: Don't let them get you down, Snoopie. They're just a bunch of goons.

SNOOP: Oh, Snaps, I want to work on the *Dive Bomber* so badly. I want to be a newspaper woman more than anything else in the world, and Dad says I have a nose for news.

SNAPS: Is that why they call you Snoop?

SNOOP: Sure. See here, Snaps, you can stay here and fold those blanks if you want to. I'm going down and sell that ad to Mr. Foose.

SNAPS: But Scribs said *No.*

SNOOP: And I say *Yes.* What's more, I have a feeling I can make Mr. Foose say *Yes.* And if he says yes, Scribs will just have to let me work on the paper.

SNAPS: But where does that leave me? I thought we were working together.

SNOOP: So did I till you began to get the jitters. Grab your camera and come along. There might be something important for you to do.

SNAPS: But, gosh, Snoops, we shouldn't walk out and leave the office empty like this with nobody in charge.

SNOOP: I'll fix that. (*Picks up card which reads "Out to Lunch."*) We'll shut the door and hang this on the outside. (*Curtains close slowly as* SNOOP *and* SNAPS *walk out on stage apron.* SNOOP *pins her sign on the closed curtain.*) There. Now everything is under control till we get back with the ad.

SNAPS: I hope you're not joking, sister, because if we come back without the ad it'll be curtains for you and me.

SNOOP (*As they exit*): Aw, don't be so pessimistic. With my brains and your camera, we can't lose. (*After a short pause,* SCRIBS, SPIKE, DAN *and* JULIE, WALT *and* GEORGE *enter on apron in front of closed curtain. They stare at the sign in surprise.*)

SCRIBS: "Out to lunch!" Can you beat that?

SPIKE: The nerve of some people's children!

WALT: I bet those kids walked out and left all those blanks for us to fold.

JULIE: Open up, Scribs, and let's see if there's anything left of the office. (*Curtains open on office.*)

WALT: What did I tell you? All those blanks — just as we left them.

GEORGE: At least they haven't dynamited the place.

SCRIBS: I'll dynamite the pair of them if they ever show their faces here again.

DAN: And I'll touch off the fuse that blows them up. Seventh-graders! Phooey!

WALT: Oh, well, we can't judge all of them by the actions of those two flutter-bugs.

JULIE: Since you are so scathing in your remarks about the seventh-grade, it amazes me that you mental giants in the ninth grade haven't conjured up a way to sell that advertising space which is supposed to save us from ruin.

WALT: Don't bring that up again, or you'll have to buy me some aspirin.

SPIKE: Now that we are back on the painful subject, why don't we toss a coin or pull straws or something to see which of us will be the one to tackle Mr. Foose the second time. I am inclined to think what he needs is a series of concentrated attacks to soften him up.

GEORGE: I have a better idea. Down at the Grille I made up one of those Thought Twisters like Dr. I.Q. uses on his program. I'll give each one of you a try at it and whoever makes the most mistakes is the victim. What do you say?

SPIKE: I'll have a try.

JULIE: Me, too. He can't do any more than eat me.

DAN: Let's have your silly old thought twister. I'll beat the lot of you.

SCRIBS: My editorial brain shouldn't let me down. Let's hear it, George.

GEORGE: Remember, you must repeat it exactly as I say it, and I'll say it only once. Spike, you can be first. Listen carefully. "Mr. Foose, you're a goose to hang on to that moose," said Alexander Swoose to Foose. "You *are* a goose, Foose, to hang on to that moose," to him said Swoose.

SPIKE (*Slowly*): Mr. Foose, you're a goose to hang on to that moose — (SNOOP *enters in time to hear the last line. She is in a state of ecstasy and excitement.*)

SNOOP: But he didn't hang on to it! Oh, Scribs, I have the most wonderful news!

SCRIBS: She's back again!

GEORGE: Get her out of here.

DAN: If you know what's good for you, young'un, you'll leave here on the double.

JULIE: I'm afraid they mean business, Snoopie. Why don't you run along and stop bothering us?

SNOOP: Oh, listen to me, please, Scribs, it's about Mr. Foose.

WALT: Foose? What about him?

SNOOP: I've been to see him, and what do you think?

SPIKE: He threw you out.

SNOOP: He did not. (*Points dramatically to* SNAPS, *who is just entering, carrying a large mounted moosehead.*) He gave us the moose! (*The whole staff is knocked speechless by this announcement.* SCRIBS *collapses on a nearby table. They all stare at* SNAPS *as he carries his burden center stage.*)

SNAPS: Where'll I put it?

SNOOP (*Airily*): Oh, anywhere. Just set it down there for the present. (SNAPS *deposits the moose in the Editor's chair.*)

SCRIBS: And I thought I had seen everything.

GEORGE: You two make me sick. What is all this anyhow?

SNOOP: It's a gift from Mr. Foose. He said we could have it to hang in our office. Wasn't that darling of him?

JULIE: Darling isn't the word for it.

DAN: If only you could tell whatever it is you have to tell from the beginning.

SNOOP: Well, I'm trying to, but somebody is always interrupting.

SNAPS: Gee! It was terrific. You should have seen how Snoopie talked to Mr. Foose and he just ate it up. Wait till you see my pictures!

SCRIBS: Pictures! Merciful Moses! Pictures!

SNOOP: You really gave me the idea, George, when you said how fond Mr. Foose was of the moose. I based my whole campaign on that.

WALT: Campaign? What campaign?

SNOOP: My advertising campaign. (*Opens notebook and tears out a sheet of paper which she hands to* WALT.) Here — here is the paper he signed promising to buy the whole back page for the season.

WALT: My great Aunt Bessie! She's gone and done it! This is the old man's signature.

SCRIBS (*Snatching paper*): I don't believe it. Let me see! Why, it's the real thing!

SNOOP: Certainly it's the real thing. What do you think I am — a forger?

SCRIBS: Right now I think you're a miracle woman.

GEORGE: I still don't believe it.

SNAPS: You'll believe it all right when you see my pictures. I got one of Mr. Foose signing the paper.

JULIE: Come on, Snoops, tell us how you did it.

SNOOP: I just used physiology.

ALL: Physiology?

JULIE (*Laughing*): You mean psychology!

SNOOP: Maybe I do. Anyhow — I just walked in and asked if I could interview his moose, and he said, "Sure, go ahead."

SCRIBS: This gets crazier and crazier. How could you interview a moose?

SNOOP: Easy. I told him we had a lot of students up here who are interested in things like hunting and fishing and trapping, and wild animals, and I wanted to write a story about the biggest moose in Elmville. So then he told me all about how he shot Felix — that's what he calls the moose — and I wrote it all down. It's right here in my notebook. Then Snaps asked if he could take a couple of pictures of Mr. Foose and the moose and he said, "Go ahead." So then, Snaps took the pictures, and —

DAN: Can't you slow up a minute? I'm losing track of the whole thing.

SNAPS: Oh, after that it was easy. He wanted to know when we were going to print the story and the pictures and Snoop told him she didn't exactly know because our paper was having budget trouble on account of not selling enough ads. And I piped up and said wasn't it a shame our paper would have to fold up all for the lack of a measly two hundred dollars.

SNOOP: So right after that he got out his check book. But I told him I wasn't on the business staff — yet — I was just a reporter, and he better wait till the real Business Manager came to see him. So I just brought this slip of paper with his signature so you would believe me.

SCRIBS: After this, I'll believe anything.

DAN: I still don't get the idea of the moose. How did you happen to get that in the bargain?

SNOOP: Oh, that was funny. The moose is sort of a peace offering. You see, Mr. Foose sort of liked Snaps and me. He said he was sick and tired of being pestered by a lot of smart Alecs who thought he should contribute to every cause in town, and he was glad to find out that kids are still interested in things like sports and hunting and fishing and outdoor life, so he thought it would be nice to put Felix where more young people could see him. I said the Office of the *Dive Bomber* would be the very place for him, and here he is.

SCRIBS: So I see.

GEORGE: So do we all see.

WALT: But what I don't see is what all this has to do with advertising.

SNAPS: That's where my picture comes in. We're going to use an enlargement of Old Long Horns there and underneath we'll print: "Felix the Moose says: Keep warm this winter with a Foose Automatic Heater."

SCRIBS: Well, boys and girls, we live and learn. I guess I not only owe you two several dozen apologies but also a place on the paper — that is, if you still care to work for such a doddering old idiot as your Uncle Scribs.

SNAPS: I'll say we do.

SNOOP: Oh, Scribs, I knew you'd come through.

SCRIBS: You're the one who came through, by having sense enough to use the human interest angle on Mr. Foose. Snoopie, you and Snaps and Felix have saved the *Dive Bomber,* so I'm going to promote all three of you. Snaps, you can be official cameraman for all seventh-grade activities. Snoop, you can be a regular reporter and assistant advertising scout. And Felix (*Picks up card which says* EDITOR) you can wear this title for a while. (*Hangs the placard around the neck of the moose.*) Fellow workers, salute your new boss. After this, we'll do what Felix says. (*All line up and salute Felix, propped up in the Editorial chair.* SPIKE *takes a place behind the chair and speaks in what he fancies is a Bull Moose Voice.*)

SPIKE: Felix says, "Get to work, you guys. This paper must go to press on time." (*All scatter to their places as the curtains close.*)

THE END

PRODUCTION NOTES

Snoop's Scoop

Characters: 6 male; 2 female.

Playing Time: 35 minutes.

Costumes: Everyday clothes.

Properties: Tabloid-size papers; placards reading, Editor, Reporters, Sports Department, Advertising Department; pencils, paper; tear sheets from newspapers showing advertisements; stack of small sheets of paper to represent subscription blanks, simulated moosehead, notebook, camera, typewriter.

Setting: Several desks and tables on which are desk lamps, a typewriter, a telephone, and stacks of papers, pen-stands, etc. Placards identifying the workers are tacked or set in stands on the desks or tables of the appropriate workers.

Lighting: None required.

CUPID ON THE LOOSE

Characters

HENRY
SYLVIA } *Patients of Cupid*
MOLLY
A POLICEMAN
CUPID, EROS, SON OF VENUS, *Heart Specialist*

SCENE: *A bench in the park.*

TIME: *The present.*

CUPID ON THE LOOSE

SETTING: *A park bench and a lamp post are all the setting required.*

AT RISE: HENRY *is leaning against the lamp post, his hands thrust into his pockets. He is whistling a mournful tune. Presently a middle-sized, pesty boy, comes flying across the stage on one roller skate. He does not see* HENRY *until it's too late to stop; but when he reaches the other side, he turns and pushes his way back to* HENRY *who ignores him. The* BOY *props his foot, the one with the skate, up on the bench to adjust the strap.*

CUPID: Don't suppose you got a skate key, Mister?

HENRY (*With heavy sarcasm*): Certainly, I always wear one around my neck on a black velvet ribbon. (*Angrily*) Of course, I don't have a skate key.

CUPID: I didn't think you did.

HENRY: Then why did you ask?

CUPID: I didn't ask.

HENRY: You did, too.

CUPID: Oh, no, I didn't. I just said, I don't *suppose* you have a skate key. And I was right. You haven't.

HENRY: All right, smarty, then you didn't ask. Now run along and sell your papers.

CUPID: I'm not selling papers.

HENRY: Then just run along.

CUPID: Where?

HENRY: Anywhere, but get going.

79

CUPID: Why?

HENRY: Because I want a little peace and quiet. That's why I came to this park — in search of peace and quiet; and all I get is a poll parrot on roller skates.

CUPID: Gosh, Mister, you sure don't believe in sticking to facts, do you? First place, I'm no poll parrot; second place I'm not on roller skates. This is only one, (*Holding up foot*) not two. Say, Mister, do you have stomach ulcers?

HENRY: Not that it is any of your business, but no.

CUPID (*Relieved*): I'm glad to hear that.

HENRY (*Sitting on bench*): These questions of yours must be contagious. You have me asking them. Just why are you rejoicing over the health of my stomach?

CUPID: Because that will make it so much easier.

HENRY: What will make what easier?

CUPID: Getting you in a good humor. You might not know it, Mister, but you show all the signs of suffering from stomach ulcers, liver complaint, or gout. Now your complexion is too pink and white for liver trouble; you're not old enough for gout and you've just denied the stomach ulcers.

HENRY: So what?

CUPID: I can cure you.

HENRY: Cure me of what? There's nothing wrong with me.

CUPID: Oh, yes, there is, Mister. A man can't be as cross as you are without some cause, and I know the cause.

HENRY: You are the craziest kid I ever saw and also one of the freshest.

CUPID: Just look at that! How excited and irritated you become over nothing at all. Steady, Mister. Steady!

HENRY (*Fairly shouting*): Stop calling me *Mister*.

CUPID: Why?

HENRY: Because it makes me nervous — gives me the jitters.

CUPID: But what shall I call you? Do you like *Sir* better?

HENRY: If you must call me anything, my name is Henry.

CUPID: Henry? That's a good enough name — a bit over-worked just now on account of the Aldrich Family, but it's better than most.

HENRY: And what might your name be, little man?

CUPID: As a matter of fact, my name is Cupid.

HENRY (*Fairly rolling off the bench with laughter*): Cupid! Oh, my sainted aunt! Cupid! That's a good one.

CUPID: Certainly, it's a good one. What's so funny?

HENRY: Don't you know who Cupid is or was?

CUPID: Sure, he is and was me.

HENRY: No, no, no. According to the old legends, Cupid was the little God of Love who went around shooting folks with a tiny bow and arrow. Don't you know that?

CUPID: Of course I know it.

HENRY: Then can't you see it's a funny name? Ye gods! Cupid! Don't the fellows tease you about it?

CUPID (*Producing slingshot*): If they do, I give 'em a load of this.

HENRY: Say, put that thing away. First thing you know, you'll be in jail for breaking windows.

CUPID: Oh, I never break windows. I use this for hearts.

HENRY: Are you crazy?

CUPID: It wouldn't do any good to deny it, for you have already made up your mind that I am.

HENRY: On second thought, I am the crazy one for wasting my time with you. Seriously, though, that monicker, Cupid, will be a dreadful handicap when you grow up.

CUPID: But I don't expect to grow up.

HENRY: Oh, but you will. I know you have every right to expect someone to murder you, but you'll probably live to a ripe old age. And I tell you you'll be a regular laughing stock. Imagine a doctor or a lawyer, or a mechanic, or a plumber named Cupid. (*Laughs*)

CUPID: I tell you I *won't* grow up. I'm as big as I'll ever be.

HENRY (*With curiosity*): You mean you're a midget?

CUPID: No, I'm not a midget. I've grown some. I got big enough to wear regular clothes, but I'll not grow much taller.

HENRY: How do you know? Did a doctor tell you?

CUPID: Heck, no. I've never needed a doctor.

HENRY: Maybe it's your glands. I had a cousin once who weighed almost three hundred pounds, and all the trouble was with his glands.

CUPID: You don't understand. My glands are O.K. I'm not sick. You're the patient and I'm going to cure you.

HENRY: Very well, if you're so smart, what's wrong with me?

CUPID: You have heart trouble.

HENRY: I have not. Listen here, my fine friend, I'll have you know I have a complete physical check-up every six months and I'm as sound as —

CUPID: Now don't tell me you're as sound as a nut. That has nothing to do with it. You have heart trouble, and I'm going to cure you. Tell me, is there a woman in your life?

HENRY (*Lunges at him, but he skates out of reach*): Just let me get my hands on you and I'll show you a thing or two.

CUPID (*From a safe distance*): Aha, I thought so. There *is* a woman. You wouldn't be so riled if there wasn't. Now please calm down a minute, Henry, and let's talk things over.

HENRY: I don't want to talk things over; I'd rather turn you over, over my knee and teach you a few manners. Then you'd find out how strong I really am.

CUPID: I have no doubt of your strength, but see here, Henry. Give me your word you'll let me come over there and sit down on that bench in safety and I'll explain a few things. Come now, promise not to be violent and I'll come over.

HENRY: O.K. I guess I have no right to wallop other people's kids.

CUPID: Phew! That's a relief. (*Sits on bench.*) Now, listen, Henry, please try to get this through that asbestos-lined skull of yours. I really am Cupid.

HENRY: Phooey!

CUPID: Listen, if I am not really and truly Cupid and if I cannot do everything I say I can, I'll let you carry out all those threats of violence and never utter a squawk.

HENRY: You must be insane.

CUPID: Answer a few questions for me.

HENRY: All right.

CUPID: What romantic holiday begins with Saint and ends with Day?

HENRY: St. Valentine's Day.

CUPID: Did you ever get any valentines?

HENRY: Often.

CUPID: With pictures?

HENRY: Sure.

CUPID: Pictures of me?

HENRY: No. No. Certainly not.

CUPID: Think hard, Henry. Wasn't there a picture of Cupid on some of your valentines?

HENRY: Sure, but it didn't look anything like you. It was a fat little fellow with wings and a tiny bow and arrow. Furthermore, he was not wearing a stitch of clothes.

CUPID: And just because I'm a little older and no longer fat. just because I'm wearing a roller skate instead of wings and carry a slingshot instead of a bow and arrow — just because the law and common decency require me to wear clothing, you refuse to believe I'm Cupid.

HENRY: I refuse to believe that your picture is used on valentines.

CUPID (*Sighing in despair*): You certainly do not have much imagination. Tell me, Henry, have you seen any baby pictures of yourself?

HENRY (*Proudly*): Sure. Lots of them. I was a beautiful baby.

CUPID: Then I'll bet that there is at least one snap showing a dear, little dimpled darling splashing in his bath or lying on his tummy in the sun — just as Mother Nature dressed him in his birthday suit. Come now, admit it. Didn't your doting parents have such a picture of you?

HENRY: I'll have to admit it, they did. It's the pride of our photograph album.

CUPID: Then you can surely understand why the whole world has the wrong picture of Cupid in mind. Why, that picture was taken when I was a mere babe. The trouble is that nowadays everybody is expecting to see a plump baby boy with a toy bow and arrow, and when I appear with my sling-shot, people just don't believe in me. They don't stop to think that times and styles have changed, and I've changed with them. Fortunately the business of falling in love is just as popular as ever.

HENRY: You're a mighty convincing speaker, my friend.

CUPID: But you refuse to call me by my real name, don't you?

HENRY: I can't call you Cupid till you've given me sufficient proof.

CUPID: I'll give you all the proof you want, if you'll just tell me your troubles.

HENRY: I guess I'm a chump. But here goes. I will confess I am suffering from a slight heart murmur caused by a certain young lady.

CUPID: Aha, now we're getting down to facts.

HENRY: The young lady in question won't even speak to me.

CUPID: Any particular reason? Say a quarrel or something?

HENRY: Oh, no, I've never even met her. I just admire her from afar. And she knows that I admire her but she won't even notice me.

CUPID: Then that's my job — to make her notice you?

HENRY: If you could do that, I'd almost believe that you really are Cupid.

CUPID: Consider it done. But you must do your part. Tell me her name and where she is most likely to be found at this hour.

HENRY: Her name is Sylvia and every day about this time, she waits for a bus on that corner. (*Points off right.*) That's why I'm here — just hoping to catch a glimpse of her.

CUPID: Sylvia. That's a romantic name and the sign of a pretty difficult case. Girls named Sylvia usually have minds of their own. But Cupid is daunted by nothing.

HENRY (*Excited*): Quick. Quick. There she is now.

CUPID (*Looking off right*): Where? Where?

HENRY: There. The little girl in the plaid jacket. Isn't she beautiful?

CUPID: I can't tell. She is looking down. Seems to be searching in her purse for something.

HENRY: Her bus fare. She always searches for it like that. Oh, dear! She's dropped her money. She's hunting for it on the pavement. I'll go help her find it.

CUPID: Nonsense! Stay right here. (*Begins to take aim with the slingshot.*) This will fix everything.

HENRY (*Horrified as he sees what* CUPID *is about to do. He tries to stop him from shooting.*) Here. Here. What on earth are you doing? Stop! Stop! (CUPID, *taking no notice of* HENRY, *pretends to snap his slingshot. There is a girl's scream offstage.*)

HENRY: Oh, my goodness! You've hit her! Oh my darling Sylvia. (*To* CUPID) You wretch. I'll skin you alive for this.

CUPID (*Hastily throwing slingshot on bench and skating off left, yelling*): I'll be back — later. (*He is hardly off stage when* SYLVIA *enters right. She is in a towering rage.*)

SYLVIA: Just let me get my hands on the person who did that. Just let me —(*Catching sight of* HENRY) Did you by chance see a small boy around here with a slingshot? (*Suddenly sees slingshot on bench*) So-o-o — it was you! I was looking for a child. I had no idea I'd find anyone old enough to know better. Well I'll teach you to play your tricks on the unsuspecting public. You can just take *that*. (*Slaps* HENRY, *who has been too dazed to move.*) And the very next time that you try any funny business like this, I'll not stop till I have you arrested and put behind bars.

HENRY (*Rubbing his cheek*): Oh, please, please don't think such a thing of me. Honestly, Sylvia, I can explain everything.

SYLVIA (*Angrier than ever*): Sylvia! The very idea of calling me by my first name! And how do you know who I am, anyway?

HENRY: Oh, forgive me. I know I am being rude, but you see — well —I've known who you are for weeks. I've seen you many times even if you haven't paid any attention to me.

SYLVIA (*Beginning to put two and two together*): Say, I seem to remember seeing you before. Several times I've seen you down at the bus stop and once or twice we've ridden on the same bus. Now I'm sure of it. I know what you've been doing. You've been following me. Now I am going to call the police. (*Yells*) Officer! Officer! Police! Help!

HENRY (*Trying to silence her*): Please! Please! Do be quiet. I haven't meant any harm. Please! I can explain everything if you just give me a chance.

SYLVIA: You can explain it to the judge. (*Continues to scream for a policeman. Curiously enough there is one in the immediate vicinity who comes running to her rescue.*)

HENRY: If ever I live to see that kid again I'll slay him with my own two hands. Please, please, Sylvia, be quiet. I tell you it's all a mistake.

POLICEMAN (*Running on stage from the left*): What's going on here? What's the trouble, lady? Has this fellow been annoying you?

SYLVIA: Yes, he has. He's been following me for weeks. Just now he shot at me with a slingshot and, what's more, he hit me.

POLICEMAN: He looks a trifle over age for schoolboy pranks. I guess he'll have to go along downtown with me.

HENRY: Officer, I can explain everything, if you'll just give me a chance.

POLICEMAN: They'll give you a chance at Headquarters. I got no time to listen to your phony alibis.

HENRY: But I tell you I didn't do it. Why, I wouldn't harm this young lady in any way. This is an outrage. You can't do this to me.

POLICEMAN: Oh, yes I can. You were disturbing the peace. That's what you were doing.

HENRY: I suppose it doesn't matter how much you disturb my peace — and for no reason at all. Look at that young lady. Do you think I would do anything to make her angry?

SYLVIA: Pay no attention to him, Officer. Right here is his weapon. (*Displays slingshot.*)

HENRY: But it isn't mine, I tell you. It belongs to a little boy. He ran off and left it here.

SYLVIA (*In disgust*): I don't think that is very manly — trying to put the blame on a little child.

HENRY: But it's true. Honest, it is. The little imp took a shot at you before I could stop him.

POLICEMAN: And just who is this juvenile Giant-Killer? If it's any kid in the neighborhood, I'll round him up. Did you get his name?

HENRY: Yes, yes, I did — but —

POLICEMAN: Well, what is it?

HENRY (*Much embarrassed*): Well, of course I know it wasn't his *real* name, but he *said* his name was Cupid.

SYLVIA: Officer, this man is crazy. It's not safe to let him run loose. I demand that he be locked up.

HENRY: I'm only telling you what he told me. You must believe me.

POLICEMAN: I've heard some weird stories in my time, but yours is the grand-daddy of them all. Where is this Cupid that you're talking about?

HENRY (*Pointing left*): He ran off there, after he shot the young lady.

POLICEMAN: Aw, no, he didn't. I was standing right there in the middle of the block, and no Cupid came past me.

HENRY: Didn't you see a little boy about so high (*Indicates height*) wearing one roller skate?

POLICEMAN: I did not and, what's more, you didn't either. Now you better be nice and quiet and come along with me peaceably, or we'll have some bad trouble here, my lad.

SYLVIA: Do be careful, Officer, that man is capable of anything. He might hurt you.

HENRY (*With resignation*): I give up. Go ahead and arrest me, but I tell you there was a boy here just a minute ago. And he did call himself *Cupid*.

CUPID (*Entering suddenly from left*): Hi-yuh Henry? How you doing?

HENRY: There he is. Catch him! Catch him!

SYLVIA (*In astonishment*) And he does have one roller skate —just as you said.

POLICEMAN: Hey, you, is this your slingshot?

CUPID: It sure is, Officer. Thanks. I must have dropped it— accidentally, of course.

POLICEMAN: I have a few important questions to ask you, Buddy. Have you ever seen this fellow before?

CUPID: Of course. That's my pal — Henry.

POLICEMAN: And this young lady?

CUPID: I've seen her from a distance, but I've never actually met her. Come to think of it, I guess I owe her an apology.

POLICEMAN: What for?

CUPID (*Holding up slingshot*): For this. I hope you'll forgive me, Miss Sylvia, but I assure you I acted purely in the interest of science.

POLICEMAN: So you're the guilty one.

HENRY: There — what did I tell you?

SYLVIA: Oh, Henry — I mean — Sir, will you ever forgive me? I am so ashamed of the way I acted. And to think I actually slapped you!

HENRY: Aw, that's all right, Sylvia. Gosh! Do you mind if I call you Sylvia? After all this I feel as if we were well acquainted.

SYLVIA: I think you are pretty wonderful not to be angry.

HENRY: I've thought you were wonderful for a long time now. (*Automobile horn*)

SYLVIA: Oh, my goodness, that's my bus. Thank you, Officer, for coming to my rescue, but as it turned out, there is no need for you to arrest this young man. I withdraw all my charges against him. Goodbye, and thank you again.

POLICEMAN: Well, I guess that's that.

HENRY: Oh, wait a minute, please, Sylvia. Won't you let me take you home?

SYLVIA: I'd be delighted, only —

HENRY: Only what?

SYLVIA: Only I should think you'd never want to see me again.

HENRY: On the contrary —

POLICEMAN: Say, wait a minute, you two. What am I to do

with this young jackanapes? By the way, Boy, what is your real name?

CUPID: Didn't *he* tell you?

HENRY: You know, Officer, I'm beginning to think it wasn't a nickname after all. I believe he really *is* Cupid. What do you think, Sylvia?

SYLVIA: I'm not quite sure yet, but time will tell. (*Horn*) But hurry. Let's not miss that bus. (SYLVIA *and* HENRY *exit running.*)

POLICEMAN: See here, Buddy, you can't kid the law. I want your real name, your parents' names and your address. (*Gets notebook ready.*)

CUPID (*Producing huge red heart from underneath his coat. He hands it to the* POLICEMAN *as a name card, reading it aloud as he does so.*) My card, Sir. At your service, Sir. (*Reads.*)

Cupid — alias Eros
Son of Venus
Residence — Mt. Olympus
Expert Love Consultant and Heart Specialist
Services Free — Upon Request

POLICEMAN: Listen to me, boy, this is neither the time nor place for monkeyshines. Do I look as if I'm the type for nonsense?

CUPID: I really couldn't say, Sir, but I know you have a most romantic heart under that uniform. And just to prove that I'm right I'm going to let you in on a little secret about yourself. Right this minute you would give your next month's pay to take Molly Murphy to the Policeman's Ball tonight. Isn't that true? Now be a sport, Officer, and own up.

POLICEMAN: How could you be knowing that, you limb of Satan?

CUPID: Never mind how I found out — I know. If I can fix things up with the little lady, will you let me go?

POLICEMAN: I'll not only let you go, I'll buy you a year's supply of these slingshots.

CUPID: It's a deal. (*Suddenly takes aim at someone in the audience.*) Steady now, and I'll make her yours in one shot.

POLICEMAN (*Horrified*): See here, you can't do that. Stop it, I tell you! Stop, in the name of the law! (CUPID *shoots slingshot toward audience. Scream from* MOLLY, *who is sitting in audience.*) Begorra, you've hit her. That's Molly's voice. (MOLLY *comes up aisle to stage.*)

MOLLY: Patrick, Patrick, where are you?

POLICEMAN: Right here I am, my darling, and if you hurry, we'll be just in time to use these two tickets to the Policeman's Ball. Unless, of course, you've still got your stubborn little head set on going with Timothy O'Shay.

MOLLY (*Taking* POLICEMAN'S *arm*): Faith, there's no room in my heart for anyone but you, Patrick Monahan, and I promise you we'll be the finest couple at the ball. (POLICEMAN *and* MOLLY *start to exit left, but* POLICEMAN *comes back on stage.*)

POLICEMAN: Pardon me, Molly, but I must have a word with this lad. Good work, me boy, good work! But mind you, be careful of this contraption. Whether it's broken windows or broken hearts — 'tis a mighty dangerous weapon. Use it with care.

CUPID: I'll be careful, Officer, I promise you. You and your lady enjoy yourselves.

POLICEMAN: That we will, me boy, that we will.

CUPID (*Advancing to curtain line and addressing the audience*): Ladies and gentlemen, I can see the stage crew are about to close the curtains so now that I have disposed of the affairs of Henry and the problems of the policeman, I would like to deliver my message to you.   (*Produces second paper heart from pocket and reads.*)

> Roses are red,
> Violets are blue,
> *You* believe in *me,*
> And I'll believe in you.
> For whether I'm Cupid,
> Or whether I'm not,
> I've a jolly good aim
> With this magic slingshot.
> So if you have heart trouble,
> Girl friend or beau,
> You better see me
> Right after the show.

THE END

PRODUCTION NOTES

Cupid on the Loose

Characters: 3 male; 2 female.

Playing Time: 20 minutes.

Costumes: Sylvia wears a plaid jacket and skirt, and carries a purse. Henry and Molly are in everyday clothes. The policeman wears a uniform. Cupid may be dressed in boy's play clothes. He carries a slingshot.

Properties: A roller skate; slingshot; notebook for policeman; two large red hearts.

Setting: A park bench and a lamp post are all that is required.

Lighting: None required.

HOMEWORK

Characters

PAPA PEPPER
MRS. PEPPER
TIMOTHY PEPPER
TRUDY PEPPER
HELEN PEPPER
MUSCLES MURRAY

SCENE: *The living room of the Pepper home.*

TIME: *The present.*

HOMEWORK

SETTING: *The living room of the Pepper home. It has been transformed into a combination workshop and study.*

AT RISE: MRS. PEPPER *is seated at a table upstage working on an electric toaster which she is trying to repair according to instructions from a manual.* PAPA PEPPER, *in his shirt sleeves, is working at a drafting board centre.* TIMOTHY *is working with some Pre-Flight tests.* HELEN *is seated at a card table piled high with textbooks on chemistry. There is a pause after the curtain opens, as everyone works at his appointed task. By facial expression and pantomime, each member of the cast should show that the going is a bit difficult. From offstage comes the sound of scales being practiced on a piano. The same exercise should be repeated several times with the same mistake being made at the same place each time.*

TIMOTHY (*Flinging down his book in despair*): For heaven's sake, cut out that racket. Mother, can't you make Trudy stop pounding on that piano?

MOTHER (*Without raising her eyes from the toaster*): She's only practicing her music lesson, dear.

HELEN: Well, hasn't she practiced long enough? She's gone over that same exercise at least twenty-five times and is still making the same mistake. It's getting on my nerves.

MR. PEPPER: And on mine too. It's bad enough I have to pay for her music lessons without having to listen to her practice. Why can't she do that when I'm not home?

MOTHER: But I always depend on you, dear, to make her stick with her practicing. I never did think Trudy was very

97

musical, but just because you had a cousin who was a concert pianist you have always been determined to give her piano lessons. Personally, I think she'd do better at elocution.

TIMOTHY: Electrocution would be more suitable if you ask me.

MOTHER: You have no room to talk, Timothy, after what we've been through with your saxophone.

TIMOTHY: But at least I can play it. Besides, she's making it impossible for me to concentrate. I'll have you know these Pre-Flight courses are no cinch.

MR. PEPPER: Tim's right, Mother. If we're all going to take these Home Study courses this winter, we'll have to have peace and quiet in the evenings. Trudy must find another hour for her practice.

MOTHER: Very well. I'll call her. (*Calling*) Trudy, Trudy... you may stop now.

TRUDY (*Offstage*): But the hour isn't up. I have fifteen minutes to go.

HELEN: Can you beat it? Any other time she'd be dying to quit before the hour was up.

MOTHER: It's all right, dear. Father says you may skip those last fifteen minutes.

TRUDY (*With a final bang on the piano*): Whoopee! That's swell! (*Runs into the room*) Thanks a lot, Dad. Come on, Tim, let's play some table tennis.

TIMOTHY: Nothing doing. I have to plug away at this engine material.

TRUDY: O.K. We'll play later. Come on, Sis, let's make some fudge.

HELEN: Not tonight, Trudy. I have a long assignment in my chemistry course, and it's going to keep me busy.

TRUDY: I never knew you were such a plugger. Well, Dad, it looks as if you and I were going to be partners. How about a game of rummy? Bet I can trim you. (*Hangs over the back of his chair.*)

Mr. Pepper: Not tonight, Trudy. And don't joggle me when I'm drawing.

Trudy: Sorry. I guess this is no place for me. Mother, will you show me how to set the sleeve in that sweater I'm knitting?

Mother: Some other time, dear. Not now. I'm too busy with this toaster.

Trudy: What's the matter with it?

Mother: Oh, it's just an old one I found down in the cellar. It hasn't worked for years.

Trudy: But there's nothing the matter with our good one. Why don't you use that?

Mother: We do. I'm just experimenting with this for my assignment in Home Repairing.

Trudy: Phew! This is the busiest family I ever saw. Do you care if I go to the movies?

Mother: You went to the movies last night, Trudy. You know I don't like you to go on school nights. Why don't you do your homework?

Mr. Pepper: Yes, for mercy's sake. Go get a book and settle yourself. It's high time you were doing your lessons.

Trudy: They're all done.

Timothy (*Incredulously*): Ha! A likely story!

Trudy (*Indignant*): They are so! I had three study periods in school today and I finished everything.

Helen: Three study periods! That's the limit! We never had more than one a week when I was in Junior High School.

Trudy: Oh, but that was years ago. Things are more modern now. Say, do you want to hear a good joke I heard today?

Mr. Pepper: No, we don't want to hear any jokes. Can't you see we're all working? Clear out of here or keep quiet so we can think.

Trudy: But my goodness, I'm not doing anything because I don't have anything to do...unless I play the radio.

HELEN: Heaven forbid! That's all we need!...

MOTHER: Can't you read a book?

TRUDY: Nope. I owe a fine at the library, and I can't get any more books till I pay it, and I can't pay it till I get my allowance, and I won't get my allowance till next week, so I can't get any more books till then.

TIMOTHY: Ye gods! Mother, can't you make her get out of here? I've read this paragraph three times and I still don't know what it means. (*Mutters to himself as he rereads a paragraph.*)

MR. PEPPER: Keep quiet. First thing I'll be doing your problems instead of my own. Trudy, I'll give you exactly three seconds to find yourself something to do or go to bed.

MOTHER: Oh, now, James, don't be so impatient. Listen, Trudy, you can see we're all busy tonight. Now be a good girl and go upstairs to your room.

TRUDY: But, mother, it's too cold up there. How about letting me go over to Louise Anderson's?

MOTHER: The Andersons are having company tonight. I met Mrs. Anderson at market today. She's entertaining her bridge club.

TRUDY: Then that's out. (*Phone rings*) I hope that's for me.

MR. PEPPER: Well, if it is, make it snappy. Don't hang on the wire the rest of the evening.

TRUDY (*At phone*): Hello...Yes, yes...this is Trudy Pepper. Who? (*Pleased*) Oh, it's you, Muscles. (*In a stage whisper*) It's Muscles Murray. (*Into phone*) Yeah...No, I'm not doing a thing. What? Well, just a minute...I'll have to ask. (*Putting hand over the mouthpiece of phone and speaking to her mother.*) Mother, it's Muscles Murray. He wants me to go to the movies with him. May I, Mother, please?

HELEN: Forever more! Don't tell me you're beginning to have dates at your age!

TRUDY (*To* HELEN): Oh, be quiet. (*To* MRS. PEPPER) Please, Mother, can't I go?

MOTHER: Of course not. I just finished telling you I don't like you to go to the movies on school nights. Besides I don't know this Murray boy.

TRUDY: Oh he's nice. Honest, he's swell. Please, Mother. We'll be home early.

MR. PEPPER: You heard what your mother said.

TRUDY: But, Dad...Please! If I don't go, he might never ask me again.

MR. PEPPER: That would be a good thing. Now tell him you can't go and hang up. (*To himself*) A man can't have a minute's peace in his own house.

TRUDY (*Almost in tears*): Hello...I'm awful sorry, Muscles, but I can't go this evening. Yeah...Yeah...Me too...I'm devastated. Maybe some other time? What? What's that? You want to come over? Well, wait a minute. I'll have to ask again. (*With hand over mouthpiece*) Mother, now he wants to come over here. Is it all right?

MR. PEPPER: It certainly is not all right. I don't want any more people around this house tonight. Tell him no. He can't come.

TRUDY: Oh, Dad, he'll think we're terrible. He doesn't know very many people. He just moved here from Chicago.

MR. PEPPER: Well, let him move back again. He can't come over here tonight.

TRUDY: Oh, Mother, can't you make Dad understand? I just can't tell him you don't want him.

MOTHER: But, Trudy, you heard what your father said. Just tell him some other time.

TRUDY (*Desperate*): I can't. I simply can't. (*Hangs up receiver.*) I'll just hang up on him. There! Maybe he'll think we were cut off. (*Begins to cry.*) I don't see why he couldn't come over. He's the nicest boy in our room. Nobody around this house even cares if I turn out to be an old maid. You're all too busy improving your minds to care what becomes of me.

TIMOTHY: Good grief! Now she's bawling. You should have let her go to the movies. Then she'd have been out of the house.

MOTHER: You keep out of this, Timothy. Trudy is too young to be running around with boys.

TRUDY: It was only one boy, and we wouldn't be running around. We'd be right here at home. I didn't care about the movies, but I don't see why he couldn't come over here. (*Crying harder*) Now he'll never call me again...never!

MOTHER: Now don't cry about it, dear. You have plenty of time for boys to call you up. Oh my! This is a distressing evening. Please, Trudy, control yourself.

HELEN: I was never allowed to go out with boys when I was her age.

TIMOTHY: Muscles! What a beautiful name! What is he? Champion prize fighter or something?

TRUDY: You keep quiet, Timothy Pepper. All you care about is airplanes, and you don't know as much about them as you think you do. Muscles knows twice as much now as you'll ever know about engines.

TIMOTHY: Pardon me! I thought his name was Muscles... not Brains.

TRUDY: Some people can have both, and then again, other people have neither.

HELEN: This is childish. Mother, can't you do something with her? I'll never get anywhere with all this confusion.

TRUDY: I suppose you think everybody will keep perfectly quiet whenever you want to do something.

HELEN: After this, I'll study in my own room even if the furnace is broken.

TRUDY: You won't have to. I'll go up to my room where I won't disturb you...even if I freeze.

MOTHER: Maybe it would be a good idea to cool off your temper a bit. (*Doorbell rings*) Answer the door, dear. I do hope we're not getting company. (TRUDY *starts towards door.*)

TRUDY (*At door*): Well, for goodness' sake! Where did you come from?

MUSCLES (*Offstage*): Hy'a, Trudy! Something must be wrong with that telephone of ours. I came over to find out if it's O.K. for me to spend the evening. We were cut off before you ever had a chance to tell me.

TRUDY (*Flustered*): Well, my goodness! Oh dear! Well... I certainly wasn't expecting you. I...You...I guess you'd better go home.

MUSCLES: What's the matter? Isn't it all right? Of course, if you have company, I'll shove off.

TRUDY: Oh, we don't exactly have company, but...

MR. PEPPER: Tell whoever that is to come in or get out; and get that door shut. You're wasting the heat.

MUSCLES (*Entering*): Gee, that's good news, Mr. Pepper. I'm sure glad to come inside. It's cold over at our house too. Every time my folks go out for the evening they turn the oil burner down so low that I practically get chilblains. I guess you never met me, did you? I'm Muscles Murray, your new neighbor. I guess you're Trudy's Dad.

MR. PEPPER: That's who I am, all right, and I suppose you're the young man who called on the phone a few moments ago.

MUSCLES (*Laughing*): Yeah, wasn't that the limit? Central cut us off before Trudy got a chance to give me the go signal ...or I guess I should say the come-ahead signal. But, thinks

I, I'll just hop over there and find out for myself, if it's not O.K., if they have company or something, I'll just hop back again. I sure am glad it's all right.

MRS. PEPPER (*Looking doubtfully at* MR. PEPPER): Well, I guess it's all right, now that you're here...but...

MUSCLES: Thanks, Mrs. Pepper. Thanks a lot. You *are* Mrs. Pepper, aren't you?

TRUDY: Sure, sure, she's Mrs. Pepper. And this is my brother, Timothy, and this my sister, Helen.

MUSCLES (*In response to nods from* TIM *and* HELEN): Glad to know you! By golly, this looks like a study hall, doesn't it, Trudy? I should have brought my homework...only...

TIMOTHY (*With sarcasm*): Only it's all done...like Trudy's.

MUSCLES: Right. With all those study periods, we kids get a break for once.

HELEN (*Grimly*): What a break!

MUSCLES: I'll say! It's swell. Nothing to do in the evenings but visit the neighbors. It's a great life.

MRS. PEPPER: I'm sorry we don't seem more hospitable, Muscles, but we're each taking a home study course this winter and we're taking our work pretty seriously, so we have to have things quiet for our study hour.

MUSCLES: Sure. I understand that. What are you studying, Mrs. Pepper? You seem to be having an awful struggle with that toaster.

MRS. PEPPER: Yes, I'm afraid I don't have a mechanical mind. I'm taking a course in Household Repairs and this toaster is my assignment. I think I could do better with a wire hairpin and the touch system than following the instructions in this manual.

MUSCLES: Maybe I could help you.

TRUDY: Muscles is awfully smart in shopwork and things like that.

Mrs. Pepper: Well...you see...here is the diagram in the manual...But I don't know if this wire here...gets twisted around this thing-amabob or whether it should tie up with this long dangly thing on the other end.

Muscles: Well, I tell you, Mrs. Pepper, I think you have your wires crossed somewhere...but let's have a look at it. Oh this is going to be easy. If you tighten this connection here... like this...and scrape off the end of this wire, I believe everything will be O.K. There... that looks better. I believe you'll have a first-rate toaster here in no time.

Mrs. Pepper: For mercy's sake, is that all it needed?

Muscles: Just a simple twist of the wrist apparently.

Mrs. Pepper: And do you really think it will work now?

Muscles: You'll have toast before you can say "zippety-doo-dah." Let's go plug it in and give it a try.

Mrs. Pepper (*Rising*): I can hardly wait to see if it works. Come along, Trudy. We'll try it out. (Trudy, Mrs. Pepper *and* Muscles *exit.*)

Timothy: Good night, Dad! Can't you get rid of that drip? He'll drive us crazy. The nerve of him coming here to see if he could come over.

Mr. Pepper: The minute he sets foot in this room again, I'm going to send him home. For the past hour I've been trying to get some sense out of this diagram and I can't figure it out at all.

Timothy (*Sarcastically*): No doubt, Muscles, the Mental Giant, could clear it up for you in nothing flat. Trudy seems to think he's Superman.

Helen: Maybe he was a chemist when he was a baby. I might ask him to help me with this.

Timothy: Just for fun, I'll ask him a question or two about airplane engines when he comes back.

Mr. Pepper: Make it snappy because he won't be here long.

TRUDY (*As they re-enter*): You sure fixed that toaster in a hurry.

MRS. PEPPER: You certainly did. Now come along, Muscles, and explain just exactly what you did, so I can write up the experiment.

MUSCLES: Oh, it was as easy as ABC. It was just a matter of...

TIMOTHY (*Interrupting*): They tell me you're quite the boy with airplanes, Muscles. Know anything about engines?

MUSCLES: Oh, not very much. Are you taking a Pre-Flight course?

TIMOTHY: Yeah. And I'm boning up on engines right now.

MUSCLES: That ought to be interesting. I used to be keen on engines. What type are you studying? Radial engines?

TIMOTHY (*Blankly*): Radial?

MUSCLES: Yes...the kind in which the cylinders are equally spaced around a single crank of a crankshaft.

TIMOTHY (*Showing surprise*): No...er...no...the question that I'm working on right now wants to know the advantages of the V or inverted type of engine.

MUSCLES (*Leaning over his shoulder to look at his book*): Well...let me see. Of course one advantage of the V-type is that it improves the visibility for the pilot. And then, of course, the V-Type gives better streamlining and at the same time lowers the centre of gravity. Then you might also mention that it increases propeller clearance over the ground. That's about all I can think of offhand but that should cover the advantages.

TIMOTHY (*In admiration*): Yeah! Gosh, it sure ought to cover everything. Say, while you're here, you might take a look at that first question. I wasn't quite sure of that one.

MUSCLES (*Reading*): "In a four-stroke cycle engine, how many strokes really produce power?" Oh, no. This is wrong. You see the answer would be only one out of four, because the power stroke is produced by the ignition and expansion of the gas within the cylinder.

TIMOTHY: That's right. Well, thanks, Muscles. Thanks a lot.

MUSCLES: Maybe I could help you with some of those other questions. Airplanes are one of my hobbies.

TIMOTHY: You sure do seem to understand them.

TRUDY: I told you he knew all about engines.

HELEN: So you did. But you didn't tell us if he knows anything about chemistry.

TRUDY: That's what Helen's taking up. I think she's crazy. And besides, chemicals have such awful smells. I'd rather study tap dancing.

MUSCLES: I'm a little rusty on chemistry, Miss Pepper, but I'll help you all I can.

HELEN: I'm not very advanced. We're just working on the molecular theory and I get atoms and molecules all mixed up.

MUSCLES: I think I can help you with that. You see, an atom is the smallest particle which enters into a chemical equation. When two or more atoms unite chemically, they form a molecule. We'll say one atom of carbon unites with 2 atoms of oxygen and forms one molecule of what, Miss Pepper?

HELEN: Umm! I guess that would be one molecule of carbon dioxide.

MUSCLES: That's right. And the equation for that would be
$$C + O_2 = CO_2$$

HELEN: I see. Thanks a lot.

TRUDY: My goodness, Muscles! You're turning out to be a big help to my family. Maybe you could even help Dad.

MR. PEPPER: I hardly think so. Electronics is college stuff.

MUSCLES: Electronics, eh? Yes, I guess you're right. I wouldn't be much help in that department. Just what are you working on, Mr. Pepper? A diagram?

Mr. Pepper: Yes. I'm showing the potential distribution in a two electrode tube in a vacuum.

Muscles: Ummmm. Pretty difficult, isn't it?

Mr. Pepper: It's not easy.

Muscles: Mind if I give it a try?

Mr. Pepper: Think you could?

Muscles: I don't know. I'm a little rusty on this sort of thing....But I'll see what I can do. (*Sits at table.*) Now let me see...(*Draws for a few moments in silence.*)

Mr. Pepper (*Looking over his shoulder*): By Jiminy! I believe you've got it!

Mrs. Pepper: How marvelous, Muscles!

Timothy: Some kid, I'd say!

Helen: We should get you to be our instructor, Muscles.

Mr. Pepper: Yes, sir...my boy...that does the trick.

Muscles: Yes, I think you'll find that O.K. Now you'll want to jot down the explanation for your notes.

Mr. Pepper: This is great. Here I've been struggling with that blasted thing all evening. Let me have another look at it.

Muscles: Shall I go over the explanation step by step?

Mr. Pepper: O.K. Shoot. (*Writes as* Muscles *dictates.*)

Muscles: Well, first you draw a two electrode tube having electrode F and B with a difference of a potential 100 volts between them. Obviously, the potential at F is zero or around potential, and as the point of view moves from F to B, the potential must rise from zero to one hundred volts. Got that straight?

Mr. Pepper: Yep. Go ahead.

Muscles: Well, then, the manner of the rise of the potential from F to B is shown by curves. If F and B consist of cold parallel plates, the change of potential along a line near the centre of the plates will be uniform and we've represented that by a straight line. If F is a small round wire (cold) and P is a hollow concentric cylinder surrounding F, the potential gradient near the wire will be high, owing to a strong electrostatic field, and then fall off as B is approached. Such a case may be represented, as we did here, by a curve.

MR. PEPPER: Well, that puts it all in fine shape. Thanks a million, my boy.

MUSCLES: You're certainly welcome. That was fun. I haven't had a problem like that in a long time.

TIMOTHY: Holy smokes! How old are you?

MUSCLES: Fourteen my next birthday. Why?

TIMOTHY: Well, I must say, I never met anybody like you. How in the world do you know all this stuff?

HELEN: Trudy didn't tell us you were a child prodigy.

MUSCLES: If she had, I'd have cut her up in little pieces. I'm not a child prodigy.

MR. PEPPER: Well, you must be something special to work out my diagram and help Tim with his engines.

HELEN: And straighten me out with my chemistry.

MRS. PEPPER: To say nothing of my toaster.

MUSCLES: Aw, heck! I didn't want to tell anybody, but you folks have been so nice about letting me come over tonight. You see, I was...well...my real name is Myron Murray. Maybe you've heard of me or something.

TIM: Not Myron Murray the Boy Wizard! Not the kid who won the National Radio Prizes on the Science Quiz Programs!

MUSCLES: I'm afraid that's me.

TIM: Well, what do you know!

MR. PEPPER: Small wonder you know your way around in the electronics field!

HELEN: Trudy, why didn't you tell us he was a celebrity?

MUSCLES: I'm no celebrity in Trudy's eyes. She corrects my spelling papers at school and sees me as I really am.

MRS. PEPPER: I was about to ask you why you were attending Junior High School.

MUSCLES: Well, you see....science just comes easy to me... but gosh! What a struggle I do have with spelling and English! And I'm not any too strong on history either. It keeps me stepping to make the grade in some of those subjects as Trudy can tell you.

HELEN: Well you sure helped me make the grade with my assignment. Now I'll have time to go down to the library for a while. (*Packing up her books.*)

MUSCLES: Glad I could help you.

HELEN: Maybe tomorrow night you'd help me work out my next set of questions.

MUSCLES: I sure will.

HELEN: So long, everybody. I'll not be out late, Mother.

MOTHER: Oh, we'll be up when you come home. (HELEN *exits.*)

TRUDY: Well, Muscles, how about a game of table tennis?

MUSCLES: All right, but you play with me at your own risk.

TIMOTHY: Not so fast, Trudy. I'd like to show Muscles that motor down in the cellar. I've been tinkering around with it for six months, and it's not right yet. How about taking a look at it, Muscles?

MUSCLES (*With a smile and a shrug of his shoulders at* TRUDY): Sure...I'll look it over.

MR. PEPPER: I'll go along. I'd like to ask Muscles a few questions about the Kenetron tube and the Klystron tube.

MUSCLES: Well, they are both pretty important. The Kenetron is a tube used in the Precipitron. That's a new device designed to wash and cleanse the air of dust, smoke, and germs. The Klystron Tube is the one used in Radar. (*As they exit*)

TIM: Radar...That's the old super-sleuth all right.

Mr. Pepper (*As they leave stage*): Then it must be the Ignitron tube that changes A.C. into D.C., isn't it, Muscles?

Muscles: Yes...They're used in the new resistance welding of aluminum. (Trudy *and her mother are left alone.*)

Trudy: Well, how do you like that? Off he goes with Dad and Tim, leaving me high and dry! Of all the nerve!

Mother (*Smiling*): Well aren't you pleased Muscles was such a success with the family?

Trudy: I didn't want him to be this much of a success. My goodness, I want him to pay some attention to me. I'm going down in that cellar and drag him back! After all, he came to see me!

Mother: Oh, no, Trudy. That would be a fatal mistake. I can see you need to take a home study course in how to influence your boy friends.

Trudy: You mean I shouldn't go after him.

Mother: Certainly not. They'll be coming back after a while ...and in the meantime you and I can stir up a batch of Peanut Delights...Never forget, my child, that no matter how scientific he might be...the road to a man's heart is still...

Trudy: Sure, sure, I know...is still through his stomach. Well, come on, Mother, you lead the way...I'll follow.

THE END

PRODUCTION NOTES

Homework

Characters: 3 male; 3 female.

Playing Time: 35 minutes.

Costumes: Everyday modern dress.

Properties: Electric toaster, books, telephone.

Setting: An average American living room, somewhat transformed into a workshop. Upstage is a small table and chair. A drafting board stands in the center of the stage. A card-table piled high with books is placed downstage right.

Lighting: None required.

BAND AID

Characters

MRS. PEPPER, *a patriotic mother.*
MR. PEPPER, *a busy father.*
TRUDY PEPPER, *little sister.*
HELEN PEPPER, *big sister.*
TIMOTHY PEPPER, *the young maestro.*
MRS. ASHTON, *a neighbor.*
BILL
JAKE } *boys from the orchestra.*
FRED

SCENE: *The Pepper living room.*

TIME: *The present.*

BAND AID

SETTING: *The Pepper living room.*

AT RISE: *A terrific blast of Boogie-Woogie blaring from a record-player is heard.* TIMOTHY PEPPER, *a rhythmic sensation of 15, is mounted on a chair in his living room conducting an invisible band. As he "swings and sways" he admonishes his players from time to time with such bits as* "Come on you, Hep-Cats, swing it! Right on the beam, now! Make it hot and sweet!" *Suddenly his mother, giving every evidence that the noise is driving her frantic, enters right.* TIM *is oblivious of her presence till she disconnects the record-player.*

TIM: Hey, what do you think you're doing? Oh, it's you, Mom!

MOTHER: It certainly is, and if I may repeat your question, what do you think *you're* doing on my needle-point chair?

TIM (*Jumping down*): Gosh, I'm sorry, Mom! But I'll brush it, and my shoes aren't so bad. Gosh, Mom, did you hear that tricky number? That's one we're warming up for tomorrow night. Did you hear that one part in there where the licorice stick carries the melody? (*Hums a strain or two and does an exaggerated dance step.*) That's the way we're doing it tomorrow night.

MOTHER: Who? Do what? I wish you'd begin a story at the beginning.

TIM: Our dance band. They're comin' to practice at four. That's why I was giving myself a workout on your best chair.

MOTHER: Coming to practice where?

TIM: Right here.

MOTHER (*Firmly*): Oh, no, they're not! I'm having a rehearsal here myself.

TIM: But, Mom, can't we go up to my room? Or downstairs to the recreation room?

MOTHER: Under our feet or over our heads, darling, the drama won't mix with Boogie-Woogie. Go practice over at Red Martin's. His mother is at bridge club.

TIM: Yeah...but their cook's home, and she threatened to quit the last time we went there.

MOTHER: It's too bad, dear, but you'll just have to go some place else. I simply can't have a jazz band blowing its head off in the midst of our play rehearsal.

TIM (*Patiently*): It's a *swing* band.

MOTHER: Jazz or swing...you'll still have to clear out.

TIM: Aw, be a sport, Mother. We just gotta practice. Why this date for tomorrow night is the most important thing in the world to my fellows. We just can't ham it up. Our whole future depends on it.

MOTHER: It looks as if we're both on a spot, son. We can't afford to "ham up" our play either. It's just too bad that a band leader and a dramatic coach have to live under the same roof.

TIM: Well, couldn't we compromise somehow?

MOTHER (*Thoughtfully*): I don't see how...unless...

TIM: Unless what?

MOTHER: Well, there's the garage.

TIM: That's perfect. Say, you're a swell guy, Mom!

MOTHER: And do try to play more softly, won't you? I'm afraid the neighbors might object.

TIM: Aw, let 'em squawk! A little music won't hurt 'em. (*Phone*) Shall I answer?

MOTHER: No, I'll take it. Run along, and be sure to meet that gang of yours outside and steer them into the garage. I don't want them tramping through here while we're rehearsing. (*Phone.* TIM *exits.*) Yes? (*Answering phone*) Yes. Oh, Clara! What? You can't come? But the Welfare play is tomorrow night. We simply can't get anyone to take your place now. (*Pause*) Oh, dear! No, I realize you can't help it that Bumpsy has measles. Well, I do hope it's a light case. I'm so sorry. Oh, well, don't worry about the play! That's my job. I'll round up somebody somewhere. (HELEN, *the 18-year-old daughter of the house, enters from the hall.*)

HELEN: Any mail for me, Mommie?

MOTHER (*In phone*): Yes, I'm sure I can. Take good care of Bumpsy and I'll call you tomorrow. (*Hangs up.*) Is that you, Helen?

HELEN: It's me all right, and no letter again from Lew. He makes me sick.

MOTHER: Then I have a cure for you. I met the postman as I came in and he gave me a letter for you. I put it in my bag, (*Taking bag from desk*) and here it is.

HELEN: Oh, Mother, you're an angel! And Lew's an angel, too! Hurry up! Give it to me, please! Quick!

MOTHER (*Holding letter out of* HELEN's *reach*): What will you give me? What am I offered for this big, fat, juicy, senti-mental, long, lovey-dovey, squish-squashy romantic epistle?

HELEN: Mother, you're as bad as Tim and Trudy. Come on, now! Give it to me!

MOTHER: Not till you promise me something.

HELEN: Anything. I'll stop my reducing diet this minute and eat a peck of potatoes a day. How's that?

MOTHER: Not good enough. Seriously, I want you to be a good child, and help me out with this play we're doing for the Welfare Rally tomorrow night. Clara Wainwright's Bumpsy has measles and you'd be perfect for her part.

HELEN: But, Mother, you know I can't act. I was never any good in school plays.

MOTHER: Now, no more excuses. Will you take the part, or do I keep this letter and read the most tender morsels to the family at dinner?

HELEN: You know perfectly well that's blackmail, but I'll take the part.

MOTHER: Then here's your precious letter. Now be sure to come when I call you. The ladies will be here in a few minutes and we can't waste any time. I'll mark your script for you. (*Takes script from desk.*)

HELEN (*Running out of room with letter*): Don't you dare call me before I've read this letter a dozen times! (*Doorbell*)

MOTHER: That must be the girls now. (*Starts to door centre, but before she arrives, there is a fanfare of horns and three Junior High School boys enter, blowing lustily on a trombone, a trumpet and a sax.*) Merciful Moses!

BILL: Hello, Mrs. Pepper. Where's our old Maestro?

MOTHER: Your what?

FRED: He means Tim, Mrs. Pepper. He's our leader.

JAKE: Yes, ma'am. He's a rarin', tearin', jivin' sensation, that boy!

MOTHER: No doubt! No doubt! Well, if it's Tim you're looking for, you'll find him in the garage.

FRED: What's he doing out there? We came for a rehearsal.

BILL: Yeah...have you heard the good news, Mrs. Pepper? We're getting our big chance tomorrow night. We're going to...

MOTHER: I don't care where you're going tomorrow night, but right now you're going to the garage. I'm having a play rehearsal in this room in a few minutes, and you wild cats will have to do your howling out there!

JAKE: Ukkle-dukkle, Mrs. Pepper. (*To boys*) Squad...Attention! About face! To the garage...March! (*Boys exit. As they leave, they almost run into* MRS. ASHTON, *a pleasant young woman who is just arriving.*)

BOYS: Excuse us!

MRS. ASHTON: Excuse me! I rang, but I guess you didn't hear me.

MOTHER: And no wonder! Honestly, I sometimes wish we had never given Tim music lessons. I wouldn't have so many gray hairs.

MRS. ASHTON: We'll both have gray hairs over this play for tomorrow night. Have you heard the latest?

MOTHER: You mean about Clara Wainright's Bumpsy's measles? Yes. I persuaded my Helen to take the part.

MRS. ASHTON: Oh, no, no! I mean about Isabel Walters.

MOTHER (*Sitting down*): For Heaven's sake! What now?

MRS. ASHTON: She's left town.

MOTHER: But she can't do that! She's the maid in the play.

MRS. ASHTON: I know. But she had a wire from her sister in Cleveland to come at once. Their mother is very ill. Isn't it too perfectly horrible?

MOTHER: Horrible? It's fantastic. This is the limit!

MRS. ASHTON: Yes, isn't it? What on earth are we going to do?

MOTHER: I haven't the faintest idea. We'll never be able to find another maid like Isabel. She was a scream!

MRS. ASHTON: I thought of calling Martha Swain, but she's up to her neck in Red Cross work. (*Voice of* TRUDY *offstage*: Mother! Mother! Have you heard the news? TRUDY *bursts in like a cyclone. She grabs her mother in a wild hug which almost knocks her off her feet.*)

TRUDY: Mother — Mother — I'm gonna be Jo Stafford.... Listen! (*Sings in a throaty voice*) "You'll never know just how much I love you!"

MOTHER (*To* MRS. ASHTON): Sometimes I wonder if there is insanity in this family! (*To* TRUDY) Trudy, what's got into you? Hush that caterwauling and say "Good afternoon" to Mrs. Ashton.

TRUDY: Jeepers! I mean, pardon me! I didn't see you had company. Good afternoon, Mrs. Ashton. No wonder I didn't see you. I'm so excited over my big chance!

MRS. ASHTON: I can understand that. But just what is your big chance, my dear?

TRUDY: Well, you see...Tim has always been so superior about that dance band of his. Won't ever let me go near a rehearsal, and just awhile ago he broke down and said I could do a number with the band tomorrow night.

MOTHER: Well, I'm sure that was very nice of Tim. Now, run along and play. Mrs. Ashton and I have a problem to discuss.

TRUDY: But, Mother, I just ran in to ask you something. Please, will you make Helen lend me her black lace to wear tomorrow night?

MOTHER: Now don't be unreasonable, Trudy. You know as well as I do that Helen would just as soon think of jumping out the window as letting you wear that dress. Your own dotted Swiss will be sweet.

TRUDY (*With a wail of despair*): Oh, Mother! Dotted Swiss! That's not tragic and disillusioned! I need a sophisticated dress to sing, "You'll Never Know." (*Repeats opening of song with extra dramatic flourishes.*) Now imagine that...in dotted Swiss!

MRS. ASHTON: Really, Trudy, I had no idea you were such a clever little actress!

MOTHER (*Grasping at an idea*): Actress! Actress! That gives me a wonderful idea! Trudy, darling, how would you like to be in the play? One of our best actresses was forced to drop out, and you could take her place with a little coaching.

TRUDY: Sure, sure, I'll help you out, if you'll help me. You get me Helen's dress and I'll be in sixteen plays.

MOTHER: But, darling, you won't need the dress if you're in the play because the play is scheduled for tomorrow.

TRUDY: But, Mother, I couldn't possibly. The boys and Tim want me for tomorrow night. I've already promised them.

MRS. ASHTON: Oh, they won't care! You can sing for them another time.

TRUDY: But there won't be another time unless there is *this* time.

MOTHER (*Firmly*): Really, Trudy, it's your civic duty to help us out. (*Getting script from desk*) Now here's your part. Fortunately you were always quick at memorizing. So sit down there and read the part of *Morning Glory*. (*Pushes* TRUDY *into chair.*)

TRUDY (*Protesting*): But Mother!

MOTHER: Not another word! We must all make sacrifices! Now I'll call Helen. She's taking Mrs. Wainwright's part. Then we can begin. (*Calling*) Helen! Helen, dear! Can you come down now? We're ready to start the rehearsal.

HELEN (*Calling from offstage*): In a minute.

MRS. ASHTON: I think it is simply wonderful the way you can recruit a cast right from your own family, Mrs. Pepper.

TRUDY: She ought to be a Recruiting Officer.

MOTHER: We can do without your suggestions, Trudy. Just study your part. Honestly, this play has been a headache from the very beginning. I wish we had never promised to do it.

MRS. ASHTON: So do I. But we'll have to go through with it now.

HELEN (*Entering*): Well, here I am. Where's my part?

TRUDY: You can have mine. I don't want it.

HELEN: Don't tell me that child is in a play with grown-ups!

MOTHER: Now, Helen, please don't start anything!

MRS. ASHTON: It's sweet of you to help us, Helen.

HELEN: Oh, I'm glad to, Mrs. Ashton! Are you the beautiful heroine?

MRS. ASHTON: That's what I'm supposed to be, but maybe the audience will have another name for me.

TRUDY: Listen, Mother...won't you please let me go out to the garage and explain? Those boys will be furious.

MOTHER: They'll get over it. You're not going to get out of my clutches till you learn that part. Now let's walk through the first scene. Trudy, you are supposed to be dusting as the curtain rises. Then the doorbell rings, you answer it and Helen enters. She says, "Is Mrs. Glastonberry-Jones at home?" And you say: "One moment, Miss. I'll see."

TRUDY: If I'm the maid, why wouldn't I know if she's in or out?

MOTHER: Never mind. Just do as I tell you. Start dusting. (TRUDY *gives a half-hearted imitation of a housemaid.*) Now, Helen, you go out on the porch and ring the doorbell. (HELEN *exits and rings bell.*)

MOTHER: Now answer the bell, Trudy, and remember what you're to say.

TRUDY (*At door*): Well, blow me down, if it isn't Dad! Hello, Daddy! How come you're home so early? (FATHER *and* HELEN *enter.*)

HELEN: I certainly was surprised to meet Daddy on the doorstep.

MR. PEPPER: Hello. What's going on here? Good afternoon, Mrs. Ashton.

MOTHER: Oh, James! I'm having such a dreadful time! This is our play rehearsal, you know. The one called, "Charity Begins At Home." Remember, you promised to put up the scenery for it; and I'm so glad you came home early. Now you can see the rehearsal and get a much better idea of what we'll need. Just sit down over here, out of the way, where you can see everything.

MR. PEPPER: But, Mother, I don't have time. I'm catching the next train to New York and I have exactly forty-five minutes to pack and get down to the station. I'm terribly sorry, but I won't be able to help with the scenery at all, because I won't be home till next week.

MOTHER: Oh, but, James, we're counting on you!

MR. PEPPER: Sorry, my dear! But the firm is counting on me, too. And business is business! As a matter of fact, I was going to ask you to run me down to the station, but I see you're tied up here.

MRS. ASHTON: I'll take you down, Mr. Pepper. I'm afraid I'll have to be leaving shortly.

MR. PEPPER: Thanks, Mrs. Ashton. You'll be doing me a great favor. I'll have to step on it. See you later. (*Exit* MR. PEPPER.)

MOTHER: Now that's just about the last straw. I can't very well put up the scenery myself.

TRUDY: Aw, Mom, this play is jinxed! Why don't you just skip the whole thing and let me sing with Tim's orchestra?

MOTHER: I can't, Trudy. They're really counting on us, and this play was specially written for the drive. We just *must* put it on.

HELEN: Well, then, here we go again! Shall I go out and ring the bell again?

MOTHER: Yes, dear. Do you remember your opening lines?

HELEN: Sure! Is Mrs. Glastonberry-Jones at home?

MOTHER: That's right. (*Exit* HELEN *to ring bell.*) Now, Trudy, try to act more like a maid. Make it more true to life.

TRUDY: If I'd make it true to life, I'd quit. That's what most maids are doing these days. (*Doorbell.*)

MOTHER: Stop arguing and go answer the bell! (TIM's *voice is heard raised in protest as* TRUDY *answers door.*)

TIM: Well for Pete's sake! What happened to you? We've been waiting a couple of hours for you. You're a fine jerk to imitate Jo Stafford. I've a good notion to fire you!

TRUDY: Honest, Tim, I couldn't help it. I just came in here for a minute and Mom's nabbed me for her play.

MOTHER: Oh, merciful Heaven! What will happen next? Tim, get out of here and go on back to the garage! Trudy, stop fussing and get on with the rehearsal!

TIM: But, Mom, you can't do this. You simply can't. We need Trudy for tomorrow night.

MOTHER: *You* need Trudy for tomorrow night? Young man, I'll have you know *I* need Trudy and, what's more, you might just as well tell those wailing banshees of yours out there in the garage that you have to help your mother tomorrow night. I'll need you to help with the scenery. Your father has to go out of town.

TIM: Aw, no! That's out! Positively out! I can't help with any scenery tomorrow night! Why, Mom, think what you're asking! Why, why...it's like askin' a man to throw down his job.

MOTHER: Now, look here, Tim! We all have to make sacrifices. There are a thousand things I'd rather do than work on this play, but the PEPPY PLAYERS are booked for the Welfare Rally tomorrow night, and we're going to give the show if I have to round up a cast at the point of a gun!

TIM: What's that again? The what Players?

MOTHER: The Peppy Players...our Civic Dramatic Club.

TIM: I'm afraid you'll have to come again. I still don't get it.

MOTHER: I refuse to discuss it any further.

TIM: But, Moms, please! Wait a second. Say that part again about the Peppy Players and the Welfare Rally. I think there's been some sort of a mix-up.

MOTHER: You're the one who's mixed up. Mrs. Ashton, maybe you can explain this complicated matter to my son.

MRS. ASHTON: THE PEPPY PLAYERS is the name of the Dramatic Club of which your mother is the Director. It is one of the organizations always on call to produce entertainment for any sort of civic cause. Yesterday your mother received a wire from the Chairman of the Welfare Rally, so we were planning to give "Charity Begins At Home," the same show we gave last week at the Woman's Club, only at the last minute our cast just fell to pieces.

TIM: Well, I'll be switched.

MOTHER: You certainly will be, if you don't stop raising all this fuss.

TIM: Look, Mother, where is this telegram you received from the State Chairman?

MOTHER: Why...it's over there on the desk, I suppose, what does it matter where it is?

TIM (*Crossing to desk and getting telegram*): Is this it? Signed "P. G. Davis, General Chairman"?

MOTHER: Yes! Yes! Certainly anyone can see it's a telegram.

TIM: But look...look what it says, Mother! Read it!

MOTHER (*Reading from telegram*): "Have reserved spot for your Players on Welfare Rally Program, Saturday, the 25th."

TIM: But don't you see to whom it is addressed?

MOTHER: Of course. Mrs. J. T. Pepper. (TIM *takes telegram.*)

TIM: Better get your specs, Mom. It says *Mr.* J. T. Pepper. That's me.

MOTHER: Why, it says no such thing. Here. (*Taking telegram from* TIM.) Helen, you look at it.

HELEN (*Reading telegram*): I'm afraid he's right, Mother. It does say *Mr.* J. T. Pepper. (*Laughing.*) This is a good one on you! It looks as if the Committee has engaged a Dance Band instead of a play.

MOTHER (*Snatching wire from* HELEN): Let me see that again! Why, that's incredible!

TRUDY: Now I'm ready to believe in Superman and Terry and the Pirates.

MRS. ASHTON: It looks to me as if you and I are a pair of actors without a job, Mrs. Pepper.

TIM: Well, you see, this is how it was! I wrote to this guy Davis a long time ago, asking him to book the PEPPER PLAYERS — that's what we call our dance band — for the big Welfare Rally. So I guess this is the answer.

MOTHER: This couldn't happen to any other family in the United States. Imagine, the Peppy Players and the Pepper Players in the same house — a Dramatic Club and a Dance Band!

TRUDY: Hot Tamale! Here I go from rags to riches in one jump! From Morning Glory to Jo Stafford!

MOTHER: Well, Timmy, I guess we owe you a vote of thanks for getting the Peppy Players out of a mighty tough spot.

TIM: Gee whiz, Mom, do you mean you're not mad?

MOTHER: Does a person get mad when somebody saves his life? I should say I'm not mad! You can take over, with my best wishes and my blessing.

MRS. ASHTON: And mine, too.

HELEN: Also mine, if you can use it.

TRUDY: We couldn't use your blessing, Helen, but I sure could use that black lace dress of yours when I sing that solo. How about it, Sis — just to show you're on our side?

HELEN: Nothing doing! I'll be needing that dress myself; that is, if Tim can use a piano player who never lets her right hand know what her left hand's doing.

TIM: Gee whiz, Helen! Do you mean you'll really play for us?

HELEN: Sure, I mean it. I've heard you boys blazing away at

your rehearsals, and I think a good piano player is all you need. Do I get the job?

TIM: Do you get the job? Boy, oh, boy! Wait till the gang hears this! We'll be a sensation! (*The three boys enter with their instruments.*)

JAKE (*Indignantly*): Hey, Tim, what are you trying to pull? A disappearing act?

FRED: Are you trying to give us the run-around?

BILL: Looks as if we're playing "Follow the leader." First we follow you down here...then out to the garage...then back here again.

MRS. PEPPER: It's a shame! But this time you can stay right here, for our rehearsal is "off" and yours is "on."

TIM: And we've got ourselves a real piano player. My sister Helen's playing with us tomorrow night.

BOYS: That's swell! Now we'll really go to town! We'll give 'em the hottest music they've ever heard!

TIM: Say, fellows, there's a new name for us! How about the RED HOT PEPPERS?

FRED: The RED HOT PEPPERS! Now you're talking, brother. That really sounds like a dance band. How do you like it, Jake?

JAKE: It's perfect! But the audience will be giving the Red Hot Peppers the "hot foot" if we don't get down to business and rehearse!

TRUDY: What about me? Am I going to be a Red Hot Pepper?

TIM: That remains to be seen. But we'll give you a try, Miss Baby Face! And you better be good!

MRS. ASHTON: Well, Mrs. Pepper, I guess these young people don't need us. They have enough pep of their own without the Peppy Players.

MRS. PEPPER: I'm sure of it. They'll never miss us at the

Rally! There's nothing we can do. (MR. PEPPER, *dressed for his trip and carrying his bag, enters during* MRS. PEPPER'S *speech.*) Well, James, the play is definitely off.

TIM: And it's on with the band for us.

TRUDY: I wish you were going to be there, Pop. The Peppers are sure gonna pep things up.

MR. PEPPER: Well, it is too bad I can't take part in it but, with the rest of the family represented, I'm sure you'll be a credit to the name of Pepper. I must be on my way. You Peppers be good, and hold the fort till I come home.

HELEN, TRUDY *and* TIM: We will. Good-bye, Daddy. So long, Pop!

MRS. ASHTON: Oh, dear! (*Searching in bag*) I must have left the keys in the car. I'll run ahead and see. (*Exit.*)

MRS. PEPPER: I think I'll ride along down to the station, James. With both of us out of the house, these children can really get to work. (*Exit* MR. *and* MRS. PEPPER.)

HELEN (*Taking her place at the piano, which may be on stage or in pit*): Come on, now, let's get down to brass tacks. (*Begins to play introduction to any popular tune. The other boys take their places and begin to tune up.*)

TIM (*Taking his place as Conductor*): Hep to it, boys! Let's give out with the best we have. (*Curtains close on the orchestra playing under the direction of* TIM. TRUDY *stands by the piano, ready to go into her solo.*)

THE END

PRODUCTION NOTES

BAND AID

Characters: 5 male; 4 female.

Playing Time: 40 minutes.

Costumes: All the characters wear modern everyday dress.

Properties: Pocketbook; letter in envelope; sheets of paper clipped together representing scripts; trombone; saxophone; trumpet; telegram blank; Gladstone bag.

Setting: There should be a sofa, a few upholstered chairs, a record player, a few end tables, lamps, and a desk on the stage to represent the living room. There is a phone on the desk. A doorway left leads to the front hall of the house, and a door right may lead to the rest of the house.

Lighting: None required.

DOCTOR'S DAUGHTER

Characters

GLORIA FULTON, *a junior high school graduate.*
MRS. FULTON, *her mother.*
DR. FULTON, *her father.*
RAY WEAVER, *the boy next door.*
MISS BLAIR, *play director.*

SCENE: *The dining room of Dr. Fulton's home.*

TIME: *The present.*

DOCTOR'S DAUGHTER

SETTING: *The dining room of* DR. FULTON'S *home.*

AT RISE: GLORIA *is seated at the table eating an early supper. Propped against her water glass is the script of her Commencement Pageant which she is studying while she eats.*

GLORIA (*Holding a glass of milk in her right hand as if it were a torch. Her eyes are closed as she declaims*): This lamp is a symbol of mercy and humanity. May its rays penetrate to every corner of this world and dispel the darkness of suffering and despair. (*Enter* MRS. FULTON *with a plate of sandwiches.*)

MRS. FULTON: Bravo, Gloria! You got through that without a mistake.

GLORIA: Yes, I really think I know every word of it now. Oh, Mother, I can't possibly eat another sandwich.

MRS. FULTON: All right. I won't urge you. But you finish your milk. I'll eat one of these myself. (*Sits at table.*)

GLORIA: Oh, Mother, I'm too excited to swallow another mouthful of anything. This is the most wonderful night of my life. Ever since I was in the grades and went to Bill's commencement, it's been my ambition to have a leading part in the Junior High Commencement Pageant. And now, just think, I'm to play Florence Nightingale. She has always been one of my favorite characters.

MRS. FULTON: Your father will be so proud of you.

GLORIA: What about you? Won't you be a little bit proud of me too?

133

MRS. FULTON: Of course I will. But you know Dad. He's always hoped that you and Bill would take some interest in medicine.

GLORIA: Ummmm. I'd love to be a nurse, if I could be like Florence Nightingale. Oh, Mother, wait till you see the scene where I walk down the long line of cots in the hospital at Scutari. The men are tossing and moaning and then I enter with my lamp. (*Rises and holds glass of milk as if it were a lamp.*) One of them looks up at me and says:

MRS. FULTON: "A woman! It must be an angel!"

GLORIA (*Surprised*): Why, Mother, do you know the lines too?

MRS. FULTON: I *should* know them considering how many times I've gone over them with you; and besides, I happen to know that's how Florence Nightingale came to be called "The Angel of the Crimea." (*Phone rings.*)

GLORIA (*As her mother reaches for phone*): Please, Mother, if that's for Daddy, he's not making any calls tonight. He's coming to my commencement.

MRS. FULTON (*To* GLORIA): Sh! (*To phone*) Dr. Fulton's residence. No, I'm sorry. The doctor isn't in. We expect him at any moment. Oh, yes, Mrs. Jacobs. Oh, I'm so glad the baby is better. Yes, indeed, I'll tell him. Yes, so long as her temperature stays normal, you won't need to worry. Thanks so much for calling. Good-bye.

GLORIA: Oh, thank goodness! I was scared to death it was old Mrs. Handley. Wouldn't it be just like her to get one of her spells tonight of all nights? Honestly, Mother, I'd just die if Daddy didn't get to see me in this play.

MRS. FULTON: Well, I don't think you'll have to die because this is his regular night for closing the office, and he said at noon that he had a pretty clear slate, so we'll just have to keep our fingers crossed.

GLORIA: He's never been able to come to see one single thing I've been in at school. Remember in sixth grade when I was the May Queen and old Mr. Evans fell off the garage roof just as you were leaving the house.

MRS. FULTON: Yes, I remember. It's always that way. The minute you plan on something, there's sure to be an accident, or an operation or an emergency of some sort.

GLORIA: Well, I bet you one thing.... I'm never going to marry a doctor and have my household upset all the time with other people's aches and pains. At least half of them are imaginary anyhow.

MRS. FULTON: Oh, I wouldn't say half...but I'll admit, a lot of them are imaginary.

GLORIA: Take Mrs. Handley's spells for example. She's been having them ever since I can remember, and Dad says himself there's nothing wrong with her but dandruff and fallen arches. Yet the minute she calls, he goes tearing over there.

MRS. FULTON: Mrs. Handley is a very old lady, dear, and there's always the chance she might be seriously ill. How do you think we'd feel then if Dad would refuse to go?

GLORIA: Like a couple of worms, I suppose; but don't worry. Dad's like an old fire horse. The minute he hears that bell, you can't see him for dust.

MRS. FULTON: You better follow his example and dust upstairs. It's high time you got into your costume. Won't Miss Blair be stopping for you before long?

GLORIA: About six. Good heavens! I didn't realize it was so late. I'll have to step on it.

MRS. FULTON: Me too. I promised to take some flowers down to the church. I'll just have time to go down there.

GLORIA: Now, Mother, please don't let Dad fool around in the office tonight till you get a late start. I want you to be on time.

MRS. FULTON: Don't worry, dear. We'll be there. You just keep your mind on your part and make us proud of you.

GLORIA: I'll do my best. (*Starts to leave and returns to get her script.*) I better take this upstairs with me and study while I dress.

MRS. FULTON: You know those lines backwards and forwards. Stop worrying about the play and enjoy yourself.

GLORIA: There's just one part I don't seem to get right. Miss Blair says I don't put enough feeling into it. By golly, tonight I'm going to put enough feeling into it to jerk tears out of a wooden Indian. So long, Mommy.

MRS. FULTON: So long, dear, and good luck. (GLORIA *exits. To herself*) Maybe I'd better save these sandwiches till after the play. She'll be starving by that time.

RAY (*Off stage*): Hi, ya, there, anybody home? (RAY *enters sucking a lemon*) Hello, there, Mrs. Fulton. Is the Doc in?

MRS. FULTON: Not yet, Ray. Did you want to see him about something?

RAY: Yeah. Wondered if he'd spray the old tonsils. You know I gotta sing tonight, and my throat feels like sandpaper. Been suckin' this lemon all afternoon, but it's no good.

MRS. FULTON: I'm sure he'll fix you up when he comes in. Stick around. He'll be here any minute. But you'll have to excuse me. I have an errand to do.

RAY: Oh, sure. Thanks. Where is La Belle Gloria? Is she reading her Paramount contract or waiting for a call from MGM?

MRS. FULTON (Laughing): Neither. She's getting into her costume. Miss Blair is calling for her at six. Help yourself to the sandwiches while you're waiting.

RAY: Thanks, I will. So long.

MRS. FULTON: So long, Ray, and good luck to your tonsils for tonight. I know they'll give a grand performance.

RAY: If they don't, I'll have Doc take 'em out. (MRS. FULTON *exits.*) Come to think of it, I better get Doc to give me a shot in the arm so I'll feel no pain when I start to warble. Maybe I better see if I'm in voice. (*Begins to vocalize with a series of Mi-mi-mi and then launches into "The Road to Mandalay."*)

GLORIA (*Off stage*): Ray Weaver, is that you down there?

RAY: No. (*Falsetto*) It's the Voice. It's "Frankie-Boy." Come on down and throw me a swoon.

GLORIA: I'll throw my shoe at you if you don't shut up.

RAY: Tush, tush! Is that any way for the "Angel of the Crimea" to talk? You should come down here and minister unto my needs. (*Phone*)

GLORIA: Oh, answer that, will you please, Ray? If it's for Dad, you have no idea when he'll be in.

RAY (*At phone*): Dr. Fulton's residence. Yes. Well, no... the doctor isn't in just now, but he's expected at any moment. Yes, yes, indeed, I'll tell him. Mrs. Henry Meyers, RD 7. Yes, I'll be sure to have him call you the minute he comes in. You're welcome. Good-bye.

GLORIA (*Running on stage. She is now wearing her Florence Nightingale costume and carries her script*): Ray Weaver, what did you tell those people? What was that message? If you told them my father would come out tonight, I'll slay you.

RAY: Pipe down, Flossie. Take it easy before you blow out a fuse. It was a Mrs. Meyers from the country. She wants to talk to your Dad.

GLORIA: And what did you tell her?

RAY: You heard me. I said I'd have the Doc call her as soon as he comes in.

GLORIA: Oh, Ray Weaver, I hate you. Why did you have to come over here and meddle in our private affairs?

RAY: Well, gee whiz! All I did was answer the phone!

GLORIA (*With heavy sarcasm*) : All you did was answer the phone! All you did was to ruin my whole commencement! You know how much I want Daddy to come. You know how much it means to me. Now he'll have to trek way out there in the country.

RAY: Gee, Gloria, I'm sorry! It's a tough break, but after all, what else could I say?

GLORIA: What else could you say? You could have said plenty. You could have said you didn't know when he'd be in. You could have told her to call someone else. You could have told her anything to get rid of her.

RAY: But, Gloria — your father's a doctor. Don't you know what that means?

GLORIA (*Vehemently*) : Sure I know what it means. It means being interrupted at meals, having people barge in on you at all hours. It means being called out at night, being called away from parties, being called out of the movies at the most exciting point. It means never going places with your family the way other fathers do.

RAY: Gosh, I never knew you felt this way about it.

GLORIA: Well, I do and more so. And let me tell you something else. When my father walks in this house tonight, you're not going to say one word about that call. Not one word, do you hear?

RAY: Nope! I can't hear a word when you talk like that, and I'm sure glad no one else can hear you talking like a selfish nitwit. Gee whiz, Gloria, when are you going to grow up and get some sense. Of course, I'm gonna tell the Doc about his call. I'm sorry he might miss our commencement. After all, I want him to come almost as bad as you do, but that's a chance we must take. I know how he feels about his calls. I guess I understand because, well, I'd sort of like to be a doctor myself someday and I...

GLORIA: You what? You want to be a doctor yourself? Ray Weaver! Why didn't you ever mention this before? Tell me why you have been keeping it a secret.

RAY: Well, Holy Moses! I didn't mean to keep it a secret. The subject just never happened to come up before. And anyhow I don't see what difference it could make to you!

GLORIA: It makes plenty of difference! I can tell you one thing, Ray Weaver, from now on I'm through with you. You can just go camp on some other girl's doorstep and get some other girl to do your homework. I don't care if you do live next door. I don't want to look at you again ever. Why, I wouldn't marry a doctor for love or money.

RAY (*Outraged*): Marry! Ye gods! Who said anything about getting married? Gloria Fulton, you're just a zany! We aren't even out of Junior High School yet, and you talkin' about who you are or aren't gonna marry! And all this fuss just because I said I had a yen for the pills and the little black bag. You're a swell kid, Gloria, but in some respects, you're a first-class dope. (*Enter* DOCTOR FULTON.)

DR. FULTON: Hello, kids. Well, well, well, here's Miss Nightingale in all her fine feathers. Turn around and let me look at you. (GLORIA *turns to show her father the costume.*) Ummm! Not bad! Not bad. In fact, very neat, I'd say. What's your opinion, Ray, or have you already expressed it?

GLORIA: Oh, don't even ask him, Daddy. We're on the outs again. Come on out in the kitchen, and I'll get you some coffee.

RAY: Oh, just a minute, Doc. You had a call.

DOCTOR: A call? Oh, dear! I might have known! Who is it this time?

RAY: A Mrs. Henry Meyers. RD 7. I told her I'd have you call her as soon as you came in.

DOCTOR: Thanks a lot, Ray. Any other calls, Gloria?

GLORIA: Only Mrs. Jacobs. Her baby's temperature is normal.

DOCTOR: Good! I was worried about that case.

GLORIA: Oh, promise me you won't go out there to the Meyers' tonight. Please, Daddy.

DOCTOR: I hope it won't be necessary, Gloria, but I'll have to call and find out what the trouble is. I'll use the office phone. You and The Boy Friend can fight better when I'm not around. If you need any help, Ray, just call me. (*Exit* DR. FULTON.)

GLORIA: Well, I hope you're satisfied with your evening's work.

RAY: I'm satisfied all right! I'm satisfied I found out what sort of a kid you are! Bah! They ought to boo you right off the stage tonight. It's a wonder some of the speeches in that play don't stick in your throat. What do you know about self-sacrifice and all the rest of it! Florence Nightingale would turn over in her grave if she could see your performance.

GLORIA: That's enough, Ray Weaver! Shut up and get out of here. Make it fast!

RAY: I'll make it fast and permanent, sister! (*He slams out of the room.*)

GLORIA (*Stamping her foot*): Of all the horrible detestable boys I've ever seen, he's the worst. (*Begins to cry.*) Oh, dear, my commencement is ruined! I'll never be any good now. I wish I could get out of the whole thing. (DOCTOR *re-enters. He is in a fine humor.*)

DOCTOR: Good news, Gloria! I was able to prescribe for Mrs. Meyers over the phone. It won't be necessary for me to see her until tomorrow. What's the matter? Have you been crying? Now don't be silly. Ray Weaver's a nice boy, but he's not worth crying over. Florence Nightingale doesn't want to sail for the Crimea with Pink Eye and a case of sniffles. (*Offering handkerchief*) Now blow your nose and

get that smile back in place. There! That's much better.
Now I'll run upstairs and shave and try to look like the father
of a real actress. You won't know me when I come down.
I'll be transformed.

GLORIA: Oh, Daddy, you're such a comfort, and I'm so glad
you're coming.

DOCTOR: So am I. Now powder your nose and get going.
(*Exit.*)

GLORIA: Boy, oh boy! What a relief! I feel better already.
Phooey on old Ray Weaver. If he thinks he can get me all
upset, he's fooled. I'll be the best Florence Nightingale this
town ever saw. Now where's that closing speech. (*Gets
script. Phone rings.*) Oh, dear! Why was the telephone ever
invented? Hello! Hello! Yes, this is Dr. Fulton's
residence...Who? Oh, Mrs. Handley? I'm awfully sorry,
Mrs. Handley, but he can't come just now, he...(*Jiggles
receiver.*) Hello. Hello. (*In disgust*)Oh, dear! She hung
up. (*Hangs up.*) Well, I'm not going to tell him. It's just
another one of her spells. I just knew she'd have one tonight.
Let her get another doctor. My goodness, I wonder if Dad
heard the phone ring. (*Tiptoes to door and listens.*) I guess
not. The water is running hard. (*In indecision*) I wonder
if I should tell him. After all...maybe...(*Making up her
mind*) Nothing doing....This commencement of mine is just
as much of an emergency call as anything else...(*Doorbell*)
That must be Miss Blair. (*At door*) Come in, Miss Blair.
I'll be ready in a jiffy. (MISS BLAIR *enters carrying an oil
lamp to be used in the play.*) Oh, I see you have the lamp.
It's a dandy.

MISS BLAIR: Yes, isn't it? Oh, your costume looks lovely,
Gloria.

GLORIA: Thank you. I'm glad you like it.

MISS BLAIR: I'm sure you'll give a splendid performance

tonight. This should be the most inspiring commencement we've ever had. With the great demand for nurses, we couldn't have chosen a more timely theme. The story of Florence Nightingale should be a real inspiration, and I want you to make her come alive as a living, breathing character who has a real message for all the girls of today.

GLORIA: I'll do my best.

MISS BLAIR: I know you will. I'm counting on you... especially to put the final tableau across. When you take your place in front of the group of young nurses and lead them in the Florence Nightingale Pledge, I want you to give it everything you have. Say every word as if you mean it with all your heart and soul.

GLORIA: I'll try.

MISS BLAIR: Would you mind going over it once more before we go up to school? Things will be so hectic up there. Let's go over it while we have some peace and quiet. Here, (*Hands her the lamp*), take the lamp and get into your position. (GLORIA *strikes a pose with the lamp and recites "The Nightingale Pledge"*)

GLORIA: "I solemnly pledge myself before God in the presence of this assembly to pass my life in purity and to practice my profession faithfully. I will do all in my power to maintain and to elevate the standard of my profession, and will hold in confidence all personal matters committed to my keeping, and all family affairs coming to my knowledge in the practice of my calling. With loyalty will I endeavor to aid the physician ...(*Her voice breaks and she repeats*) with loyalty will I endeavor to aid the physician in his work...and...and...

MISS BLAIR (*Prompting*): And devote myself...

GLORIA: And devote myself...(*Starts to cry.*)

MISS BLAIR: Why, Gloria — what's the matter? Don't tell me you have stage fright....What's making you break up like this?

GLORIA (*In tears*): Oh, Miss Blair...I can't say it... I can't...I can't. They'd boo me off the stage if they only knew.... I can't say those lines...

MISS BLAIR: What lines? I don't understand what you're talking about.

GLORIA: I can't say that pledge....I can't say I will endeavor to aid the physician in his work when...I...(DR. FULTON *enters.*)

DOCTOR: Good evening, Miss Blair. Why...what on earth? Gloria, what's the matter?

GLORIA: Daddy, it's Mrs. Handley. She called just a few minutes ago. Says it's an emergency. She wants you right away.

DOCTOR: Good grief! Of all times for her to kick up a fuss!

GLORIA: You'll have to go, Daddy. She sounded terrible.

DOCTOR: O.K., Office Girl. I'll run over right away and take care of her. Is that why you're crying...cause I'll miss the play?

GLORIA: Not entirely...it's...well...it's just everything.

DOCTOR: Well, don't cry....That's what you get for being a doctor's daughter. Cheer up. Maybe I can see you graduate from college.

GLORIA: Or maybe from nursing school?

DOCTOR: Say that again.

GLORIA: You heard me, Doctor. Now grab that satchel and get going.

DOCTOR: You're a good little sport, Gloria...and whether I get to see that play or not, I know you'll knock 'em in the aisles. How about it, Miss Blair?

MISS BLAIR: I'm sure of it, Dr. Fulton. There's something about Gloria that made me know from the start she had the stuff to play Florence Nightingale.

Dr. Fulton: I call that a compliment, Miss Blair. Thank you and goodnight. Good luck, Gloria.

Gloria: Thanks, Daddy, and hurry. (*Exit* Doctor.)

Miss Blair: I know that's a big disappointment, Gloria, but maybe he'll get back in time.

Gloria: You know Mrs. Handley's spells. They last for hours....But I don't care, Miss Blair...because now I can really say that pledge...without being ashamed to look the audience in the face. You see, I wasn't going to give Daddy that call from Mrs. Handley. I wasn't going to say a word about it...just because I was a selfish little pig...(Ray *enters out of breath and much excited. He doesn't even notice* Miss Blair.)

Ray: Gloria! Gloria! Where's your Dad? Is he still here?

Gloria: No, he just left. Ray, what's the matter? What's wrong?

Ray: Where did he go? Where is he? Are you sure he's not in?

Gloria: Of course, I'm sure. He's gone over to see Mrs. Handley; I gave him the call myself.

Ray: You what?

Gloria: I said I gave him the call myself. Mrs. Handley called a few minutes ago all upset. Another one of her emergencies.

Ray: And after all you said awhile ago...you gave him the call?

Gloria: Sure, I did.

Ray: But I thought...

Gloria: Yeah, I know what you thought. And you were right. I was a nitwit. Well...Florence Nightingale taught me a thing or two. I got wise to myself and this time I had sense enough to aid a physician in his work regardless of whether or not it interfered with my well-being.

Ray: Oh, boy! What a relief! Gee, I was scared to death

you wouldn't give him the call. I ran all the way over here...I...

GLORIA: I still don't get it. Why have Mrs. Handley's spells suddenly become a matter of life and death to you? Is she really ill this time?

RAY: You see...well, oh my gosh, Gloria, I hate to tell you this, but...

MISS BLAIR: Is something wrong, Ray?

RAY: Excuse me, Miss Blair, I didn't even see you...I guess I'm kind of upset...You see...it isn't Mrs. Handley this time...it's Gloria's mother.

GLORIA: My mother? What's wrong with mother? Where is she? What's happened?

RAY: It was a car...it happened right in front of Mrs. Handley's house and they took her in there.

GLORIA: Is my mother hurt? Oh, Miss Blair, take me over there right away.

RAY: No, wait a minute, Gloria. Let me tell you. Your mother was crossing the street and this big black Buick swung around the corner and sideswiped her. They carried her into Mrs. Handley's and Mrs. Handley called for the Doc. When I found out she put in the call, I was afraid you might not tell the Doc and maybe...

GLORIA: Oh, Ray, suppose I hadn't told him.

RAY: But you did, Gloria. Everything will be all right now. I don't think she was hurt badly. Really I don't...I think she probably slipped in front of the car instead of being knocked down.

MISS BLAIR: This is pretty bad, Gloria, but you'll have to control yourself. Run upstairs and get out of your costume, and I'll take you over right away.

GLORIA: Oh, no...I won't wait to change. Let's go right this minute.

MISS BLAIR: Just as you wish, my dear. We'll go at once.

GLORIA: And you, Ray, won't you come with me...please?

RAY: Sure, Gloria. I'll stick right by you. I think it was pretty swell of you giving the Doc that call when you thought it was just Mrs. Handley. I guess you're O.K. after all.

GLORIA: Thanks. Let's get going. (*Phone*) I'll get it. (*Phone*) Hello. Oh, yes, Mrs. Handley. Yes, I just heard. Oh, thank goodness! Are you sure? Oh, thanks! Thanks a million for calling! I was worried sick. I was just starting for your house. All right. No, I feel much better now. Tell Mother I'm fine and not to worry, and tell Dad I won't even open my diploma till he sees it. Thanks again. Good-bye. (*Hangs up.*) Thank heavens! Mother is going to be all right. Dad was afraid I might hear the news and be scared to death. He says she is suffering from shock and when she's rested, he'll bring her home. She's just bruised...nothing broken. Oh boy, oh boy! Is that a relief! That Mrs. Handley can call us morning, noon and night from now on. I'll have no complaints. This time her emergency was the real thing.

RAY: Gosh, Gloria, that's swell!

MISS BLAIR: That's wonderful news, dear. You certainly have had a bad time. Do you think you'll be able to go through with everything tonight?

GLORIA: Go through with it? Golly! Miss Blair! Nothing could stop me now. Give me that lamp. (*Strikes pose with lamp.*) "With loyalty will I endeavor to aid the physician in his work and devote myself to the welfare of those committed to my care." (*Holds pose as* MISS BLAIR *speaks her final line and curtains close.*)

MISS BLAIR: That's it, Gloria...That's the true spirit of Florence Nightingale...the real challenge of the Lady with the Lamp.

THE END

PRODUCTION NOTES

Doctor's Daughter

Characters: 2 male; 3 female.

Playing Time: 30 minutes.

Costumes: Everyday modern dress. Florence Nightingale costume for Gloria.

Properties: Script, glass of milk, plate of sandwiches, lemon, man's handkerchief, oil lamp, doctor's bag.

Setting: Dining room of average American home. On the serving table, close to a big comfortable chair, there is a telephone and a memo pad. The dining table is set for one place with dishes, water glass, etc.

Lighting: None required.

SAY IT WITH FLOWERS

Characters

Mrs. Fairchild

Scotty Fairchild

Kitty Fairchild

Junior Fairchild

Buzz Jones

Molly

Hoppy

Wayne Crawford

Messenger

Scene: *The living room of the Fairchild home.*

Time: *The present.*

SAY IT WITH FLOWERS

SETTING: *The living room of the* FAIRCHILD *home.*

BEFORE RISE: A MESSENGER *enters.* *He carries a florist's box
under his arm and is apparently looking for a house number.
In pantomime he refers to the number on the box, looks at the
imaginary numbers on the curtain and finally halts at the
curtain opening.* *After pretending to ring the doorbell, he
waits until the curtain opens slightly, an arm reaches out and
with a polite bow he delivers his package.* *Exit whistling
softly to himself.* *Pause.*

AT RISE: JUNIOR *and his friend* BUZZ JONES *are just entering.*

BUZZ: I ask you, is that any way to treat a pal?

JUNIOR: Aw, gee whiz, Buzz! Can't you see it's not my fault?
I want to go to the old dance as bad as you do. I can't help it
if Carriebelle won't go.

BUZZ: What made her change her mind? She was going
yesterday, wasn't she?

JUNIOR: Sure she was going. We were all set. Now this
morning she writes me this note and says the deal's off. I
don't know what's got into her.

BUZZ: Well, I know one thing...I'm not going to that
Valentine Dance by myself.

JUNIOR: Stop talking about going by yourself. Susie will be
with you, won't she?

BUZZ: I mean I'm not going without you. It was your idea in
the first place. You'll just have to dig up another date.

JUNIOR: I don't want another date. If I can't take Carriebelle, I'm not going and that's that.

BUZZ: Then I'm gonna call up Susie and tell her I can't go either.

JUNIOR: What excuse will you give?

BUZZ: I don't know yet, but I'll think of something.

JUNIOR: Sounds like a rotten trick to me. Susie will be disappointed. Look, Buzz, you don't need me at the dance. After you get there and start circulating, everything will be okay. Sit down here and cool yourself off. I'll see if I can't find us a coke in the icebox. (*Exit* JUNIOR. BUZZ *walks around the room, scuffing at the rugs and showing by his restlessness that he is undergoing mental strain.*)

BUZZ: Of all the luck! Me a confirmed woman-hater talked into going to this old brawl and then he walks out on me. It's enough to give a guy a good dose of tropical fever.

JUNIOR (*Re-entering with flower box*): You should talk about bad luck, Buzz. Look at this. Here are the flowers Mother ordered for tonight. Aren't they beauties?

BUZZ (*Looking at flowers dismally*): Gee! Gardenias. They're neat. Say...why don't you call her up and tell her you can't let the flowers go to waste. Go on. All women like flowers. Maybe that'll melt her.

JUNIOR: I'm not going to coax her. If she doesn't want to go to the dance with me, let her go jump in the lake.

BUZZ: But, gee whiz, man. You don't want to throw your money away like that. Go on, call her up.

JUNIOR: Oh, all right. I'll call her, but it won't do any good.

BUZZ: That's swell. I'll look up the number.

JUNIOR: Don't bother. I could dial that number in my sleep. (*Dials number*) 3-7-5-8-3- Hello. Is Carriebelle there? (*To* BUZZ) This ought to be good! Hello, Carriebelle.... This is your big moment. Sure....Sure it's me. Listen,

Babe...are you sure you haven't changed your mind about the hop tonight? I just thought I'd call you up and warn you you're missing out on a beautiful spray of gardenias... Yeah...gardenias....That's what I said. Of course, I'm not kidding. No...Mother ordered them and they're here now. Of course not...I didn't want to take a chance on having them delivered. Thought it would be safer to bring them myself. Well...for crying out loud! Is that why you were calling it off? Well, you make me sick....You might have known I'd crash through with a corsage....No...no... I'm not mad...okay...okay....We'll be seeing you about eight. All right....No....Nope...save it for tonight. All right...bye.

BUZZ: Jeepers....That's what I call fancy fixin'.

JUNIOR: Can you beat it? Just because all the other girls got their flowers this morning she got sore because she thought I hadn't sent her any. Aren't girls the limit?

BUZZ: I'll say! Well...now that's all settled I feel better.

JUNIOR: I'll have to put this right back in the ice box. Gardenias are awful touchy. They're like girls. You have to know how to handle 'em.

BUZZ: There's a card in the box.

JUNIOR: Gee, Mom thinks of everything. (*Pulls out card.*) Look... "To my Valentine."

BUZZ: That's not your writing.

JUNIOR: Of course not, Dope, the florist writes the card. You just tell him what to say.

BUZZ: Well...I must beat it. I'll stop for you and then we'll pick up the girls together.

JUNIOR: Right. Come on, let's go out the kitchen door. I have to go down to the cleaner's for my suit. We'll stuff this in the ice box on the way out. (*Starting to exit*) Whoever said...*Say it with flowers* sure said a mouthful. (*As the boys exit,* SCOTTY *comes in the opposite door. With her is her current admirer,* WAYNE CRAWFORD. *They are quarreling.*)

SCOTTY: I don't care what you say, Wayne Crawford, I'm not going to that dance. You only asked me at the last minute anyhow.

WAYNE: What do you call the last minute? I've been asking you every day for the last two weeks.

SCOTTY: And in between times, you've been asking Myra Thompson.

WAYNE: Myra Thompson! What ever gave you that idea?

SCOTTY: Lots of things gave me that idea. The way you're always borrowing her algebra papers for one thing.

WAYNE: Ye gods! Can't I borrow a girl's algebra papers! What does that have to do with a dance?

SCOTTY: Well, just the same...I'm not going... and that's final.

WAYNE: Okay, okay. If that's the way you feel about it, I'm glad you're not going. We'd probably have a rotten time, anyway.

SCOTTY: A rotten time! So that's how you feel about going to dances with me. Well, just put this in your pipe and smoke it, Wayne Crawford, you'll never have any more rotten times with me. I'm through.

WAYNE: Oh, Scotty, be reasonable. I never said anything about having a rotten time with you. We always had wonderful times.

SCOTTY: Sure, sure...that's what I thought too up until now. You can just go and take Myra Thompson and I hope she tramps all over your feet up to the knees.

WAYNE: Okay. Thanks for the suggestion. Maybe I will... and in the meantime, if you change your mind...my telephone number is in the book. Goodbye.

SCOTTY: Goodbye. (*As soon as* WAYNE *exits she bursts into tears.*) Oh, dear...oh dear! Why did I have to act so mean and hateful! And I wanted to go to this dance more than any other. Oh, well...I'll just have to tell Hoppy not to bother pressing my dress. Hoppy...(*No answer. Calls again*) Hoppy...Oh, dear, I suppose she's out for the afternoon. Now I suppose I'll have to get supper. (*Exits to kitchen still calling "Hoppy." In just a minute she re-enters, all smiles. She is carrying the florist's box.*) Oh, they're gorgeous! Perfectly gorgeous! And to think I talked to him like that when all the time he had ordered these beautiful flowers. Bless his old heart! I'm going to call him right up. (*At phone*) 5-7-8-6. Hello, Mrs. Crawford? Has Wayne come in yet? Well, the minute he comes, would you ask him to call me? Oh, yes...I almost forgot. This is Scotty... Scotty Fairchild. All right, thanks. And Mrs. Crawford, tell him the flowers came and they're simply super. Yes, thanks again. Goodbye. (*Hugging the flowers as she starts to exit.*) And you, you great big luscious, beautiful beauties, you're going right back in the refrigerator until tonight. (*Exits. Immediately after her exit there is a ring at the doorbell and she re-enters.*) Oh, that doorbell! I hope it's nobody for me this time. I'll have to step on the gas if I am to press my dress and be ready by eight. (*Exit in opposite direction. Off stage*) Yes, yes. Fairchilds live here. No, Mrs. Fairchild isn't in just now, but I'll sign for it. (*She re-enters with telegram*) A wire for mother. That must be from Dad. I'll stick it right here by the phone where she'll be sure to see it. And now, to make myself beautiful. (*Exits. After a brief pause,* KITTY *enters with* MOLLY, *her girl friend.*)

KITTY: Just flop down any place, Molly, while I take a quick look in the refrigerator. If they're not here, we're sunk.

MOLLY: Well, they better be here because if they're not, it's too late to order any more. After all, you were chairman of the flower committee.

KITTY: I did my part all right. I ordered them in plenty of time. (*Exit*) But let's not get in an uproar till I look. (*Re-enters with flower box.*) Thank heaven! Here they are.

MOLLY: Let's have a look. I hope they're what we ordered.

KITTY: What do you mean...what *we* ordered?' I thought you just said I was the chairman.

MOLLY: Oh, don't quibble. Let's look. (*Opening box and giving gasps of admiration*) Oh, they're marvelous.

KITTY: Aren't they perfect? Oh, she'll love them. I've heard her say thousands of times that gardenias are her favorite flower.

MOLLY: Well, our class really is lucky to have Miss Wilson for our advisor. She's the prettiest one on the faculty.

KITTY: Yeah...I'd sure hate to waste gardenias on some of those old do-does. Now Miss Wilson is something else again.

MOLLY: Don't let them get in a draft. Gardenias are very delicate.

KITTY: You sound as if they'd catch pneumonia.

MOLLY: Well, no kidding, I read somewhere you have to keep them out of drafts.

KITTY: Then why put them in a refrigerator where they're likely to freeze to death?

MOLLY: Refrigerator cold isn't the same as a draft. Put the lid back on and get them back where they belong.

KITTY: All right, but be careful. I must wrap the waxed paper around them.

MOLLY: Oh, look! There's a card.

KITTY: "To My Valentine!"

MOLLY: That's cute. I hope she doesn't think it's too fresh.

KITTY: Oh, not Miss Wilson. She's broad-minded.

MOLLY: I'll say she is. Well, I'll dash over home and come back about seven. We'll have to go early to help with the decorations.

KITTY: Wait a sec till I put these back in the refrigerator. (*Exits and re-enters.*) There! They'll be nice and fresh for tonight. I hope she wears her black velvet. Gardenias look wonderful on black velvet.

MOLLY: I'll say. Well, I must scram. See you tonight and don't forget to bring the flowers.

KITTY: I'd like to see myself forget the flowers. They'll be the high spot of the party. So long. (*As* MOLLY *exits,* MRS. FAIRCHILD *enters.*)

MRS. FAIRCHILD: Oh, hello, Molly.

MOLLY: Hello, Mrs. Fairchild. Kitty and I have just been polishing off the last-minute details for our class Valentine Party.

MRS. FAIRCHILD: We've heard nothing else at our house for a week but that party. I hope it goes off smoothly.

MOLLY: Oh, it will. Goodbye.

MRS. FAIRCHILD: Goodbye, dear. (*Exit* MOLLY. *To* KITTY) Is everything under control in your department?

KITTY: I guess so. We're going up to school early so we can put the finishing touches on the decorations.

MRS. FAIRCHILD: Then you'd better fly. I must speak to Hoppy about supper.

KITTY: If you can find her, you're a better detective than I am.

MRS. FAIRCHILD: Isn't she in the kitchen?

KITTY: Not unless she's in the oven. I haven't seen her at all. Well, I'll go take my bath before the rest of the tribe starts hammering at the door. Even now it sounds as if Scotty beat me to it. (*Exits yelling "Gangway...here I come....Clear the decks!"*)

MRS. FAIRCHILD: Never a dull moment in this house. Well, I might as well go see what's in the refrigerator for supper. (*Exits and re-appears with the now-familiar flower box.*) Gardenias — Somebody in this house is pretty lucky. I suppose they're for Scotty. She's the belle of the ball these days. I wonder if she's seen them. (*Starts to set the box on telephone table and sees telegram*) Oh...oh...here's a little something for Mrs. Fairchild. I hope it's from my Valentine in Washington. (*Opens it.*) And that's just who sent it....The old darling! (*Reading*) "Hope the flowers reach you in time for Valentine's. Love to all. Dad." Well, that explains the mystery....If he isn't an old sweetheart! He's sent me gardenias every year on Valentine's Day. I should have known they were from him. Well, I'll just put them away and wear them at dinner tonight to surprise the children. (*Starts to exit as* JUNIOR *enters. He carries a cleaning bag containing a suit.*)

JUNIOR: Hya, Moms. I see you got the flowers.

MRS. FAIRCHILD: Oh, so you found them first. How do you like them?

JUNIOR: They're keen.

MRS. FAIRCHILD: I'm just putting them back in the icebox. (*Exit.*)

JUNIOR (*Calling*): They sure saved my neck...those posies. When's supper ready?

MRS. FAIRCHILD (*Re-entering*): What did you say, dear?

JUNIOR: I said, when's supper ready?

MRS. FAIRCHILD: That's a hard question to answer. Hoppy doesn't seem to be in evidence. I'll have to rustle a few things together.

JUNIOR: Want me to help? Buzz and I have to get an early start.

MRS. FAIRCHILD: Oh, no. You don't need to help. Just take

your suit upstairs. You'll have time to dress before supper if you like. Hoppy will probably be along any minute. I have an idea she went to the store.

Hoppy (*Entering on* Mrs. Fairchild's *last line*) : That's just where I've been, Mrs. Fairchild. The minute I saw those gorgeous flowers, I said to myself...Hoppy, you march yourself down street and buy this family a valentine. And here it is, the biggest box of candy I could find...for you and the whole gang.

Mrs. Fairchild (*Accepting big heart box of candy*) : Why Hoppy! What a surprise!

Junior: Gee, Hoppy. That's swell.

Mrs. Fairchild: But what flowers are you talking about?

Hoppy: The flowers you sent me for my Valentine. (*Wiping eyes with handkerchief*) I was downright touched...and that sweet card..."To My Valentine." I bet Miss Scotty fixed that up.

Mrs. Fairchild: But, Hoppy, oh, my goodness, this is embarrassing. You see, those flowers weren't for you...

Junior: Gosh, no! They're for me.

Mrs. Fairchild: For you? What in the world makes you think they're for you?

Junior: Well, didn't you order a corsage for me to give Carriebelle?

Mrs. Fairchild: Yes, but... (*Phone*)

Junior: I'll get it...Fairchild residence...Yeah...she's here. (*Yelling*) Scotty...phone.

Scotty (*Off stage*) : Coming!

Hoppy: This is beginning to sound like a merry mix-up.

Mrs. Fairchild: It certainly is....You see...I happen to know that the flowers are for me....That card proves it. (Scotty *enters.*)

SCOTTY: Oh I hope that's Wayne... (*At phone*) Hello, hello, Wayne. Oh, I'm so glad you called. Oh, Wayne, I can't tell you how sorry I am about this afternoon, but those flowers fixed everything. Did I get them? Of course, I got them... and I love them. Certainly, I'm going to the dance. That is, if you still want me.....All right...Well, I can't talk right now...I'll tell you when I see you. Okay. I'll be ready at eight. Goodbye. (*Hangs up*) Oh, Mother, Wayne and I had the most awful fight and then I found these flowers in the refrigerator. (*Stares at flowers and then at* JUNIOR.) How did they get out here? Junior Fairchild, what's the idea of meddling with my flowers. You put these right back.

JUNIOR: What the heck? Your flowers? They're my flowers.

SCOTTY: They are not. They're mine. Wayne sent them to me. See...gardenias...and there's the card..."To My Valentine." You don't suppose anyone would send you flowers with a card like that, do you?

JUNIOR: No, but they're not for me.

SCOTTY: That's what I'm telling you, they're for me.

JUNIOR: They're not! They're for Carriebelle. Mom bought them. Didn't you, Moms?

MRS. FAIRCHILD: I've been trying to tell all of you, they're for me. Here is a telegram from Dad. He sent them to me. He's sent me gardenias on Valentine's Day every year since we were engaged.

SCOTTY: Really, this is too silly for words! I just talked to Wayne this very minute...and he said...

JUNIOR: Did he say they were for you? Did he say he sent them?

SCOTTY: Well, no...not exactly but I know he did. I'm positive.

HOPPY: This is too much for me. And there's no name on the box, that's why I was so sure they were for me.

KITTY (*Entering in a bathrobe*) : I just thought I'd better run down and see if I remembered to put the lid on those flowers. ...Well, for mercy's sake. How did they get in here?

JUNIOR: I suppose you think these are your flowers?

KITTY: And whose do you suppose they are? Of course, they're mine.

JUNIOR: Ye gods! Who'd be sending you flowers?

KITTY: Myself. I ordered them for Miss Wilson. I'm chairman of the flower committee...and I chose them myself. Don't you think they're beautiful, Moms?

MRS. FAIRCHILD: They're lovely, Kitty, but they're not for you.

KITTY: Not for me...Oh, I see...you mean...they're not for me because they're for Miss Wilson.

MRS. FAIRCHILD: They're not for Miss Wilson either, Kitty. They're for me. I just had a wire from your father saying he had sent me flowers for Valentine's Day.

KITTY: Holy smokes! Then where are my flowers?

JUNIOR: And mine?

SCOTTY: And mine?

MRS. FAIRCHILD: Well, I can explain where Junior's are. I had them sent directly to Carriebelle. (*Doorbell*)

JUNIOR: I'll go.

KITTY: Oh dear. I'll never get on any committees again if this is a sample of my luck.

JUNIOR (*At door*) : Yes, this is 29 Elm Street. Yes, we have some gardenias. Well, for the love of mike, come in. (*Enters with dazed-looking messenger boy.*) This guy says he delivered a box of gardenias here by mistake.

MRS. FAIRCHILD: By mistake! You mean these flowers aren't for me.

MESSENGER BOY: No, lady, they're for 39 Elm Street. I'm kinda near-sighted and I made a mistake.

MRS. FAIRCHILD: And what a mistake!

SCOTTY: Here, take them and be sure you deliver them to the right place next time.

KITTY: And take the card with them.

HOPPY: Somebody else will be getting a valentine.

MESSENGER: I'm awful sorry but that's how things are in the flower business. Thanks a lot. I see they're still fresh. Gee, I'm glad you didn't take 'em out of the box. This might have cost me my job.

MRS. FAIRCHILD: Well, go along, son, and look where you're going next time.

MESSENGER (*Exits*): Thanks, lady, I will. Happy Valentine's Day.

JUNIOR: Aw, say it with flowers.

MRS. FAIRCHILD (*Laughing*): Well, that's a good one on me. I guess Dad's flowers have been held up somewhere but this wire is good enough for me.

JUNIOR: Well, anyhow, if you had mine sent to Carriebelle, the country's saved. When they arrive, she'll think she's getting two bunches.

HOPPY: Well, I might as well get supper.

MRS. FAIRCHILD: And if you look on your bureau, Hoppy, you'll find a Valentine that's really for you.

SCOTTY: I wonder if Wayne sent me flowers after all.

MRS. FAIRCHILD: There's still the six o'clock delivery, you know.

KITTY: And what about me?

MRS. FAIRCHILD: Cross your fingers, Kitty, and keep your mind on that six o'clock delivery. (*Doorbell*)

KITTY and SCOTTY (*In a rush*): That's for me...

MRS. FAIRCHILD: I hope it's for both of you and I hope it's gardenias.

OFFSTAGE VOICE: Flowers for Fairchild — 29 Elm Street... Three boxes...

MRS. FAIRCHILD: Dear me...that must be for me... (*Runs off*)

JUNIOR: Ye gods! Aren't women funny! Don't take any wooden gardenias, girls... (*Quick curtain.*)

THE END

PRODUCTION NOTES

SAY IT WITH FLOWERS

Characters: 4 male; 5 female.

Playing Time: 30 minutes.

Costumes: Everyday modern dress. The messenger boy is dressed in messenger's suit.

Properties: Florist's box containing tissue paper, small white card. Since the flowers are not seen, it is not necessary to have any. Telegram, cleaning bag, heart-shaped box of candy, handkerchief for Hoppy.

Setting: A modern American living room. The furniture is comfortable but simple. There is a large sofa, a couple of arm chairs, and occasional tables and lamps are placed about the room. The telephone stands on a small table to one side. There are two entrances, one leading to another part of the house, and the other leading to the hall and front door.

Lighting: None required.

PAPA PEPPER'S BOMBSHELL

Characters

PAPA PEPPER
MRS. PEPPER
TIMOTHY PEPPER
TRUDY PEPPER
HELEN PEPPER
A STRANGER

SCENE: *The living room in the Pepper house.*

TIME: *The present.*

PAPA PEPPER'S BOMBSHELL

SETTING: *Living room in the Pepper home.*

AT RISE: *The Pepper family is assembled in the living room —
that is — all but PAPA. MOTHER is knitting; HELEN is
writing a letter at a desk on which there is a photograph of a
young man in uniform. TIM, swathed in bandages, occupies
the sofa where he is victim for TRUDY's First Aid practice.
TRUDY is struggling with a large triangular bandage which
has a knot tied in one corner. From time to time she consults
her Manual for directions.*

TRUDY (*Reading from Manual, bandage in hand*): "Tie a knot
at the point of the bandage, beginning the knot about six
inches from the point." Well, I've done that much. Now
what's next?

TIM: I can tell you what's next. Get a new patient. I'm
through.

TRUDY: Oh, not yet, Timmy. This one will be fun. Just wait
a second till I make sure I'm going in the right direction.
(*Reads*) "Place knot at crown of head. Carry the base down
over the face and chin to neck. Carry one end around to back
covering the cheek, ear, and back of head and neck." (*Suits
actions to the words.*)

TIM (*Struggling*): Hey! Hey! For Pete's sake! What are
you trying to do? Suffocate me?

TRUDY: Shut up and sit still. Remember you already have a
broken arm and a cracked rib.

167

Tɪᴍ: That cracked rib must have come from splitting my sides laughing at your bandaging technique. (*He pronounces it Tek-ni-cue.*)

Tʀᴜᴅʏ: You'll laugh on the other side of your face when I get this one on you. It says (*Reading*) "Now carry the other end around in a similar manner crossing over the first. Bring ends to front and tie under chin."

Tɪᴍ: Tie what under whose chin? (*Grabbing book*) Let me see that crazy book.

Tʀᴜᴅʏ: You give that back.

Tɪᴍ: Hold your horses. I gotta locate my wounds.

Tʀᴜᴅʏ: Oh, Tim, you're spoiling that lovely sling. Please do be careful. If you'll just keep still, I'll show you the picture. (*Recovers the manual.*) Here it is, Figure twenty-four, Bandage for Face or Back of Head.

Tɪᴍ: Holy Catfish! That's not a bandage. That's the Ku Klux Klan.

Tʀᴜᴅʏ: It is not. It's for scalds and burns.

Tɪᴍ: And I'm burned up enough with you and your old First Aid. Come get me out of this. Mother, make her unwind me.

Mᴏᴛʜᴇʀ (*Mildly*): Maybe he has had enough for one treatment, dear. After all, you don't want to overdo a good thing.

Tʀᴜᴅʏ: But he could easily have a broken arm and a cracked rib, and be scalded too, all in one smash-up. It often happens.

Tɪᴍ: O.K. Then what's the use of all this bandaging? I'd be dead anyway or hang myself in all these old rags.

Mᴏᴛʜᴇʀ: You two give me the shivers with all that gory talk. Trudy, can't you count his pulse for a while or listen to his breathing? Something more quiet?

Hᴇʟᴇɴ (*Looking up from her writing*): I second the motion. I can't concentrate at all.

Tɪᴍ (*Falsetto voice*): Oh dear me! Our Helen can't write to her Llewellyn.

HELEN: You stop making fun of Lew's name. After all, he's still in the service and you should be proud of him.

TIM: Just think how funny it's going to be when you two stand up there at the altar and he says: "I, Llewellyn take thee, Helen."

HELEN: Oh, Mother, make him stop.

MOTHER: Remember how furious you get, Timothy, when Trudy calls you — you know what.

TIM: Don't say it. Don't say it. I surrender, and if I wasn't tied up like a mummy, I'd get down on bended knee and apologize.

HELEN: It would be better for all of us if Trudy could put a strait jacket on that mouth of yours.

TIM: Why, sister Helen, you amaze me. You utterly astonish me. In short, I don't like your attitude.

TRUDY: I never in all my life heard anyone who could rattle on and on like you, Timothy Pepper.

MOTHER: Well, when Dad comes home, please try to soft pedal this chatter for a while.

TRUDY: I can guarantee a soft pedal on Tim if you'll just make him let me adjust this bandage.

TIM: Nix on that feed bag. Put it on Pop when he comes home.

TRUDY: What do you want? A war on our home front?

MOTHER: For once, Trudy, you are using your head. Please, whatever you do, don't try any of that First Aid business on your father.

HELEN: I wonder what makes him so irritable lately. He's not one bit like himself.

TIM: Wouldn't even lend me two bits yesterday.

MOTHER: And no wonder. You have your regular allowance.

TIM: Yeah? But look at the high cost of living, taxes and everything and no increase in my income.

MOTHER: I can think of a few extra jobs around the house and garage that might add to your income.

TRUDY: Nobody around this house seems to care if I pass my Scout First Aid test or not. Here, Tim, I'm ready for the bandage. This might be a trifle uncomfortable, but I'll cut eyes and nose after it is in place.

TIM: Oh, no, you don't! You'll not go poking around my beautiful blue eyes with any old scissors. I'd rather stay blindfolded.

MOTHER (*To* HELEN): If you've finished your letter, dear, I wish you'd hold this yarn for me.

HELEN: I've just finished.

TIM (*From under bandage*): Did you put in lots of love and kisses?

HELEN: When will you ever grow up? (*Moves to footstool beside mother.*)

MOTHER: Not for years, so don't expect it!

HELEN: Seriously, Mother, why do you suppose Dad acts so funny?

MOTHER: He doesn't act funny. He doesn't say much when he comes home, because he is worn out. He has a lot on his mind.

HELEN: You mean he's worried about the factory?

MOTHER: Of course. All the strikes and labor troubles are enough to keep him stirred up all the time.

HELEN: But Dad never had any trouble with labor before.

MOTHER: That's why he's so worried. Plenty of things go on at the factory that we don't understand.

TRUDY: Oh, that factory! It's a wonder he doesn't eat and sleep there!

TIM: Yeah! And a ribbon factory at that! I thought sure he'd convert to something useful during the war, but nothing doing!

TRUDY: Come to think of it, Pop didn't take a very active part in the war, did he?

MOTHER: You youngsters make me sick and tired, criticising your father, when he works so hard for us all. Here it is, nine o'clock and he's not even home yet! (*Phone rings.*)

HELEN (*Leaping to her feet*): I'll get it. Maybe it's for me.

HELEN (*At phone*): Hello? Yes, this is the Pepper residence. No, he hasn't come home yet. No, but we're expecting him at any minute. Can I give him a message or tell him to call you? Oh, very well. Goodbye. (*Returning to her place.*) These people who can never tell their names always give me a pain.

TRUDY: Who was it?

HELEN: Didn't I just tell you he wouldn't leave his name? Maybe he couldn't pronounce it. It seemed all he could do to talk English at all.

MOTHER: Maybe it was Mr. Dupree. But he would have given his name. At least he always does when he calls your father.

HELEN: Oh, no, it wasn't Mr. Dupree. I know his voice. This was a different accent, sort of guttural and growly.

MOTHER: What did he want?

HELEN: Just wanted to know if Dad was in and hung up when I asked who was calling.

MOTHER: Well, he just missed him. I think I hear your father coming in now.

TRUDY: Yep, that's Pop. He's putting his bicycle away. Honestly, Mother, he's a sight for the gods on that velocipede he insists on riding.

MOTHER: It's not a velocipede, and you know it. Besides, how would he get back and forth to the plant since we have no car?

HELEN: If we had ever dreamed we would be riding bicycles to and from town, we would never have built this house way out here in the country.

MOTHER: Hardly the country, dear.

TIM: No, no, nothing so common as the country, sister mine. Just a little suburban paradise, the real estate agents call it. Happy Highlands — the Hill of Happy Home-Owners. (*Sound of door.*)

MOTHER: Is that you, James dear?

FATHER: Yes, where is everybody?

MOTHER: In here. Come in and join us. Did you eat in town?

FATHER (*Entering with evening paper and brief case. He has removed his coat and hat, but he is rumpled and dusty. One cheek is scratched and smudged. His hair is mussed*): Yes, I had a bite at the drug store. Hello, everybody.

ALL: Greetings. Hello. Hy'a, Pop, etc.

FATHER (*On seeing Tim's bandages*): Good gravy! What's wrong with you? Were you in an accident?

TRUDY: Not yet, Daddy. It's just my First Aid. Look, see, I've given him arm and leg bandages and the masked-rider effect is for burns and scalds.

FATHER: That's a fine, cheerful sight to confront a tired businessman, I must say.

HELEN: Well, you look a bit mussed up yourself, if you ask me. Your face looks as if somebody stepped on it.

MOTHER (*Alarmed*): Why, James, you do look upset. What happened?

TRUDY (*Eagerly*): Let me put a compress on that cheek, Daddy. I know exactly how it's done.

FATHER: There's nothing wrong with me, and don't come near me with a compress, if you know what's good for you. I just had a tumble from my bike, that's all.

TIM: Ho, ha! It threw you, did it? I always knew that old bike had a lot of vim and go in her. Maybe you better stop feeding her vitamins.

HELEN: Never you mind, Daddy. Anybody can fall off a

bicycle. How about a nice piece of cake? I baked it myself and it's simply divine.

FATHER: O.K., daughter. That will just hit the spot. What kind is it?

HELEN: It's called Golden Delight.

MOTHER: One of those new thrift recipes Helen learned at nutrition class.

FATHER: Don't bother. I'm not hungry.

HELEN: But, Daddy, it's wonderful. It's eggless, butterless and milkless and instead of flour, you use...

TRUDY: Let me guess! Some nice fresh feathers out of an old sofa cushion.

FATHER: No doubt. It's probably flourless, sodaless, baking-powder-less, and tasteless. Two cups of sawdust and a dash of T.N.T.

HELEN: Oh, Daddy, you're never willing to try anything new. You always wanted me to learn how to cook.

FATHER: And I still do. But I'd prefer you'd learn to make a cake that tastes like a cake instead of a hair-mattress.

HELEN: But this is delicious. Honestly. Come on, Daddy, just take a teensy-weensy piece.

FATHER: All right, chicken. To please you, I'd eat a sausage made out of an old inner tube. Better bring me a glass of milk to wash it down, but remember I want the real thing— out of a real cow.

MOTHER (*As* HELEN *leaves the room*): Now, James dear, try to relax. You must have had a hard day.

FATHER: And while I'm relaxing, I'd enjoy a glimpse of my only son without that winding sheet on his head and with his arm and legs uncovered.

TRUDY: O.K., Dad. I'll have them off in a jiffy. Golly, I wish something drastic would happen around here to convince you people that First Aid is a wonderful thing. (*Unwinds* TIM.)

MOTHER: By the way, James, someone called you on the phone just before you came in.

FATHER: That so? Who was it?

MOTHER: Some man who wouldn't give his name and Helen said it wasn't anybody we know.

TRUDY: He no spoke-da-Eengleesh.

FATHER: You mean he talked with an accent? (*Displays interest.*)

TRUDY: That's right.

FATHER: What kind? Did she say what kind of accent?

MOTHER: Not exactly. She said he had a deep, growly voice and spoke in a harsh, guttural tone.

FATHER (*Jumping up*): How long ago was that call?

MOTHER: Just a few minutes ago. Why?

HELEN (*Offstage*): Hey, Daddy, you left the back door wide open. What do you think this is, a barn?

FATHER: The back door — open? Why, I'm sure I... (*Loud piercing scream from* HELEN *offstage. All the lights go off. Everyone on stage screams. In the darkness,* MR. PEPPER *thrusts his brief case, which has been on the table, under the cushion of his chair. The beam of a flashlight plays over the room and a voice says: "Efferybody stand where you are. Don't move, please." The words are spoken in a heavy foreign accent. (To* HELEN) *"You, Mees, walk straight ahead and turn on the light in the room." In the beam of light* HELEN *is seen walking in front of a man wearing a mask. He is directing her movements and keeping her under control by a pistol which he keeps trained on her. As she turns on the light above the desk, nobody but* TRUDY *notices that* TIM *is missing. He has climbed over the back of the sofa and is crouched behind it. She starts to call attention to his disappearance, but changes her mind. As the lights flash on the* STRANGER *speaks.*)

STRANGER: That ees fine. Now, nobody move, please. My beesness ees wis Mr. Pepper only. Eet concerns no one else, so long as no one else eenterferes.

MOTHER: James, who is this person?

HELEN (*Sobbing*): Oh, Mother, he jumped out at me from behind the dining room curtains. He's a burglar.

STRANGER: Mees Pepper ees meestaken. I am not a burglar. I will disturb nothing of your valuables. My beesness ees wis Mr. Pepper only.

FATHER: What do you want?

STRANGER: You know what I want. Hand it ofer, please... before your wife and children see a great unpleasantness.

FATHER: I don't get you. And I'm not afraid of you.

STRANGER: No? You may have the chance to prove your courage later. But now, the brief case, if you please.

FATHER: My brief case? What could you possibly want with that?

STRANGER: Shall we say it is a ribbon pattern that I desire?

TRUDY: Daddy, who is this man?

STRANGER: Mr. Pepper does not know my name, but mine beesness he understands. The brief case, eef you will be so kind.

MOTHER: But, James, you never bring your brief case home with you. This gentleman should have made you an office visit.

STRANGER: Ve do not need suggestions from the ladies. Eef eet vill conwince you, Mrs. Pepper, I am in a posetion to know that these night your husband have brot wis heem home the brief case. Eet ees in these house and een these room.

HELEN: You, you thug! You bandit! How dare you break in here and threaten us?

STRANGER: Neither your bad menners nor your questions vill help your father. The brief case. I must have it and my patience ees not long.

FATHER: What makes you so sure that the case is in the house? My wife has told you that I always leave it at the office.

STRANGER: But not these evening. My partner — how do you say? — my co-worker, did he not pay you a small veesit these evening as you rode home on the bicycle? But you were so rough wis heem, he had to call on me to feenish his work myself.

HELEN: Daddy, were you attacked?

TRUDY: I knew you couldn't *fall* off that bicycle. Somebody pushed you.

MOTHER: James, were you in a fight?

FATHER: Please, all of you, this is no time for questions. But if you must know, someone did attack me tonight on the way home. Whoever it was tried to take my brief case, but that doesn't matter now.

STRANGER: Quite right. Eet does not matter now. Nothing matters now except the brief case.

TRUDY: For heaven's sake, give him the old brief case, Daddy, it's practically worn out anyhow.

FATHER: But you do not understand. It is not the case this fellow wants. It is what is inside.

MOTHER: And what on earth is inside that could stir up such a rumpus and bring this murderer upon us.

STRANGER: Mrs. Pepper, please, your words are geeving me beeg ideas.

FATHER: There's no use bluffing. You might as well know I don't intend giving you the brief case. If you want it, you'll have to take it yourself.

STRANGER: Obviously I cannot search these room the while I must keep you covered wis these one small gun. But I warn you, there are ways to force you, Mr. Pepper, unpleasant ways.

FATHER: You'll have to do your worst then, Mister. The brief case is not for you or for anyone else in your outfit.

TRUDY: Hey, who are you anyhow, a spy?

STRANGER: My profession do not concern you. You American children have many lessons to learn and soon ve vill teach you — how you say? — plenty. Meanwhile — the brief case?

MOTHER (*In a businesslike way*): Now look here, my good man, my husband has told you he won't give you the case, so that's that. When James puts his foot down, he won't budge.

STRANGER: Nefair fear, Mrs. Pepper, ve vill budge heem. Now leesten, all of you. I have been most patient. Now I stop using words of persuasion. These gun ees loaded. Mr. Pepper, you are a family man. You luff your wife and children. Very well. (*With one sweep of his arm, he grabs* TRUDY, *and by twisting her wrist forces her to the sofa beside him. He holds her with one hand and places the pistol at her head.*)

TRUDY (*Struggling as much as she can*): You let me go. Ouch! Ouch! You're hurting me. Ooooh! You let me go! Help! Help!

STRANGER (*As* MOTHER *starts toward the sofa*): One more step, Mrs. Pepper, and I will live up to the name you called me — murderer!

TRUDY (*Really frightened*): Oh, Daddy, Daddy, make him let go of me. He's hurting me.

FATHER: Try to be quiet, Trudy. Sit still, if you can. He won't hurt you.

STRANGER: He speaks the truth. I vill not hurt you. A bullet through the head is painless. (TRUDY *screams and then falls to sobbing.*)

MOTHER: You monster! Oh, James, James, what can we do? What can we do? (MOTHER *falls into chair and begins to cry.* HELEN *tries to comfort her.* MR. PEPPER *stares dazedly at the* STRANGER *holding* TRUDY *prisoner on the sofa.*)

STRANGER: Have you a watch, Mr. Pepper?

FATHER: Yes.

STRANGER: Then look at the hands. When five minutes are up, I vill pull these trigger — unless, of course, I have the brief case.

TRUDY: Oh, Daddy, he means it. He means it. Make him let me go.

STRANGER: Quite right, young lady. And your father knows I mean eet. But you vill not die. I know fathers too well.

HELEN: Oh, Daddy, Daddy, give him the case. We can't just stand here and watch him actually —

MOTHER: James, do something. Give it to him. Do anything he wants...quickly.

FATHER: You don't understand. I can't give it to him. The case contains important plans — government plans.

HELEN: What would you be doing with government plans?

FATHER: It's about the factory.

MOTHER: But James — a ribbon factory isn't important.

FATHER: I can't explain now. But I can't hand over the brief case...no matter what happens.

TRUDY (*In terror*): Daddy, you aren't going to let him kill me?

FATHER: No, no, I'm not, Trudy. I'm not. There must be some way.

STRANGER: Only one way, Pepper. Where have you hidden that brief case?

FATHER: I can't tell you. I can't. I can't.

STRANGER: A bullet hole in a child's head...it ees an ugly sight. You will nefair forget eet.

MOTHER: James, James, I can't stand it. Trudy, she's our baby.

FATHER: You swine, you rotten, dirty swine! I can't stand it either. No one could. (*Pulls brief case from under cushion on chair.*) Here it is. Take it and take your hands off that child.

STRANGER: Aha! You are becoming more fatherly, I see. Now open eet. (FATHER *opens case.*) Now hold up the papers — one by one. I must make sure I am not deceived. I have seen the papers once — I vill know them. No tricks, now, eef you please. (*During this last speech,* TIM, *who has taken refuge behind the sofa, slowly rises to view. In his hand he has the triangular bandage which had been tied around his head. He is aiming for the head of the* STRANGER. *If anyone sees him, there is no sign. The* STRANGER *and* TRUDY *have their backs to him.* MR. PEPPER *stalls for time.*)

FATHER: There will be no tricks, on my part. But how am I to be sure that you will clear out and leave us all unharmed?

STRANGER: I suppose my word would be of no importance to you. There — there — that is enough. I am sure they are the papers I want. Bring them to me. I vill release the girl when you lay them here beside me. (*By this time* TIM *is almost ready to sling the bandage over the* STRANGER'S *head.*)

TRUDY: Oh, Daddy, hurry, please.

MOTHER: Oh, James, I knew you'd save her.

FATHER: I guess any father would do the same, but you — you unspeakable wretch, your methods may not always be successful.

STRANGER: Allow me to be the judge of — (*His words are choked off as* TIM *throws the bandage over his head and pulls it tight. The* STRANGER *flings up his arm to guard his head thereby releasing* TRUDY *and diverting his aim with the gun.* MR. PEPPER *rushes on him and grabs the gun out of his hand.* TIM *pommels him from the rear.*)

TRUDY (*Running to her* MOTHER): Mother! Mother! Mother!

MOTHER *and* HELEN (*Fussing over* TRUDY): Oh, you darling, are you sure you're not hurt?

FATHER: You forgot something that time, Stranger. You

forgot to reckon with that completely unknown quantity — the American Boy.

STRANGER (*From under bandage*) : Glub — glub, etc. (*Which might be interpreted to mean* — *"You let me go."*)

TIM : I've got enough bandages left, Pop, to bind him hand and foot.

FATHER : I'll do the holding and you do the tying. Your Boy Scout knots should do the trick.

TIM : Boy, oh boy, oh boy! A real spy on our good sofa! We'll have to air it for six months! (*They have the* STRANGER *stretched out on the sofa and are doing a first-rate job of tying him up.*)

FATHER : Well, Tim, I guess you're the hero of the hour.

TRUDY (*Brokenly*) : He saved my life. He honestly did.

FATHER : To say nothing of your dad's honor and the government papers.

TIM : Say, I think Trudy should have a chance to work out on this patient. Let's leave one knot for her to tie.

TRUDY (*Shuddering*) : No, no, I don't want to touch him.

MOTHER : And you don't have to, Honey. *Keep away from him!*

FATHER : Well don't you think it's high time somebody called the police? Or do you want to have this fellow as our guest for the night?

HELEN : Heaven forbid. I'll call them myself. (*Runs to phone.*) Police Headquarters? Send a police car right away to 225 Happy Highland Road. Yes, yes, please...and do hurry. We've caught a spy. Yes, honest we have. He tried to — Oh, all right, but please hurry. Thank you. (*Hangs up.*) They'll be out in a few minutes. Oh, my goodness, I feel faint!

TIM : Can you beat that? *She* feels faint. Trudy's the one who has a right to do the fainting.

TRUDY (*Master of the situation*) : Quick, Helen, sit right here and put your head down between your knees. (*Pushing* HELEN's *head down.*) That's the best way to prevent fainting.

HELEN: Ouch! Stop it! You're mussing my hair.

TIM: What are we going to do with this lug, Pop?

FATHER: Leave him where he is till the police arrive. They'll attend to him.

MOTHER: But, James, what is all this mystery about the brief case and the War Department and the factory and the government?

FATHER: You see, the ribbon factory is only in the front of the building. During the war, we tore out all the machinery from the rear of the shop and installed a sort of laboratory.

MOTHER: A laboratory?

FATHER: Yes, Mr. Dupree and I have been working on it. We secured the services of Dr. Zuroski, the exiled chemist, to direct us, and, well, we've done some pretty important work on the atomic bomb!

ALL: The Atomic Bomb!

FATHER: Lately there have been some new developments...a new short-cut formula!

TIM: So those were the mysterious plans! Gee willikins! This is too much for my feeble brain!

FATHER: I have been worried all along for fear this labor agitation has been the work of a spy ring. Now I have proof.

TIM: Gee, Pop! No wonder you've had things on your mind!

TRUDY: He's a hero! That's what he is! And the dearest daddy in the world.

TIM (*Calling attention to the prisoner's efforts to free himself*): Hey, you there! No tricks. Quick, everybody, don't let this guy escape. (*Hurls himself on the prisoner.*)

TRUDY: I'm not afraid of him now, Tim. Let me at him. I'll give him some real First Aid — an example of Artificial Respiration. (*Sound of siren*)

FATHER: No need for that. Let's leave the rough stuff for the strong arm of the law. As for me, I'm ready for a good big slice of that cake Helen was going to get for me a while ago, and a gallon of milk to go with it.

TIM: Not till we see this guy loaded right onto the Black Maria. Here they come, Pop. I'll open the door. (*Runs to door*)

MOTHER (*Walking to curtain line*): And I'll just close these curtains so no idle curiosity-seekers will have the satisfaction of seeing the patrol-wagon drive up to this house. (*Curtains begin to close.*) I think the Peppers have put on enough show for one night!

THE END

PRODUCTION NOTES

Papa Pepper's Bombshell

Characters: 3 male; 3 female.

Playing Time: 30 minutes.

Costumes: All characters are in everyday clothes. The Stranger wears a mask.

Properties: Knitting material; pen; paper; bandages; First Aid Manual; stamp book; evening paper; brief case; flashlight; gun.

Setting: A comfortable middle-class living-room with chairs, a couch, a desk, lamps, etc. No elaborate furnishings are needed.

Lighting: Footlights are used as well as lamps on stage. Lights all go off on cue and then on again.

HORRORS, INCORPORATED

Characters

MONSTER X, *Karloff Incarnate.*
THE COUNTESS, *a sinister dame.*
HERMAN, *the Mad Scientist.*
JOYCE *and* JIMMY, *Human Beings.*
GHOSTS, GOBLINS *and* WITCHES } *the Spectral Strikers.*

SCENE: *Office of the firm of Horrors, Incorporated.*

TIME: *The present.*

HORRORS, INCORPORATED

BEFORE RISE: *As the house lights dim, the strains of the "Chopin Funeral March" are heard and a strange procession marches slowly across the apron of the stage. There are witches, ghosts, goblins, skeletons, black cats and any other spectral figures available. Each one bears a placard with these and other inscriptions:* ON STRIKE! DOWN WITH HORRORS INC. SHORTER HOURS FOR SPOOKS! UNION WAGES! JOIN THE SPOOK UNION! HORRORS UNFAIR! WE WANT WARMER GRAVEYARDS! MORE HOLIDAYS FOR HAUNTS! *As the last figure leaves the stage, the curtains open.*

SETTING: *The firm of* HORRORS, INCORPORATED.

AT RISE: *Pacing up and down the office is* MONSTER X, *a tall, formidable-looking man whose shoulders are padded to resemble a hump. He walks with his head thrust forward, his arms dangling loosely at his side in the approved Karloff fashion. Seated at the typewriter is his secretary, a tall, thin girl in a long, tight-fitting black dress. Her hair should be parted in the middle and drawn tightly down over her ears. She has a dark and sinister manner.*

MONSTER X: Tell me, Countess, are those strikers still picketing the plant?

COUNTESS: Yes, they're still at it. I don't see how they keep it up. Three days without eating or sleeping. It's positively inhuman.

MONSTER X: Don't I know? Inhuman is right. Oh, if they were only flesh and blood human beings, I could cope with them. These hands of mine could twist their skinny necks and squeeze their last breath from their gasping throats. But what can I do with these supernatural monsters?

COUNTESS: You'd better say what can you do *without* them.

MONSTER X: Enough. Enough. Go on with your typing.

COUNTESS: I have nothing to type. We have had no mail to answer in three weeks.

MONSTER X (*Tearing his hair*): I shall go mad if this keeps up. Countess, do you know what this means? With those miserable wretches on strike, the shortage of materials, and this falling-off of orders, the firm will have to close. HORRORS, INCORPORATED, in continuous operation for over a thousand years, will have to shut down. This is a terrible state of affairs and yet there must be some way out. There must be.

COUNTESS: I see very little hope. But why worry. You don't need the money. You can retire and live off your income.

MONSTER X: Fah! Retire! And what would I do all day and all night? How could I put in my time? I have no friends. Where would I go? No, when you have spent a thousand years building up the most horrible and frightening business in the world, you don't give it up without a struggle. (*Points to large armchair*) What other firm in the world could ever produce a chair like that? The famous chair used by The Demon Barber of Fleet Street for his victims. Every customer who ever sat in it had a close shave.

COUNTESS: Yes, that was one of our most popular numbers. Is it still in working order?

MONSTER X: Certainly. I oil it twice a month. Just let a customer sit down in that chair, touch the spring...and customer, chair and all disappear in the wall. The Demon Barber would then slit the customer's throat, ransack his pockets and sell the body to the old woman next door who made meat pies in a gigantic oven. Oh, he was a clever one, the Barber of Fleet Street, but it was HORRORS, INCORPORATED who made the wonderful chair.

COUNTESS: Yes, but we have no call for that sort of thing these days.

MONSTER X: The world has gone soft. We once made a specialty of sword canes and poison rings and invisible daggers. And as for sealed-up rooms, we had a monopoly on that business during the Middle Ages. We sealed up some of the best families in Europe. Whenever a duke or an earl or a lord wanted to dispose of a troublesome relative, we just walled him up in some unused part of the castle and left him to his own devices. But that, too, is out of style.

COUNTESS: Yes, people can hardly get bricklayers and plasterers for ordinary purposes nowadays.

MONSTER X: The same thing is true of haunted houses. We used to have more calls than we could handle, but now hardly anyone has a house to haunt. Yes, things have come to a pretty pass.

COUNTESS: Perhaps our advertising is at fault. Maybe folks need to be reminded of our existence. They've forgotten some of our darkest deeds because they happened so long ago. Maybe if we put on a good publicity campaign with some sensational advertising we could revive public interest.

MONSTER X: Countess, I believe you've got something there. We should be more sensational, more daring, more breathtaking. By all the satanic powers of darkness, I think you've hit the nail on the head. We must do something so awful, so awe-inspiring, so hair-raising that the whole world will be talking about HORRORS, INCORPORATED.

COUNTESS: But what can we do?

MONSTER X: I dont' know. Call in the Mad Scientist. Perhaps he can help us.

COUNTESS: I'll call him, but perhaps he is on strike with the others.

MONSTER X: Not Herman. He's probably so absorbed in one of his crazy experiments that he doesn't even know the strike is on.

COUNTESS (*Talking into office phone*): Herman, the Boss wants to see you right away. No, he won't wait five minutes or five seconds. Put down your test tubes, turn out the gas flames and come at once. (*To* MONSTER X) He'll be right in.

MONSTER X: Herman must help us. He must conjure up some new experiment in Horror that will set the world by the ears.

COUNTESS: Don't count too much on Herman. He's getting madder by the minute. Sometimes I wonder if he even remembers he is a scientist. (*The* MAD SCIENTIST *enters. He wears a white jacket and carries a test tube of bright red liquid. He is greatly excited.*)

HERMAN: Master, Master, the Elixir is complete! It is perfect at last. We are ready for the final experiment...but for that, we need human beings—real flesh and bone people with rich, flowing blood, lots of blood!

MONSTER X: Quiet, Herman! Quiet! We have important business to discuss. Sit down.

HERMAN: But nothing is as important as the Elixir. It is just right. I tried it a few minutes ago on a pair of white rats, and guess what happened.

COUNTESS: They turned green.

HERMAN: No, they dissolved, leaving nothing at all except a few grains of white powder. But now we must try it on a human being.

MONSTER X: Herman, I know how much this Elixir means to you, and you know how much HORRORS, INCORPORATED means to me. Perhaps we can work out a deal.

HERMAN: What sort of a deal?

MONSTER X: If I could arrange to get a human being for your experiment, and if we were to give it the proper amount of publicity, HORRORS, INCORPORATED would be back on its feet, and you would be famous.

HERMAN (*Rubbing his hands*): Splendid. When do we start?

MONSTER X: Are you quite sure this Elixir really dissolved those rats?

HERMAN: Oh, absolutely. They dissolved in three seconds. Now it might take longer with human beings. It will be interesting to study their reactions. The Countess can take everything down in shorthand for our records. (*Sound of doorbell*)

MONSTER X: Quick, Countess. The unexpected has happened. Look through the peephole in the vestibule and see who is at the door. Perhaps our luck is turning and we have a customer. (*Exit* COUNTESS.)

HERMAN: A customer would be just right for my experiment.

MONSTER X: If we have the good fortune to entertain a human being here today, I promise you, you may go ahead with your experiment.

HERMAN: Then I must go back to the laboratory at once and distill a large quantity of the Elixir.

COUNTESS (*Reentering*): There are two children at the door, sir — a boy and a girl.

HERMAN: Excellent, excellent. It will be interesting to see which one dissolves more rapidly. The boy perhaps will show more resistance, but the girl will doubtless emit shrill piercing screams.

MONSTER X: Quick, Herman, to the laboratory. I'll take care of things in here. Countess, show in our callers. (*Seats himself at desk and pretends to be very busy writing as the* COUNTESS *ushers in* TWO CHILDREN *of high school age.*)

COUNTESS: Monster X, there are two young people to see you on urgent business.

JIMMY: Good morning, sir.

MONSTER X: Oh, good morning, young man, what can I do for you?

JIMMY: We've come to see about renting some Halloween costumes for our school party.

MONSTER X: Halloween costumes?

JOYCE: Yes, and we thought you might also have some Halloween novelties — maybe some paper skeletons, or cardboard witches that we could use. You see, we're on the decorating committee.

MONSTER X: And what in the world made you come here for a party?

JIMMY: Well, when we saw your sign, HORRORS, INCORPORATED, we thought it would be an ideal place for Halloween fixings.

JOYCE: We want this party to be a regular humdinger. The other parties have all been so tame, we want this one to be something the kids will always remember.

MONSTER X: Aha! Well, maybe we can fix you up. Won't you sit down, Miss...er...what is the name?

JOYCE: I am Joyce Weatherby and this is Jimmy Charles.

MONSTER X: Delighted to have you. Just sit down and make yourself at home. I think you will find this chair (*Points to the Demon Barber Chair*) quite to your liking.

JOYCE (*Seating herself*): Thank you.

JIMMY: Quite an interesting place here. I like the way you have your samples arranged.

MONSTER X: Ah, yes...glad you like it...very glad indeed.

JIMMY: What a big old chest that is! Is that your costume chest?

MONSTER X: No, my young friend, that is a body chest.

JOYCE: What in the world is that? I thought a body chest contained your heart and lungs and things.

MONSTER X: It does, my dear, very often. It is a chest designed especially for the concealment of bodies. That very one you are looking at has contained at least twelve bodies — all dead by violent means.

JOYCE: Good heavens!

JIMMY: You can't be serious, sir.

MONSTER X: ...and very very soon (*Assumes a menacing attitude*) it will contain the thirteenth. I think, Master Jimmy, that it is just about your size.

JOYCE: Jimmy, let's get out of here. (*Starts to get up.* MONSTER X *grabs her by the shoulders and forces her back in the chair.*)

JIMMY: Don't be afraid, Joyce. We'll be out of here in a jiffy. (*Heads for door, only to be met by the* MAD SCIENTIST.)

HERMAN: Not so fast, young man. You almost spilled this vial of Elixir and that would have made our experiment take place prematurely. (*Holds* JIMMY *with other hand and places bottle on desk*) Shall I tie this one up, Monster X?

MONSTER X: Yes, you'll find rope in the chest. And hand me a piece for this squirming female. She wriggles like an eel.

BOTH CHILDREN: Let me go! Let go of me! Turn me loose— Help! Help! (COUNTESS *enters.*)

COUNTESS: Oh, I see you have everything under control. Shall I gag them so they cannot scream?

MONSTER X: No, that would disappoint Herman, and I want him to have his fun.

COUNTESS: Very well. What nice-looking children they are too. It seems a pity in a way to destroy them, but then there are millions more. They'll hardly be missed.

JOYCE: Oh, Jimmy, what are they talking about?

JIMMY: Don't cry, Joyce. This is only a stunt to scare us.

MONSTER X: You'll find out soon enough what sort of stunt it is.

JIMMY: What's your game anyhow?

MONSTER X: I'll explain shortly. Herman, are you sure you have plenty of Elixir?

HERMAN: I am afraid not. On such short notice I was not able to produce enough for both. I'll try this on the boy and dispose of the girl by other means.

MONSTER X: That's in your department. Do as you like.

HERMAN (*Rubbing his hands in glee*): Excellent! I'll consult my formula books for a novel method. (*Exit.*)

JIMMY: I demand to know what all this is about.

JOYCE: Oh, Jimmy. Make him let us go.

MONSTER X: Not yet, my dear, but soon. This bottle contains a magic Elixir which, when the Mad Scientist pours it over your friend here, will dissolve him into a fine white powder we can carry out on a dust pan. (JOYCE *screams.*)

JIMMY: Cut it out. Can't you see you're scaring the wits out of her?

MONSTER X: And what about yourself? Are you quite calm?

JIMMY: I don't believe a word of it.

MONSTER X (*Gloating*): You'll believe, when you see your fingers and toes and arms and legs dissolve before your very eyes. And I don't think we need wait for Herman to dispose of Joyce. The chair will do the trick. As soon as I press this spring in the back, it will slowly recede into the wall where a razor will do the rest.

JOYCE (*Screaming wildly*): Jimmy, Jimmy, these people are insane. Help! Help!

MONSTER X: Quiet! There's plenty of time. No need to get upset — at least not for a few minutes. Relax. (JOYCE *cries more softly.*)

JIMMY: What's the idea of all this? We never did anything to you.

MONSTER X: Of course not, and there are no hard feelings. Because of labor troubles, shortage of materials, plus a general lack of public interest, we are forced to go out of business. This I cannot bear. We must do something to put the name of HORRORS, INCORPORATED before the public. That is where you come in my friends. The sheer horror of your disappearance, the fact that you have met such dreadful fates by means supplied by our firm will set the whole country talking about us.

JIMMY: But you'll be arrested and executed. The law will catch up with you.

MONSTER X (*Snapping his fingers*): That for the law. The law cannot touch the members of the spirit world. We are a law unto ourselves.

JOYCE: You mean you aren't real. Oh, Jimmy, he's a spook.

MONSTER X: Be careful how you use that term, girl. I am not a spook. I am a Monster...MONSTER X is my name. And here in this building I am master of all I survey.

COUNTESS: Sorry to interrupt you, sir, but the strikers insist upon seeing you.

MONSTER X: Send them away. I am in conference.

COUNTESS: They refuse to budge, sir. Already they are coming up the stairs. (*The* STRIKERS *burst into the room, all screaming, "Justice, we want justice. Down with Monster X."*)

MONSTER X (*Backing up against the desk*): What is all this? Quiet! Hush that infernal clamor and tell me what you want. Who is your spokesman?

SKELETON: I am. Look at me. I've worked my fingers to the bone for this firm and where has it gotten me? My co-workers and I demand better working conditions.

GHOST: Those graveyards are too damp. I have rheumatism now in all my joints.

WITCH: My broomstick was worn out ten years ago. I want a new one.

BLACK CAT: I second the motion. Her old one is so short there's no room for me to ride on it. I have to walk or take a street car.

GOBLIN: I haven't had a day off in twenty years. I demand all legal holidays.

MASKED FIGURE: We want a shorter-hour week.

GHOST: I'm tired of haunting apartment houses. I want a house in the country closer to the cemetery.

MONSTER : Later, later. Come back and see me later when I have more time.

SKELETON: That's what you always say...later...later. But *now* is the time — right this instant. (HERMAN *enters with book.*)

HERMAN: I have here a very interesting case, sir, of how we destroyed a young lady in 1492.

GHOST: There he is, the dirty scab...

WITCH: Catch him for my caldron. He wouldn't join in the strike, and now he shall pay for it. (*Laughs. Some of the* STRIKERS *seize* HERMAN *and hold him.*)

HERMAN: Help! Help! Let me go. I am a scientist. My work is important!

COUNTESS: He's really innocent. Poor Herman doesn't know what goes on half of the time.

SKELETON: And what about you? You are not one of us either.

COUNTESS: But I have my union card and I have always paid my dues.

MASKED FIGURE: That's right. She's a member of The Spook Union in good standing.

SKELETON: Enough of this twiddle twaddle. What shall we do

with this fellow   (*Pointing to* MONSTER) and who are these children?

JIMMY: We're here by no fault of our own, and if you are aiming to do anything terrible to these two fellows, we'll help you if you'll just turn us loose.

MONSTER: Quiet...quiet. Give me a chance to talk. Don't you realize I have worked for the best interests of all of you by trying to keep the firm of HORRORS, INCORPORATED in operation? Now when we are in a jam, you threaten to walk out on us. Give me a chance to pull off this publicity stunt of doing away with these two human beings, and maybe we can get the plant back into full operation. Then we can talk business.

JIMMY: If that's what bothering you, maybe we could help. We've both taken a course in business administration at high school.

MONSTER: What's that?

JOYCE: That's a course that tells you how to run a business.

MONSTER: Does it tell you how to run other people's business?

JIMMY: Sure. Why, I could run this business single-handed.

MONSTER: Oh, you could, could you?

JIMMY: Sure thing. I'll make a deal with you.

MONSTER: A deal?

JIMMY: A bargain. You turn us loose and we'll tell you how to make HORRORS, INCORPORATED a going concern.

MONSTER: A likely story.

JIMMY: What have you to lose? These laborers of yours are as likely to grind you to mincemeat as not. If I can satisfy them and put your firm back on its feet, you'd be happy, wouldn't you?

MONSTER: We monsters are never actually happy, but it would satisfy me for a time.

HERMAN: And what about our experiment?

MONSTER: Quiet, Herman. You talk very sensibly, Master Jimmy, and as you say, I have nothing to lose. Countess, untie that boy and let him take over.

JIMMY: Untie Joyce first.

COUNTESS: Quite the little gentleman, aren't you? (*Unties* JOYCE)

JOYCE: Oh, Jimmy — let's run.

JIMMY: Not yet. We'll have to settle this mess first. Now listen to me, you strikers. Your demands are reasonable. First of all you need a holiday and you shall have it. (*All cheer.*) Halloween is your legal holiday. Not a stroke of work from any of you from midnight till midnight, and full pay in the bargain. (*All cheer.*) You shall be free from this time forth to scare people, and haunt people, frolic through the graveyards, jump out at passers-by in dark alleys and have a good time in general. Does that satisfy you?

WITCH: What about my broomstick?

JIMMY: I'll get you a vacuum cleaner first thing tomorrow. They're easier and faster. Plenty of room for the cat too.

WITCH *and* CAT: Oh boy! Hot diggety!

GHOST: What about those damp graveyards?

JIMMY: I'll set you up in a marble burial vault. It's as dry as dust there. And here (*Takes horsechestnut out of pocket*)— here's a horsechestnut to carry in your shroud. It's a sure cure for rheumatism and arthritis.

GHOST: Thanks...thanks...

JIMMY: Now for your share in the bargain. Report for work tomorrow at 9 A.M. sharp.

MONSTER: You mean seven.

JIMMY: I said nine. Spooks can't get up early when they're out all night spooking. They have to get their beauty sleep between midnight and dawn. (*All cheer.*) Now scram, all of you, and get back on the job tomorrow.

ALL: We will, we will. (*Sing "For you're a jolly good fellow" as they exit.*)

JOYCE: Oh, Jimmy, you're wonderful!

MONSTER X: And what about our business?

JIMMY: We're coming to that? How big a mail order business do you do?

COUNTESS: Hardly any. We've had only two orders for skeletons in closet size in over a year.

JIMMY: No wonder! Who wants a skeleton in their closet these days? There's not enough closet space at best.

MONSTER X: And that's the trouble. We just don't get the orders any more.

JOYCE: Then your supply is exceeding your demand.

JIMMY: That means you must manufacture more things that the public needs? Let's see your fall and winter catalog.

COUNTESS: Here it is. (JOYCE *and* JIMMY *look at it.*)

JIMMY: Ummm...Bad, very bad.

JOYCE: Listen to this...a skeleton in armor. Number 72222.

JIMMY: They went out of style with Henry Wadsworth Longfellow. Phantom of the opera. No good. There's not enough opera.

JOYCE: Brimstone and sulphur smoke.

JIMMY: That's out...it's against the health laws. I can see this whole catalog needs revision.

MONSTER X: But what can a horror company manufacture if they don't go in for horrors?

JOYCE: Oh, there are lots of horrible things left in the world.

JIMMY: Sure, but ghosts and banshees and witches and black cats went out of style with the bustle. As for you, you Mad Scientist, I can get you a job in a toy factory making miniature atomic bombs. The kids will go for them in a big way.

HERMAN: Atomic bombs. What are they?

JIMMY: Never mind. You'll find out in the papers. You might

also turn out some rocket pistols and rocket cars, and rocket candles, and plain rockets. That should keep you happy all day long.

HERMAN: Splendid. But what about my Elixir? It was beautiful the way it dissolved the rats.

JOYCE: If it was good for rats it would be good for other animal and insect pests. Maybe we could use it to replace DDT.

JIMMY: Swell. We'll brew it by the billion gallons and sell it in spray guns. Herman, you have work to do. Back to your laboratory. (*Exit* HERMAN *smiling happily and crooning to himself.*)

MONSTER X: What about the Countess and me?

JIMMY: You both belong in Horror Pictures. I'll wire Hollywood today. In between pictures you can do radio work. Let me hear you laugh.

MONSTER X: A monster never laughs. That would be out of character.

JOYCE: Modern monsters laugh. They chortle and cackle and gasp and wheeze something awful. You'll never succeed if you can't give a wild demoniacal laugh like this. (*Demonstrates.*)

JIMMY: Go ahead and try. (MONSTER *and* COUNTESS *make feeble tries to imitate The Shadow.*)

JOYCE: Not that way. It must be louder and longer, more drawn out — like this. (*Demonstrates again. The* MONSTER *and the* COUNTESS *try again and are more successful.*)

JIMMY: Splendid, splendid. You got the hang of that in no time. Now just sit down over here and practice. (*Seats* COUNTESS *and* MONSTER X *on the chest and Barber's Arm Chair.*) I'll run and get Herman to make a recording of this to send to the Mystery Theatre of the Air. Now keep right on laughing till I get Herman. Don't stop for fear you can't get started again. Come on, Joyce. We'll be right back with Herman. (MONSTER X *and* COUNTESS *keep on laughing and laughing. They pause for breath, look for the children and then resume their efforts. They are still laughing as the curtains close.* JOYCE *and* JIMMY *stick their heads around opposite corners of the curtains.*)

JIMMY: He who laughs best...

JOYCE: Laughs last.

JIMMY: And we have the laugh...

JOYCE: On HORRORS, INCORPORATED!

BOTH: Irritating, isn't it?

THE END

PRODUCTION NOTES

HORRORS, INCORPORATED

Characters: 3 male; 5 female.

Playing Time: 30 minutes.

COSTUMES: Monster X wears a black suit with back and shoulders padded to resemble hump. He has a black moustache and pointed beard. The Countess wears a long, tight-fitting black dress. Herman wears a white jacket and dark trousers. The cat wears a black costume (similar to one-piece sleeping clothes) to which tail and hood are attached. The Ghost wears a white sheet with holes for eyes and mouth. The Witch wears a black robe and black pointed hat and carries broom. The Skeletons may wear white robes with black stripes to indicate bones. Jimmy and Joyce are dressed in everyday modern clothes.

Properties: Test tube with red fluid; books; signs bearing inscriptions indicated for strikers; bottle for Elixir; chest; horsechestnut or any nut that could pass for one.

SETTING: The office of Horrors, Incorporated is furnished with a desk and desk chair; another high-backed wooden arm chair to represent the Barber Arm Chair; a typing table, filing cabinet, and several odd chairs. There is a chest to one side. There may be a black backdrop used. On the typing table is a typewriter.

Lighting: None required.

THE RUMMAGE RUMPUS

Characters

DONNA SHAFFER ⎱ *members of The Junior*
NORMA JEAN LANE ⎰ *Booster Club.*
CYNTHIA CHRONISTER ⎰
MRS. LYAN, *owner of the Melrose Apartment House.*
PANSY BROWN, *tap dancer.*
HENRY BROWN, *mouth organ artist.*
MRS. LAMERTO, *a customer.*
ELDERLY CUSTOMER

SCENE: *The empty storeroom of the Melrose Apartment House.*

TIME: *The present.*

THE RUMMAGE RUMPUS

SETTING: *The empty storeroom of the Melrose Apartments.*

AT RISE: DONNA, NORMA *and* CYNTHIA *are running the sale.* DONNA *is assisting two small colored children in their inspection of the shoe table;* NORMA *is trying coats on a large Italian woman, and* CYNTHIA *is adding up accounts and checking the money at the cashier's table.*

DONNA: I doubt very much if we have any shoes to fit either one of you children, but if you'll just give me an idea of the kind you want, maybe we can find something suitable.

HENRY: Well, it's like this, lady. We don't want any shoes at all, unless you all's got a mouth organ to go with 'em.

DONNA: A mouth organ! Goodness! How would a mouth organ go with a pair of shoes?

PANSY: It's for our act. We're a team.

DONNA: A team?

HENRY: Yes, ma'am. I play the mouth organ and Pansy, she tap dances.

PANSY: Only we're no team unless we get back our utensils. I wore out my tap shoes, and Henry here lost his mouth organ so we're out o' business unless we can locate something at this here rummage.

HENRY: We came around last month, but you all had no musical instrument 'ceptin' a guitar, and that won't fit my mouth.

DONNA (*Laughing*): No, I don't believe it would. Well, look, here's a pair of slippers that seem to be about your size, Pansy. You sit down there and try them on while I look through some things that just came in. Maybe we can find a mouth organ for you some place. I can see you'd make a wonderful mouth-organ and tap-dance team if you had the mouth organ and the tap shoes. (*Goes back of counter and looks through boxes while* HENRY *helps* PANSY *try on the slippers.*)

NORMA (*Struggling to help her customer out of a coat which is much too tight*): Oh dear! I'm afraid we have nothing in your size. Maybe if you could come back this afternoon....

WOMAN: No...no...Thees afternoon eet ees mucha too late. The so stylish funeral...eet begin at two o'clock pronto. Oh, please, leetal lady...I musta getta the so stylish black coat. My uncle he a vera, vera grand man. He have stylish funeral. These green coat...eet ees impossible. Eet would be vera vera great deesgrace. Please, helpa me. (*Grabbing a coat on rack*) Here! Here ees such a beega one. Let us try.

NORMA: Oh, but we did try that one. It's miles too little. I'm terribly sorry, lady, but there just isn't another coat on this rack that you could possibly squeeze into.

WOMAN: Oh Santa Maria! (*Begins to sob*) All the friends, the relatives... all weel have the so long black veils, the black gloves, the black coats...only I weel have such hateful ugly green coat. Such I cannot wear. I weel not bring heem such shame. Rather should I stay home and never see the flowers, the candles, the so handsome relatives....

NORMA: Oh, please, please, don't cry. Listen! Let me have your name and address, and I promise you that if we should get a black coat in your size before two o'clock I'll let you know.

WOMAN (*Brightening up*): Oh, leetal lady...you so sweet... so kind. I geeve you the name...Angela Lamerto...

NORMA: Angela Lamerto...That's a pretty name. Now where do you live?

WOMAN: 229 South 10th Street. You sure you letta me know the meenute you finda the beega black coat?

NORMA: I promise. But don't count too much on it. We never can tell what's likely to come in. We might not get a thing, but on the other hand....Well, I'll keep my fingers crossed just for luck.

WOMAN (*As she exits*): I keepa the feengers crossed too... for the besta, besta luck and the so beeg black coat.

NORMA: Phew! I was beginning to think I'd have to take two of these coats and sew them together for that woman. She just wouldn't take *no* for an answer.

CYNTHIA: I will say, you girls sure do take an interest in your work. How are you coming, Donna? Any sign of a mouth organ?

DONNA: Believe it or not, I have one. It was in the very bottom of this box of junk. (*To children*) Well, kids...here you are...a mouth organ!

HENRY: Whoopee! Kin I play it?

DONNA: I don't know, can you? (*Handing it to him.*)

HENRY (*Blowing a trial blast*): That sure is wonderful. I can play most anything on this here little ole mouth organ piece.

DONNA: That's fine. Now, how's Pansy coming along? Why, that's a pretty good fit!

PANSY: They fit fine but they're not taps.

DONNA: Oh, but you can have taps put on them over at the shoemaker's across the street.

PANSY: How much?

DONNA: Oh, I don't know just how much...maybe a quarter.

HENRY: How much is this here mouth organ and the shoes?

DONNA: Well...now...let me think.

CYNTHIA: The price is marked on the bottom of each shoe.

DONNA: Yeah, I know but...

HENRY: We only got fifty-five cents.

DONNA: Fifty-five cents...well...let me see...twenty-five from fifty-five...that leaves thirty cents! Well...now can you imagine that? That's just the price of the shoes and the mouth organ. Ten cents for each shoe and ten cents for the mouth organ...that's thirty altogether and that will give you twenty-five cents in change for the taps.

HENRY: This is sure our lucky day!

PANSY: It sure is. Now we can go back in show business.

DONNA (*Crossing to* CYNTHIA's *table for change*): Thirty out of fifty, please.

CYNTHIA: I'll say it's their lucky day. It was their lucky day the minute they got you for a clerk. You just make up any old price to suit the pockets of our clients.

DONNA (*In a whisper*): Sh! You'll hurt their feelings. Now, kids, here's your change. Now skip right over there and have those taps put on the shoes and maybe you can come in sometime and go through your routine for us.

HENRY: Yes, ma'am. We will.

PANSY: I'll do a double shuffle just for you. (*Exits with* HENRY.)

DONNA: You do that. Good luck to you. (*Note: If* HENRY *and* PANSY *can really perform, a short specialty number can be introduced here.*)

CYNTHIA: Donna Shaffer, you ought to be fired!

DONNA: Who? Me? And what for?

CYNTHIA: For cutting prices. Every time you get to feeling sorry for somebody, you just slash our prices.

NORMA: I'll bet those shoes were marked twenty cents a piece if they were marked a cent.

DONNA: Well, the mouth organ wasn't marked. We hadn't even unpacked it.

CYNTHIA: Maybe not, but we could have gotten at least fifty cents for that. Don't you know they are almost extinct?

DONNA: Sure. That's why Henry and Pansy were up against such a tough proposition. I wanted to help them out. They're Mr. Brown's children. You know Mr. Brown. He's the janitor here in this building.

CYNTHIA: So what?

DONNA: Oh, well...what's the use of having these rummage sales every month if we can't throw in a few good deeds along with the rummage?

NORMA: Yes, but it's not good deeds we're after. It's money for the Day Camp.

DONNA: You haven't much room to talk, Norma Lane. You sold a sweater this morning for fifty cents that we had all agreed should bring a dollar.

NORMA: I know...but...well....The poor little girl who bought it looked frozen stiff and anyhow, it was my sweater. I donated it and it looked nice on her. I wanted her to have it.

CYNTHIA: Sure. I was glad to see her get it too; but can't you see this is no way to do business? We can't cut our prices every time we feel sorry for someone. I've just been going over our accounts, and I find that we make less money when you and Donna are selling than at any other time.

DONNA: No kidding? Is that really the truth?

CYNTHIA: Cross my heart.

NORMA: In that case, maybe we better quit.

CYNTHIA: Oh, don't get mad, Norma.

NORMA: I'm not mad, but my goodness, if we're costing the firm money, we better vanish.

CYNTHIA: You're both too soft-hearted...and Donna, you're the worst of the lot.

DONNA: O.K....Here, let me take over the cash box for a while and you do the selling.

CYNTHIA: Sure you're not insulted?

DONNA: Of course not. I see your point, and I want to raise money too. After all, these sales are a lot of work and if we can't make money, they're not worth the trouble.

NORMA: I thought sure with all this stuff we'd be able to raise fifty dollars today. But business hasn't been so brisk. It's almost time for lunch and we haven't hit the half way mark yet.

CYNTHIA: Oh, well, maybe we'll have better luck after lunch. Sh! Here comes a customer. (*An old lady enters. She is poorly dressed, but very gentle and sweet.*) Good morning. May I help you?

OLD LADY: Thank you, yes. That beautiful lamp...how much is it?

CYNTHIA: It *is* a very lovely lamp, isn't it? And such a bargain. It's just one dollar and a quarter.

OLD LADY (*Disappointed*): Oh dear! A dollar and a quarter! I'm afraid that's more than I can...

CYNTHIA: But it's really a wonderful buy at that price. The base is genuine brass and the shade, with a little cleaning, will be just like new.

OLD LADY: Yes, I know, but...you see, it is for my daughter's birthday. I know she would love it...only...well...I had planned to spend just a dollar...I thought I could find something at that price.

CYNTHIA (*Looking at* NORMA *and* DONNA *helplessly. They shake their heads firmly*): Oh, I'm sure you can find something for a dollar. (*Picks up battered electric toaster.*) Now here is something very useful...and very scarce these days too...an electric toaster, and it's only seventy-nine cents.

OLD LADY: No, no...she would not like a toaster nearly so well as this beautiful lamp. Besides, the toaster does not look very strong.

CYNTHIA: No, no, I'm afraid it isn't 100 per cent, but I'm sure it could be fixed.

OLD LADY: No doubt...but for my daughter's birthday I would like something very special. You see, her husband is in the hospital this year so she has only me, and that's why I would so like to give her a real surprise.

CYNTHIA: Oh well...in that case, I guess...

DONNA (*Clearing her throat loudly*): Excuse me, Cynthia, but I believe our cash sales are a little short...

CYNTHIA: Yes, yes...I'm afraid so too, but well, I tell you, Lady, I sure would like to see your daughter have that lamp. ...Now suppose we... (NORMA *coughs loudly.*)

OLD LADY: Land sakes, child. Let me give you a peppermint.

CYNTHIA: Oh, no. Don't bother. She'll be all right. It's just the dust getting into her throat. Now about this lamp.... Here's an extra shade we happen to have in stock that is considerably less expensive than the shade on the lamp. Now let's switch shades and see how it looks. (*Tries on new shade.*) There! How do you like that?

OLD LADY: Oh, it is beautiful! Beautiful! Even lovelier than the first one. And is this one actually cheaper?

CYNTHIA (*Ignoring coughs and sneezes from the other two girls*): Yes...it is. This shade is only...only...(*Swallowing hard*) fifteen cents. That brings the price of the lamp down to one dollar exactly.

OLD LADY: Oh that's wonderful. I'll take it and you don't even need to wrap it. I'll carry it right with me. Oh dear! My daughter will be so pleased. She loves presents, and she doesn't get very many of them.

CYNTHIA: I do hope your daughter enjoys her present.

OLD LADY: Oh I know she will, and I'll tell her how nice and kind you were to me. Goodbye.

CYNTHIA: Goodbye. Come again. We have a sale every month.

NORMA (*Clearing her throat*) : And is that an example of how to make friends and influence customers by not cutting prices?

CYNTHIA: Well...er...well...I didn't exactly lower the price, did I? I just put on a cheaper shade.

DONNA: A cheaper shade, my foot! We had agreed that that second shade was to sell for fifty-nine cents, and the lamp base was to cost a dollar. By switching the shades, you gave the old lady a fifty-nine cent exchange for a twenty-five cent shade, put it on a dollar base, and sold the whole thing for one buck. Figure out for yourself how much money you cost the firm on that transaction.

CYNTHIA: Oh, dear! I can't even figure. It would take geometry to dope that out. Besides I...Oh, well, what's the use? I'm just as big a softy as you two.

NORMA *and* DONNA (*Throwing their arms around her*) : Sure, you are! That's why we love you.

DONNA: I would have scalped you if you hadn't let the old lady have that lamp.

NORMA: It would have been a crime. And speaking of crimes, there'll be a death around here, if I don't go out for lunch. Don't forget, I opened this place at seven this morning.

CYNTHIA: Go ahead. Donna and I can hold the fort.

NORMA: Even if we haven't been such super-salesmen, I hope we can continue all winter. We can send a lot of kids to camp.

CYNTHIA: We can as long as Mrs. Lyan gives us the store room rent free.

NORMA: Oh, she will.... She's a peach.

DONNA: Take a look in the Janitor's office when you go upstairs to see if we got any more merchandise.

NORMA (*As she exits*) : O.K....I'll take a look.

DONNA: The most wonderful thing to me about these sales is that we can always sell this junk. I often wonder who in the world will buy the stuff, but someone always turns up.

CYNTHIA: Sure. Look...here's one roller skate. When that came in, I thought we had a lemon for sure, but it's sold. A man bought it this morning for twenty-five cents...pleased as punch too. He's using the wheels to make a pushmobile for his little boy. I'm keeping it for him till this evening. Just goes to show you, if you keep a thing seven years you find a use for it.

DONNA: Which reminds me... Cynthia, I hope you don't mind, but I donated this pen wiper you made me for Christmas when we were in the third grade. So far nobody has found a use for it...not even at two cents.

CYNTHIA: That's an idea. I have some Christmas presents I can contribute to the next sale. Uh—oh...another customer. (MRS. LYAN *enters very much agitated*) Good afternoon, may I help you? Oh! Oh my goodness! It's Mrs. Lyan! I didn't recognize you.

MRS. LYAN: And no wonder! Oh, girls I'm so upset! So terribly upset!

DONNA: What's wrong? Are you ill?

MRS. LYAN: No, not ill, but something terrible has happened.

CYNTHIA: Well, what is it? Can we help you?

MRS. LYAN: It's my new coat! My brand new, imported broadcloth coat trimmed with genuine Kolinsky!

CYNTHIA: Oh, it sounds gorgeous! But what's happened to it?

MRS. LYAN: It's gone.

GIRLS: Gone? You mean...stolen?

MRS. LYAN: I don't know what I mean. (*Walking the floor*) It was to have been delivered to the apartment while I was away last week. When I came home, there was no sign of it, and when I called the store, they said it had been sent out on

Wednesday. The janitor remembers signing for it, and leaving it in my vestibule, and that's the last trace of it. It has utterly disappeared.

CYNTHIA: Oh, how dreadful! But surely it must be around here some place.

MRS. LYAN: I was wondering if by any possible chance it could have been mixed up with this stuff down here. So many things were collected last week, it just might be possible that...

DONNA (*Running to rack of coats and dresses*): I'll look, Mrs. Lyan.

CYNTHIA: But I am sure we would have noticed anything so handsome.

MRS. LYAN (*Sinking down on chair*): Indeed, it just makes me sick all over. When I think what I paid for that coat! Have you sold any coats today?

DONNA: No, not a one. At least, not that I remember. I know Norma was trying to sell one, but I don't think she made the sale.

CYNTHIA: When the girls unpack the things, they sometimes take out some of the better clothing and send it to a relief society.

DONNA: I wasn't here last evening when the things were unpacked.

CYNTHIA: Neither was I, but I can call the agencies and have them make a search.

MRS. LYAN: Oh, please do. I must find it. I simply must. I'll offer a reward. I'll do anything....Only I must get my coat.

CYNTHIA: I'll call right away. Donna, you take care of things while I'm gone. You say it was black broadcloth trimmed with Kolinsky? (*Exits.*)

MRS. LYAN: Real Kolinsky. Oh, dear! I know I should not have been so extravagant.

DONNA: Oh, don't give up, Mrs. Lyan. Cynthia's awfully lucky. She'll probably locate it for you right away. If it was taken to either of those agencies you'll have it in a short time.

MRS. LYAN: I was so hopeful that it might be down here. Indeed, if I don't get it back and have to buy another winter coat, I'll just have to rent this storeroom on Saturdays to make up the loss.

DONNA: Oh dear, Mrs. Lyan. We were hoping to continue our sales all winter. So far, the Junior Boosters have been able to raise enough money for twelve campers.

MRS. LYAN: Yes, I know, and I'm only too glad to let you have it. It works out so well renting it to the Woman's Club for their classes during the week and leaving it free for you girls on Saturdays. But I'm afraid I'll have to do something to make up this loss.

DONNA: Of course, we can understand that, Mrs. Lyan, but oh dear...I guess I'm too optimistic but I just know you'll find it...I have a feeling.

MRS. LYAN: I do hope your feeling turns out to be reliable. I've questioned every man, woman and child around the place and...That reminds me...I haven't questioned everybody. There's Henry. I haven't seen him all morning or Pansy either for that matter. I wonder if they'd know anything about it.

DONNA: Oh, I think Henry and Pansy are absolutely honest, Mrs. Lyan.

MRS. LYAN: So do I, but children get funny notions sometimes. I think I'll go upstairs and see if they have come home yet.

DONNA: They were in here quite a while ago, but we haven't seen them since. Here's Cynthia...but her face doesn't look like good news. (CYNTHIA enters.)

CYNTHIA: No luck, Mrs. Lyan. Sorry. Not a trace of your coat.

MRS. LYAN: I was afraid of that. Now I am convinced the coat has been stolen.

DONNA: Oh, don't give up, Mrs. Lyan.

MRS. LYAN: I'll try to be as hopeful as you are, child. And now I'm going on the trail of Henry and Pansy. Maybe they know something about it. Thank you very much, girls, for your help.

CYNTHIA: I wish we could do more, Mrs. Lyan.

DONNA: So do I.

CYNTHIA: If you find it, do let us know. We'll be terribly anxious.

MRS. LYAN: Don't worry, I'll let you know. I'll be so happy I'll let the whole town know if I find it. Goodbye. (*Exits.*)

DONNA: Oh dear, Cynthia, there goes our Rummage Sale for next month and all the other months. Mrs. Lyan says she'll have to rent this room full time to make up her loss, if she has to buy a new coat.

CYNTHIA: Can you beat it? Here we are, slaving away and now this has to happen. I wonder what will turn up next?

DONNA: Nothing more than Norma coming back from lunch, I suppose. Talk of the angels, and they appear. Here she is.

NORMA (*In high glee*): Oh, girls, the most wonderful thing happened during my lunch hour.

CYNTHIA: I'm glad somebody has good news. Spill it.

NORMA: Remember that Mrs. Lamerto I waited on...the Italian woman who simply had to have the "so beega blacka coat for the so stylish funeral"?

DONNA: Well, what about it?

NORMA: Well, I found one for her...that's what about it! And was she pleased! Girls, you should have seen her. She simply beamed. She'll be the best-dressed woman at the funeral.

CYNTHIA: But I don't understand. Where in the world could you have ever located a coat during lunch?

NORMA: Oh, it wasn't actually during lunch. You see, as I was leaving the building Henry and Pansy came tearing up to me with a big box that had just come in and when I opened it...lo and behold there was...

GIRLS (*Screaming*): Mrs. Lyan's new coat!

NORMA: What are you talking about? Sure there was a coat... a lovely black one, plenty big too...just right for Mrs. Lamerto.

CYNTHIA: Norma Jean Lane...You go right out and bring that coat back here. Hurry.

NORMA: But, I can't. And anyhow, I wouldn't if I could.... Not till I find out what this is all about.

DONNA: You'll find out plenty fast. It's about Mrs. Lyan. Her new coat was delivered while she was away and somehow or other it disappeared. She's frantic about it. Threatens to rent this storeroom on Saturdays if she doesn't get it back.

CYNTHIA: She just left here a few minutes ago.

DONNA: Oh, wait till she finds out we sold it to that woman.

NORMA: Oh, but I didn't sell it.

CYNTHIA: But you said...

NORMA: I said Mrs. Lamerto wore it to the funeral. Well, she did, but I didn't sell it to her. I just rented it.

DONNA: Rented it? Honestly, Norma, I sometimes think you must amaze yourself.

NORMA: Well what's so amazing about renting a coat? Plenty of people rent special clothes for special occasions.

CYNTHIA: Sure, but we're not in the costume renting business.

NORMA: I know that; but, well, one look at that coat told me poor Mrs. Lamerto could never afford to buy it. Even I could see that it was worth more than eight dollars.

DONNA: Eight hundred dollars is more like it.

NORMA: Since you read me that lecture about costing the firm so much money, I knew I'd never dare cut prices on that, so I just made her a proposition.

CYNTHIA: And just what proposition did you make her for Mrs. Lyan's eight-hundred-dollar coat trimmed with real Kolinsky?

NORMA: A dollar an hour...starting at two o'clock. That means she can bring it straight back after the church service or she can go and wear it to the cemetery or wherever she pleases...depending on how much she wants to spend.

DONNA: And did it ever occur to you that she just might keep it?

NORMA: Oh, she'd never do such a thing. Why, it isn't hers; it's just rented.

CYNTHIA: You are an innocent. It's a wonder you know enough to come in out of the rain. If she ever finds out she has a valuable coat like that, it's entirely possible she might decide to hang on to it.

NORMA: Cynthia Chronister, I'm ashamed of you! You're losing your faith in human nature. I guess I know an honest woman when I see one. What do you want to bet Mrs. Lamerto shows up with the coat and the money?

DONNA: Let's not waste our time and money on bets. I only hope you're right, because if you're wrong, it's going to be up to us to make good with the real Kolinsky.

NORMA: Oh, stop talking about Kolinsky. It sounds like a Russian general.

CYNTHIA: I'm ready to stop talking about the whole thing, so you can just do the talking yourself if and when Mrs. Lyan pops back in here which she may do at any moment.

NORMA: O.K., I will. I'll just tell her the truth. (PANSY *and* HENRY *enter followed by* MRS. LYAN.)

PANSY: Here she is, Mrs. Lyan. Here's the gal we gave the coat to.

HENRY: I told you she'd be right here, but I sure is most mighty relieved to see her.

MRS. LYAN: Oh, dear....Oh, it's you, Norma. I couldn't make head or tale of Henry's story except that he had given the box to a rummage girl. I'm glad to see it's somebody reliable. Now where did you put it? Oh, girls, can you imagine my relief? These two rascals thought the box was standing in the vestibule to be given to the rummage. Well, Norma, where is it?

NORMA: Well, right at the moment, Mrs. Lyan I don't exactly know.

MRS. LYAN: You don't know? Oh, come now. Of course, you know.

NORMA: Well, in a way, I do know, Mrs. Lyan, but if I tell you, I'm afraid you'll be awfully upset.

MRS. LYAN: I can't be very much more upset than I am now.

NORMA: O.K. You asked for it, Mrs. Lyan, your coat is attending a funeral.

MRS. LYAN: You're out of your mind.

NORMA: No, I'm not. I'm telling the truth, the whole truth and nothing but the truth, so help me. It's at a very handsome funeral on Dupont Avenue near Tenth Street, Church of Saint Martin, to be exact.

MRS. LYAN: Never have I heard of anything so ridiculous!

PANSY: Are they goin' to bury Mrs. Lyan's new coat?

DONNA: Sh! For Heaven's sake, Pansy, don't talk about burying it!

CYNTHIA: It's more likely they'll bury one of us!

DONNA: It does sound preposterous, Mrs. Lyan, but it seems Norma rented your coat to a Mrs. Lamerto who needed it to wear to a funeral.

NORMA: A very stylish funeral!

MRS. LYAN (*Angrily*): I don't care if it's a stylish or unstylish funeral. I want my coat and I want it right now. Just march yourself over there and get it, or I'll call the police.

NORMA: Oh, please, Mrs. Lyan. Not the police! It does sound a little queer, I'll admit, but Mrs. Lamerto needed a black coat something fierce. Everybody else would be wearing black, and her coat is bright green. After all, I only rented it to her and I had no idea it belonged to you.

MRS. LYAN: But you could see it wasn't a rummage sale coat!

NORMA: I didn't see anything except that it was black, and big enough to fit Mrs. Lamerto.

MRS. LYAN: So nice to be the same size as Mrs. Lamerto!

NORMA: Oh, she's a lovely woman, really, Mrs. Lyan. You'd love her.

MRS. LYAN: I'd love her if she'd bring my coat back safe and sound.

NORMA: Oh, she will. I know she will. You see she's paying a dollar an hour for it, and I know she doesn't have much money, so she should be coming in any minute now.

CYNTHIA (*As* MRS. LAMERTO *enters*) Look! Look! There she is! And she has the coat. (MRS. LAMERTO *enters wearing her old green coat and carrying the black one*)

MRS. LAMERTO (*Out of breath*): Oh, how I have hurried. It has taken my lungs! But see...only one hour and a half I am gone! One dollar and feefty cents I owe for the so beautiful coat.

MRS. LYAN (*Seizing the coat*): Thank goodness! Oh, what a relief! (*Examining the coat*) And not a mark on it!

MRS. LAMERTO: What do you think? I let spots get on these coat? No, ma'am. I want I should hire it again next week. These time for wedding. How much you want for wedding, eh?

NORMA: I'm sorry, Mrs. Lamerto, but I am afraid we can't rent any more of our clothing. It seems this coat was not intended for the rummage sale. It belongs to this lady.

MRS. LAMERTO: Oh, but these so stylish people, they theenk these coat belong to me. I must wear it next week to the wedding.

CYNTHIA: I am afraid that's out of the question, Mrs. Lamerto.

MRS. LAMERTO: But I take good care. I breeng heem back just so.

MRS. LYAN: Never mind, Mrs. Lamerto. Since you have brought it back this time and in such good condition, I think I might be able to fix you up for the wedding. Since we are the same size, maybe I could fit you out with a dress and a coat...another one...not so new as this one, but very nice. Would you care to come with me and try them on?

MRS. LAMERTO: Yes, and thank you. I come right away, but first I must pay my rent. One dollar and feefty cents.

MRS. LYAN: I hardly think that will be necessary. Let's consider it paid. After all, it was my coat and I'd like to reward someone for bringing it back to me. As for you girls, I'll see to it that you won't lose anything on the transaction. (*Opening purse*) Here. Maybe this little contribution will help make up your quota for today. Since I didn't donate any rummage this time, let this be my share.

CYNTHIA: Oh, thank you, Mrs. Lyan...but after all the trouble we caused you, it seems a shame to take your money.

MRS. LYAN: You're not taking it, my dear. You're giving it. I think your Booster Club is doing a wonderful job running these sales to help underprivileged children, and now that I have my winter coat back again, you can count on this room for the rest of the year.

ALL: Thanks a million, Mrs. Lyan.

MRS. LYAN: And now, come along, Mrs. Lamerto, we'll see what we have for you in the line of wedding finery. (MRS. LAMERTO *and* MRS. LYAN *exit.*)

NORMA: We can thank our lucky stars and Mrs. Lamerto that our troubles are over.

HENRY: 'Scuse us, ladies, but me an' Pansy would like to help y'all out with these here rummages.

CYNTHIA: For goodness' sake! Are you still here?

PANSY: Yes ma'am. We stayed right here till that coat mystery got straightened out.

DONNA: Well, it seems to me most of it was your fault. You better be more careful after this what you turn in for rummage.

HENRY: Yes ma'am. You sure are right. But, say, can we stick around here and help out?

NORMA: I don't know what you could do. We don't have enough customers now to keep three of us busy.

HENRY: Then shut your eyes and see what I made for you. I'll be back in a jiffy. Come on, Pansy. (*Children exit.*)

CYNTHIA: What in the world do you suppose they've cooked up now?

DONNA: I hope it's no more merchandise that belongs to somebody else.

NORMA: Oh well...let's be good sports and close our eyes.... They want to surprise us.

CYNTHIA: I'm ready to be surprised at anything.

NORMA: Sh! They're coming. Shut your eyes tight. (HENRY *and* PANSY *enter wearing Sandwich Board Signs that say:* RUMMAGE SALE—MELROSE APARTMENTS.)

HENRY: Now you can look. We're goin' out and rummage for customers...like this. (HENRY *plays the mouth organ, and he and* PANSY *march around stage singing:* "*Mammy's little baby loves Rummagin', Rummagin', Mammy's little baby loves Rummage Sales.*" *The girls laugh, and children continue their parade until curtains close.*)

THE END

PRODUCTION NOTES

The Rummage Rumpus

Characters: 1 male; 7 female.

Playing Time: 30 minutes.

Costumes: Everyday modern dress.

Properties: All sorts of properties may be used as merchandise for the sale, but there must be a rack of coats and dresses, a table of shoes, one roller skate, an electric toaster in bad shape, a rickety floor lamp, an out-of-date table lamp, a cigar box to be used as a cash box, and a mouth organ.

Setting: The properties arranged about the room, several folding chairs, and a cashier's table are all that is needed.

Lighting: None required.

THE SOFT-HEARTED GHOST

Characters

EGBERT ⎫
FATHER ⎬ *the Ghost Family.*
MOTHER ⎭
PIERRETTE
GYPSY
MASTER OF CEREMONIES
BILL TEMPLETON
MR. SILAS P. STATIC
MASQUERADERS

SCENE: *The living room of the Ghost family.*

TIME: *Halloween.*

THE SOFT-HEARTED GHOST

SETTING: *The living room of a respectable ghost family.*

AT RISE: *The head of the house, dressed in a long, white robe, and all the trappings of a real ghost, is pacing the floor. His wife is nervously trying to read a magazine, but is distracted by her husband.*

WIFE: I do wish you would sit down, dear, and try to control yourself. Here, read this article in *The Saturday Evening Ghost*. It's really wonderful, a firsthand account of a goblin raid.

FATHER: I'll read it later. Right now I can't do a thing till that nincompoop boy of ours comes home.

WIFE: Well, don't worry. He'll be along any minute now.

FATHER: He'd better! And I'm warning you that if that young whippersnapper has nothing to report from this trip, I'm through with him. I'll not have a piece of milk toast for a son and be the laughing stock of the whole graveyard.

WIFE: Oh, Henry, don't be so hard on the poor boy. After all, he hasn't had much experience in these things.

FATHER: Not had much experience! Of course he hasn't. He's had none whatever. And that's just what makes me so infernally mad at him. He refuses to take advantage of any opportunity that comes his way. He won't start out for himself. Why, when I was his age, I had already frightened the Countess de Verne into a spasm, and had terrorized an entire village so that no one dared show his face in the street after dark.

227

WIFE: I know, dear, but you were unusual, and you always seemed to have a natural gift for horrible things.

FATHER: And what about yourself? Didn't you panic an entire neighborhood in the disguise of the headless witch and the phantom lady? You have amazing talents, my dear, and I cannot understand why Egbert is such a complete flop when he has such horrible examples right here in his own home.

WIFE: It's just that the poor dear boy is so tender-hearted, he can't bear to see anyone frightened.

FATHER: And what kind of spirit is that? No self-respecting ghost or goblin would ever admit such a feeling. I've taught that boy every trick I know. He can turn himself into an absolute facsimile of the Phantom of the Opera; he can laugh exactly like the Shadow. He can disconnect his ankle and wrist bones and drop off his hands and feet as cleverly as a contortionist. He knows every trick of gibbering and grimacing. He really almost gave me a scare one time when we were coming home from Vampire Inn, just by assuming the shape of a drowned man and twining seaweed around my neck. Of course, it was all in fun, but it was an act that would make him famous if he would only apply it to business.

WIFE: Oh, I know Egbert has great talent and ability once he finds himself, but you'll just have to give him a little more time to get over being so soft-hearted.

FATHER: Time! He's had all the time in the world...And I am determined to disinherit him unless he has something to show for this night's work.

WIFE: Oh, Henry...you couldn't be so cruel.

FATHER: You just wait and see. I'll show him he can't disgrace the family by any more of this shilly-shallying. Unless he frightens someone out of his wits tonight, he's no son of mine.

WIFE (*Starting to cry*): I don't see how you can be so heart-less. Isn't it enough that Egbert is a good, honest, well-meaning ghost? He's never given us a minute's trouble except for this one weakness. Why are you so determined that he must frighten people?

FATHER: Because that's the whole point of being a ghost. Unless you can scare people to death, or at least into hysterics, there's no reason for your existence. Tonight is Halloween, just the time of year when mortals are most susceptible to "Ghosties and ghoulies and things that go bump in the night." Now, I say if Egbert can't work up a successful case of hysteria tonight, he's not worth his salt, and I'm through with him. That's positively my last word on the subject.

WIFE (*Moaning*): If only you'd let me go along with him. Maybe I could give the poor boy confidence. I could wear my skeleton costume with clanking chain necklace and brace-let, and loom up behind him just at the critical moment. That way, he wouldn't lose his nerve so quickly.

FATHER: Nothing doing! Egbert must be strictly on his own. Sh! He's coming. Not a word to him about my decision. (*Assumes a commanding attitude with crossed arms as he waits for* EGBERT's *entrance.*)

WIFE (*At entrance*): Good evening, son.

EGBERT: Hello, Mother. Hello, Dad.

FATHER: Ah, er good evening! How's the weather?

EGBERT: Fine. It's a wonderful night. The wind is howling in the trees and it's pitch dark. No sign of a moon.

FATHER: Wonderful! I only hope it lasts so we have a real spooky Halloween. Did you meet any people, humans, I mean, on the way home?

EGBERT: There were a few children down by the Old Mill.

FATHER: Children, eh? Out by themselves this time of night? And by the Old Mill too; they would be easily frightened, especially tonight. Did you scare them out of a year's growth?

EGBERT: Well, no, er — that is...not exactly. You see, they were just *little* children.

FATHER: They scare most easily.

EGBERT: But that's just it. I couldn't bear to frighten them. In fact I had to make myself invisible and stay close to the side of the building until they had gone safely past.

WIFE: Didn't you even give a few moans and groans just to startle them a bit?

EGBERT: Oh, no. Children are terrified of moans and groans. They wouldn't have slept a wink all night.

FATHER: Nonsense! What difference would it make if they didn't sleep the rest of their natural lives? Might have made you famous. Well, letting the children escape was bad enough but perhaps you really went to work on some of the grown people. You surely met someone else besides children on your walk.

EGBERT: Oh, yes...There was a young girl standing at the cross roads...right where the old prison used to be.

WIFE: Now young girls are very, very easily frightened. They'll yell bloody murder if you just reach out a bony hand and tickle the back of their necks.

FATHER: Right you are. And what amazing good luck to find one right near the old prison. If I remember correctly that's just where the gallows used to stand. It would have been a simple matter for you to have appeared to her as the ghost of a headless murderer...or better yet...you could have done your old trick of hanging by the neck from the branch of a tree. That would have probably driven her out of her senses. Did you think of that, my son?

EGBERT: Well, as a matter of fact, I did think of it...but she was such a young girl, sort of timid and she was all alone... so...well....It just didn't seem quite fair.

FATHER: Fair! What kind of talk is that? What does being fair have to do with your business of frightening people? I might as well tell you here and now, Egbert. I am fed up with you. Unless you can tell me of one genuine case of the jitters that you have brought about this night...you can get out of this house and never darken my door again. But come...surely you met other people.

WIFE: Oh, my poor, poor boy. Can't you tell us of a single solitary soul you have scared or startled or frightened?

EGBERT: I'm afraid not. I guess I just don't have the right stuff in me. I don't know why it is...but the minute I get all set to scare someone, I just sort of freeze up and lose my nerve.

FATHER: A coward! That's what you are. Nothing but a lily-livered coward.

WIFE: Henry! What a thing to say about your own son!

FATHER: He's no longer any son of mine. From this night forth he can shift for himself. I'm through with him. Get out of my house.

EGBERT: But, Father, where would I go?

FATHER: It's no concern of mine. From now on you can support yourself in any way that you see fit. You have disgraced this family long enough. You come from a long line of successful ghosts, spirits, phantoms and zombies. You have a family heritage that is unrivaled in the spirit world. You alone have failed to live up to it.

WIFE: Oh, Henry, please...for my sake... give him one more chance. Please. I beseech you.

EGBERT: It's no use, Mother. I can see his mind is made up.

FATHER: Get out before I really lose my temper and turn you into a Japanese beetle.

EGBERT: But wait, Father! Surely you'll give me till the stroke of midnight to see what I can do. After all, the evening is still young. The streets will be filled with Halloween merry-makers. Maybe...now remember, I promise nothing, but it might just happen that the spirit of this night will help me and that I might be able to pull it off. How about it, Dad? Will you give me a few more hours?

FATHER: A few more hours? After all, you've had years and years...and you've never done the slightest thing to justify our faith in you.

WIFE: Oh, Henry, maybe his luck will change. Perhaps he could just give someone a teeny weeny scare...just to give him confidence.

FATHER: I won't settle for a teeny weeny scare. Nothing less than a faint or hysterics will satisfy me. Well, son, I'll give you a last chance...But mind you...if you have not made a human being scream or faint or throw a fit by midnight, your name will never be mentioned in this house again.

EGBERT: Oh, thanks, Dad. You're the best father a ghost ever had. I'll try to make you proud of me.

WIFE: I'll be thinking of you every minute, Egbert. Remember, if all else fails, you can always effect a good scare with a few well-chosen moans...work up to a crescendo and wind up with a demoniacal shriek.

EGBERT: I'll try, Mother.

FATHER: As a final word of advice, I would suggest that you try to haunt the young people. They are most susceptible to ghostly pranks. If I were in your place I'd scout around till I found a gathering of young people, a Halloween party would be the ideal place, and then I'd really do my stuff.

EGBERT: I'll do my best.

FATHER: I'm sure you will, my boy, and now good-night.

MOTHER: And good luck to you. (*Exit* EGBERT.)

FATHER: Quick, mother! We'll make ourselves invisible and follow him. We'll see for ourselves what he does.

MOTHER: Oh, please, Henry, won't you let me help him the least bit?

FATHER: Not the slightest bit. He's on his own. Come on, we must hurry.

CURTAIN

SCENE 2

SETTING: *The gymnasium of Sheridan High School.*

AT RISE: *A Halloween party is in progress. As the curtain opens the Masqueraders are seated in a circle around a gypsy fortune teller who is reading palms.*

GIRL: Read mine next, please, gypsy. I want to know if I am going to marry a Marine or a Coast Guard.

GYPSY: Neither one, my child. You are going to be an old maid with a poll parrot and three cats. (*General laugh*)

GIRL: I don't believe a word of it. I think you are a horrible fortune teller.

GYPSY: In that case there will be no more fortunes. I was ready to quit anyhow and besides, the mystic hour of midnight is approaching. Time for us to go on our spook hunt through the building.

GIRL: A spook hunt?

SEVERAL GIRLS: Ooh! I'm afraid.

GYPSY: Come on, all of you, line up. I'll lead the way. Piano player, get set and give out with some of that melancholy jive. (*The Funeral March is played.*) Hold tight to the hand of the person ahead of you; and if any long arms reach out to grab you in the dark, you'll be comparatively safe. (*Shrieks of dismay.*) Remember, no matter what happens, don't let go of hands. (*As the music plays, the long line of masqueraders marches slowly off the stage. As the line reaches the exit, the last girl drops out and lingers behind. She is wearing a black and white clown suit.*)

PIERRETTE (*As the line moves off without her*) : I told Bill I'd wait for him right here in the gym. It's nearly midnight and he hasn't come. I wonder what could have happened to him. Oh, dear! I bet two cents he's gone to Mary Ellen Martin's party instead of coming here to our school masquerade. If he doesn't show up I'm through with him for good. (EGBERT *makes his entrance. As he enters,* PIERRETTE *has her back to him and he draws himself up to his full height, arms raised as if to grab her, but as he stealthily approaches, she opens her vanity case to powder her nose and sees him in the mirror.*) Oh, no you don't, smarty! What do you think you're doing, trying to scare me just because you're dressed up in your mother's nightgown and a sheet! I'd know you anywhere.

EGBERT (*Speaking this line and the others in a deep, sepulchral tone*) : And who do you think I am, my pretty maid?

PIERRETTE: Don't "pretty maid" me! I'm good and sore at you, Bill Templeton. The others have all gone on a ghost hunt and here I am, waiting for you, like a goon.

EGBERT: A ghost hunt! They don't need to go hunting to find a real spirit, not when I am here.

PIERRETTE: Stop talking nonsense and tell me where you have been all this time.

EGBERT: I've been walking for hours in the realms of the dead.

PIERRETTE: Phooey!

EGBERT: You talk as if you don't believe I am a real ghost.

PIERRETTE: What do you take me for? A moron? That isn't even a very good disguise. Anybody would know you.

EGBERT: Don't you feel chilly as I approach you? Can't you feel the atmosphere of the grave when I touch you? (*Reaches out to touch her arm.*)

PIERRETTE: Don't touch me, Bill Templeton. You're just trying to get my mind off the main question which is why you are so late to this party.

EGBERT: I am not late. I have until the stroke of midnight to turn you blue with fright.

PIERRETTE: I'll turn you black and blue if you don't stop this silly chatter and give me some logical explanation of your behavior.

EGBERT: A spirit has no logical explanations.

PIERRETTE: O.K. I'm through. If you can't talk like a human being, get out of here.

EGBERT: How can I talk like a human being when I'm a ghost?

PIERRETTE: You're only a ghost in that mask. Take it off.

EGBERT: Take what off?

PIERRETTE: That false face you're wearing, stupid.

EGBERT: I wear no face but my own. Oh dear, why can't I make you understand? Why can't I frighten you?

PIERRETTE: You could never frighten me, Bill Templeton. You're a bigger fraidy cat than I ever was.

EGBERT: Alas, you speak the truth. Oh, dear, and this was my last chance.

PIERRETTE: Honestly, Bill, I think you must have a fever. Let me feel your head.

EGBERT: One touch of my brow and you'll find my forehead is as cold and damp as the tomb.

PIERRETTE: Mildew on the brain, that's what you have. I always said you were a drip.

EGBERT: That settles it. I will not stay here to be insulted. I'll vanish in a blue flame.

PIERRETTE: You'll do nothing of the sort. You'll stay right here and do the number we promised the kids. Why do you think I've been waiting for you all this time? I suppose you thought it was because you are just naturally so irresistible. Well, it's nothing of the sort. It's only that I believe in sticking to our promises. We signed up for this floor show act a week ago and that means we're going through with it. So you can just give out with one of those crooning specialties.

EGBERT: You talk like a mad woman.

PIERRETTE: I am a mad woman, mad at you, and as soon as our act is over I'm going home. (*Talking and laughing off stage as masqueraders return.*) Here comes the gang, so let's get set over here at the piano. (*The party guests return to stage with much laughter. The* GYPSY *is still in the lead.* EGBERT *and* PIERRETTE *move over to piano at one side of stage.*)

GYPSY: Now, remember, you've taken an oath never to tell what we found on our ghost hunt. Cross your hearts and hope to die. And now, fellow masqueraders, we're going to turn our party over to our master of ceremonies and let him introduce our floor show. Let's give our M.C. a great big hand. (*A tall boy wearing a long tailed coat, high silk hat and a pair of gym shorts moves forward.*)

MASTER OF CEREMONIES: Since this is to be a floor show in the literal sense of the word, let's all sit down on the floor. No pushing or shoving. The best seats in the house are yours for the taking. Just flop down anywhere and get set for the big event of the evening. (*To* STAGE HANDS) Now if one of you gents will just bring the old microphone forward, we'll have the thrill of a lifetime. (BOYS *bring microphone to center of stage.*) And now before we unmask and reveal ourselves to each other in our true colors, the management wishes to present the most sensational of all entertainers, that super-colossal heartbreaker, that inimitable moaner and groaner and crooner of tunes and croons, Bill Templeton, "The Voice" of Sheridan High. (*There is loud applause.* EGBERT *is shoved into the spotlight at the microphone.* PIERRETTE *at the piano gives a few opening chords,* EGBERT *steps to the mike and begins an exaggerated crooning number. As he gets under way with his song, his* MOTHER *and* FATHER *enter and stand at one side, interested by-standers. As* EGBERT *approaches the climax of his crooning, the girls in the stage audience start to make "Sinatra" noises and swoon with delight.*)

GIRLS (*In audience on stage*): Ooooooh! He's divine! He's wonderful! He's making me swoon. I feel faint.

MASTER OF CEREMONIES: Atta boy, Bill. Atta boy! Slay 'em. You're knockin' 'em cold.

MOTHER: Look, look, Henry! Already some of the girls are fainting.

FATHER: He's a natural. A chip off the old block.

MOTHER: I told you all he needed was a little confidence.

FATHER: That caterwauling is enough to send the whole crowd into hysterics.

MOTHER: He's better than any wailing banshee I ever heard. (*As* EGBERT *finishes his "number," the* MASTER OF CEREMONIES *leads in applause.*)

MASTER OF CEREMONIES: How about a great big hand for "The Voice" of Sheridan High...good old Bill Templeton!

TEMPLETON (*Entering*): Who's taking my name and my fame in vain? Who's the guy in the winding sheet? (*Striding up to* EGBERT) Say, who are you, wise guy? And what's the idea of stealing my act? I stole it from Sinatra in the first place and I have a right to it. Speak up. (*Grabbing him by the Sheet.*) Who are you?

EGBERT (*Giving a wild laugh in imitation of "The Shadow"*): Ha! Ha! Ha! I am the Ghost of Egbert Edwin Edison Engleheart, the third. Ha! Ha! Ha! (*There are wild peels of laughter, the lights black out and nothing is heard but the screams of the terror-stricken masqueraders. When the lights go on, the stage is empty except for the original* GHOST FAMILY.)

FATHER: Congratulations, my boy! You really pulled it off in fine style. Those kids won't stop running and screaming for an hour.

MOTHER: It was magnificent, son, simply magnificent! I never knew you had such a blood-curdling voice.

FATHER: At last we can hold our heads up with the best of them. From now on, you can haunt the finest families in two continents. (*A stranger enters. He is wearing ordinary clothes.*)

STRANGER: Just a moment, sir. You'll pardon me for interrupting you, but I have a proposition to make to this young man. My card, Sir. (*Hands card to* EGBERT *who reads it aloud.*)

EGBERT: Silas P. Static, Program Director of the Allied Broadcasting Company.

STRANGER: As you see, I am scouting for radio talent and I believe this young man has a great future. I can make him a star of the airways.

FATHER: Not with my consent. That boy was born to haunt people and haunt people he shall.

MOTHER: Sh, Henry. Listen to what the man has to say.

STRANGER: But think for a moment, sir, what opportunities he'll have on the radio. His voice will carry into millions of homes.

MOTHER: Think of it, Henry, millions of people shivering in the dark, hearing Egbert's voice. What do you say, my boy?

EGBERT: I think it's a swell idea. After all, there's not much future to ghosting, at least not on the old basis. I'd just as soon be a ghost star as anything else.

STRANGER: That settles it, my boy, come down to my office in the morning and sign the contract...a thousand dollars a week and a double bonus every Halloween.

MOTHER: You see, Henry, that's what he gets for being a soft-hearted ghost.

THE END

PRODUCTION NOTES

The Soft-Hearted Ghost

Characters: 5 male; 3 female; male and female extras.

Playing Time: 30 minutes.

Costumes: The Ghost Family is dressed in long, white robes or sheets; their faces are pale. Scene II: The fortune teller is dressed in a gypsy costume. Pierrette wears a black and white clown costume. The Master of Ceremonies wears a long-tailed coat, high silk hat, and a pair of gym shorts. Mr. Static is dressed in everyday clothes. The Masqueraders wear various Halloween costumes.

Properties: Magazine, compact, microphone.

Setting: Scene I: An everyday, modern living room can be suggested or a more macabre setting can be used. Scene II: No setting is required. All that is necessary is a piano placed at one side of the stage.

Lighting: The lights black out in Scene II according to script.

THANKSGIVING FOR FRIEDA

Characters

MR. AND MRS. MARSTON, *average American parents.*
TESSIE MARSTON, *a teen-ager.*
FIDDLE MARSTON, *the little sister.*
ROCKY MARSTON, *the kid brother.*
FRIEDA, *an Austrian maid.*
TEXAS, *a college boy.*
TWELVE EUROPEAN BOYS AND GIRLS.

SCENE: *The Marston living room.*

TIME: (Scene 1)   *The afternoon before Thanksgiving.*

(Scene 2)   *Thanksgiving Day.*

THANKSGIVING FOR FRIEDA

Scene 1

SETTING: *The Marston living room.*

AT RISE: TESSIE, *the teen-age daughter of the house, is trying on a party dress.* FRIEDA, *the Austrian maid, is adjusting the hem.* MRS. MARSTON *is busy with letters at her desk.*

TESSIE: Aren't you finished, Frieda? My feet are nearly killing me.

FRIEDA: Almost feenished I am. Vun meenute, please.

TESSIE: Oh dear! I'm so thrilled about the dance tomorrow night! I can hardly wait.

MOTHER: If you ask me, I think it's pretty nice of Frieda to fix your dress at the last minute. You should have told her sooner.

TESSIE: But, Mother, this is a last-minute affair. Tex only called me this morning, so I couldn't do very much about it.

MOTHER: I'm afraid your father isn't going to like your being away from home for Thanksgiving dinner. You know how he feels about the family being together on high days and holidays.

TESSIE: Oh, he won't care.

MOTHER: Well, I do wish you could have dinner here before you go.

TESSIE: But the bus leaves at one o'clock sharp and it's a long drive to Collegeville, so I couldn't possibly make it.

MOTHER: I suppose not, but I still say your father's not going to like it.

FRIEDA: Now, Mees Tessie, I think everysing dokey-okey.

TESSIE: My goodness, Frieda, you're catching on fast to our slanguage, and no wonder with Fiddle and Rocky in the house.

MOTHER: And that's another thing! Why do my children have to have such ridiculous nicknames when your father and I started them out in life with perfectly good Christian names?

TESSIE: Oh come, now, Mother, you know you think Fiddle is a more suitable name for Sis than Fidelity; and I think it was pretty smart of that kid brother of mine to change Cliff to Rocky. You must admit he stuck pretty close to the original idea. May I take this dress off now, Frieda?

FREIDA: Nein....I mean, not yet. So crooked on this one side still.

TESSIE (*Sighing*): What a girl must go through for her public. (*Phone rings.* MRS. MARSTON *answers.*)

MOTHER: Marston's residence. Yes, this is Eleanor Marston speaking. Who? Oh, yes — Clara. What can I do for you? What? Tomorrow afternoon? Oh, but Clara, I couldn't possibly. We're having our usual family Thanksgiving dinner. Oh, dear...well, that is too bad! But I don't see how I can help you this time. Sorry. All right. Call me again sometime and I'll do my best to help. All right. Goodbye. (*To* TESSIE) That was Clara Wheeler asking me to take calls at the Visiting Nurses' Association.

FRIEDA: Now, please, Mees Tessie, make vunce across the room so I can see to the straightness. (TESSIE *parades across the stage for inspection.* FRIEDA *watches the dress critically.*)

MOTHER: Very nice, indeed. In fact, there's just a chance you might be the belle of the ball. (*At this point* FIDDLE *enters, carrying several rolls of white and black crepe paper.*)

FIDDLE: Hy'a, termites. How's your sawdust?

MOTHER: Please, Fiddle! Why must you always be so crude?

FIDDLE: What goes on? A fashion show? Or is it just the Marston dummy dressed up for a store window display?

TESSIE: Well, will you look at that child, all dressed up fit to kill in my raincoat. How are you going to explain that one?

FIDDLE: There's not much to explain (*Removing coat*). You certainly wouldn't want your blue sweater to get wet, would you?

TESSIE: Why, you — you — you —

FIDDLE: Now don't go calling me names. Mother won't like it. And besides, you're too old for that sort of thing!

TESSIE: You march yourself right upstairs and take off that sweater, young lady. Mother, aren't you going to punish that child for wearing my sweater?

FIDDLE: I've already been punished plenty. That old sweater has pricked the skin off me all afternoon. If that's rabbit's wool, the poor bunny must have spent his days in a briar patch.

MOTHER: You two are enough to try the patience of a saint. Maybe it's a good thing, Tessie, that you're going away tomorrow. We'll be spared this petty bickering between you girls.

FIDDLE: Going away! On Thanksgiving? Hey! I don't like that. Our family's always together on Thanksgiving.

TESSIE: You sound exactly like father.

FRIEDA: Shall I help you with the dress off, Mees Tessie?

TESSIE: Yes, thank you, Frieda, we'll go upstairs where it isn't so crowded. (*Exit* FRIEDA *and* TESSIE.)

FIDDLE: Honest, Mother, is this on the level? Is Tessie really going off some place instead of celebrating Thanksgiving day with us?

MOTHER: Yes, dear, but it's not so terrible. Tessie was invited to go along to the dance at Collegeville.

FIDDLE: I think she's a downright drip to go away when she

knows that's the one day in the year when we're all together. That's a family transmission.

MOTHER: Tradition, dear. It *is* too bad, but it can't be helped.

FIDDLE: But Thanksgiving Day has always been my favorite day and I don't want it spoiled. What about Aunt Ruth and Uncle Henry and Grandma and Grandpa? They'll be hurt if Tessie just walks out on them.

MOTHER: No, they won't, because they're not coming this year.

FIDDLE: Not coming! What's the matter? Are they sick?

MOTHER: No, but they're not as young as they used to be, and they're afraid of the driving in this weather.

FIDDLE (*Sinking into a chair*): Well I never heard of anything so perfectly putrid. Do you mean to tell me there's just you and Dad and Frieda and Rocky and me for dinner tomorrow?

MOTHER: That's right. Oh, my goodness! What's that? (*A door bangs and* ROCKY *appears in entrance. He wears a football helmet, a torn sweater; one leg of his trousers is rolled up, the other down. He carries a football which he places on the floor in kick-off position. He leans over, places his hands on the ball and calls out signals in a lusty voice.*)

27-31-9 Shift!

41-12—Hip-hip!

Then he snaps up the ball, clutches it to his stomach and charges down the living room in the direction of imaginary goal posts.) Rocky, stop! Stop that! Do you hear? Stop it, I say!

ROCKY: O.K., O.K., O.K.! I was only showin' you the way I carried the old pigskin down the field during the last quarter at practice this afternoon. And say, Mom, do you know what? Coach says I can be the water-boy at the big game tomorrow.

MOTHER: Why, that's fine, dear. I'm very proud of you. I'm sure you'll make a very nice water-boy, indeed.

FIDDLE (*In high disdain*): Water-boy! Ha! I guess the sport page will carry your picture tomorrow night with headlines: "Gunga Din Marston Kicks the Bucket in Big Game of the Season!" Hey...wait a minute! I just thought of something. What time is your old game?

ROCKY: Two o'clock, but we must be at the field by one o'clock at the latest.

FIDDLE: Now *you're* deserting us. A fine family this turns out to be! Mother, don't let him go!

ROCKY: What do you mean — "don't let him go?" What's it to you?

MOTHER: Now there's nothing to quarrel about. Fiddle doesn't want you to go because it will break up our family dinner party. You should be glad that your sister thinks so much of you.

ROCKY: But, Mom, it's the big game. Oxford High plays Abingdon High. This is my big chance.

FIDDLE: Your big chance for what? To run up and down the field with a dirty old water bucket. I don't call that very important.

ROCKY: Nobody asked you for your opinion, so how about doing what the sun told the mud puddle — dry up!

MOTHER: Listen to me, both of you. I'll have no more of this argument. I can understand how you feel about this, Fiddle, but I can also see Rocky's point of view. Naturally it would be exciting to have only a little part in a big game, but it's really up to your father. If he's satisfied, it's all right with me; but you know how father feels about family holidays.

ROCKY: Yeah — I know.

FIDDLE: Then that's settled. He'll never let you go. That's one time Daddy puts his foot down. He wants us all here for Thanksgiving dinner.

ROCKY: Well, it won't hurt to ask him anyhow. Will it, Moms?

MOTHER: No, it won't hurt, but I have a feeling it won't do much good. Now, suppose you run along upstairs, son, and clean up for supper. Fiddle, you hang up your coat, or rather, Tessie's coat, and go set the table for Frieda. She'll be late with supper if you don't help her.

ROCKY: O.K., Moms. Signals. (*He repeats his entrance maneuvres with the football as he exits.*)

FIDDLE (*Picking up coat, hat and crepe paper*): Gee! I wouldn't have needed all this crepe paper.

MOTHER: Crepe paper? What's it for, dear?

FIDDLE: I was going to make Thanksgiving favors for the dinner tomorrow.

MOTHER: It's really sweet of you, Fiddle, to feel so strongly about our family celebrating Thanksgiving together, and I understand your disappointment; but very often as families grow up, they grow apart. It's not that they don't love each other; it's just that their interests are different.

FIDDLE: Sure, I understand, but Thanksgiving's a day for families to be together.

MOTHER: Of course, dear, but... (*Phone rings.*) Oh dear... that telephone. (*To phone*) Hello. Yes...Yes, Bill, this is Eleanor. (*To* FIDDLE) It's Daddy! (*Back to phone.*) You what? Oh, my goodness! Not today. Fiddle will be broken-hearted.

FIDDLE: What's wrong? Is Daddy sick?

MOTHER: No, no, but he has to go away. (*To phone*) Yes, yes, dear. Of course, I understand. When will you be back? Not till Monday. Well, it is too bad, but I guess it can't be helped. Yes....Yes. Can't you get home before you have to leave? The six o'clock train? Oh, then you *will* have to step on it. Yes...yes, I'll tell them. Goodbye, dear, and good luck. Be sure to take time out for a good Thanksgiving dinner tomorrow. (*Hangs up.*)

FIDDLE: Don't tell me Daddy's not going to be here tomorrow.

MOTHER: That's what he said. The firm is sending him to Washington on business. He couldn't explain it over the phone.

FIDDLE: Well, that's that. Now there's just the three of us. I never heard of anything so mean. Nobody has a right to work on Thanksgiving day.

MOTHER: What about doctors and nurses and bus drivers and engineers and radio announcers?

FIDDLE: O.K., Moms. You have me convinced. But I'm still not happy about it.

MOTHER: To tell the truth, neither am I, but we have to make the best of it. Now, since the whole party is ruined anyhow I think I'll call Mrs. Wheeler and tell her I'll help her out. I'll give you the money to treat Frieda to a super-deluxe Thanksgiving dinner down at the Hotel Standish.

FIDDLE: It's a deal....But I guess I'll skip the crepe paper favors. Frieda and I won't need them at the Hotel Standish.

MOTHER:...You're a good little sport, Fiddle, and I'm proud of you.

FIDDLE: But what about that turkey and all the trimmings in the icebox?

MOTHER: They'll keep till Sunday and we'll have a post-Thanksgiving dinner then. Now I'll run upstairs and see how Tess and Rocky are getting along. I'll phone Mrs. Wheeler from the upstairs phone.

FIDDLE: All right. Boy, oh boy! It doesn't take long to wreck a Thanksgiving dinner in this household. (MOTHER *exits as* FRIEDA *enters.*) Hello, Frieda, it looks as if you and I are left holding the bag.

FRIEDA: Bag? Bag? What bag?

FIDDLE: Oh, that's just another one of our dopey expressions, Frieda. It means we're left...left out in the cold. You see,

the whole family is going to be busy tomorrow, so there
won't be any Thanksgiving dinner here at the house.

FRIEDA: No Thanksgiving? But I thought here in America...
Thanksgiving it vas like...how shall I say...like the law...
like national holiday.

FIDDLE: Well, it is like that, Frieda, but our family all seem
to be busy and —

FRIEDA: I not understand. In old country I read about
Thanksgiving....The families coming under one roof...the
good sings to eat at the end of the autumn... the harvest
festival....Effer since I come here...it seems gut this new
land...I vant to make Thanksgiving too with America vays
...I vant to feel like an American on Thanksgiving Day.

FIDDLE: I think I know how you feel, Frieda, but don't be disappointed. Mother is treating you and me to a big turkey
dinner down at the Hotel Standish. It'll be fun.

FRIEDA: But not like the Thanksgiving I read about and see in
pictures. Long time now I half such an ache in my heart...
here...such a lonesomeness...and yet such a gladness for the
new home...for the people who have me such kindness
shown. I vas...how you say — forward-looking to the feast
of Thanksgiving here in this house vhere efferyone is so free
...so happy...so loving each with the other. It is different
in old country...different in my Vienna. The families can
no longer be together. The brothers, the sisters, the father,
the mother...all separated....No Thanksgiving in Vienna.
It...it makes me sad.... (*Begins to cry quietly.*)

FIDDLE: Oh, please, please, Frieda, don't cry....Listen...
we'll have a Thanksgiving — a real American Thanksgiving
right here in this house. I'll find a way to manage...and
you'll get a real American Thanksgiving — just the kind
you've always dreamed of — only please don't cry. Here, take
my handkerchief. (*Gives* FRIEDA *her handkerchief.*) Now

wipe your eyes and blow your nose, and as soon as the supper dishes are put away you and I will get to work on those favors. There's going to be a Thanksgiving dinner in this house tomorrow or I'll know the reason why. And that brother of mine is going to help me — water-boy, or no water-boy....I'll find a way.... (*Off stage there is the sound of* ROCKY'S *voice yelling* — *"Signals"...followed by a terrific crash and a yell...plus long drawn out moans and howls.*)

FIDDLE: Holy Moses! What's that?

MOTHER (*Offstage*): Rocky, Rocky, what's the matter? Are you hurt? What happened?

ROCKY (*Offstage, in an outraged voice*): I've killed myself. I fell down the steps. OOOOOOOOH....Get a doctor or something....I tell you I'm dying. (*More moans.*)

FIDDLE (*To* FRIEDA): Fate has taken a hand in things! Something tells me they'll be needing another water-boy at the game tomorrow. Come on, Frieda...to the rescue!

CURTAIN

* * *

SCENE 2

SETTING: *Thanksgiving Day, same setting as previous scene.*

AT RISE: FIDDLE *is standing by a card table on which there are piles of white and black crepe paper. Seated at the table, his foot and ankle heavily bandaged is* ROCKY. *Beside his chair is a crutch.* FIDDLE *is modeling a Puritan apron and a white crepe paper cap and fichu.* ROCKY *is putting the finishing touches to a black paper Puritan high-crowned hat.*

FIDDLE: Do I look anything like my original Puritan ancestor, Dame Fidelity?

ROCKY (*Putting on Puritan hat*): Couldn't say...I never met her, but I'll bet I'm a dead ringer for Governor Bradford or Elder Brewster.

FIDDLE: Oh, Rocky, I *am* sorry about your ankle, but I can't help being glad you're here to help me with the party. You'll make it a lot more fun.

ROCKY: Now that I'm into it, I sort of think it's fun myself. Between us we should be able to give those refugee kids a Thanksgiving they'll never forget.

FIDDLE: That was really Frieda's idea, inviting the children from the New Citizens League. She sure is sold on the idea of giving all these new citizens a sample of a real American Thanksgiving.

ROCKY: I'm sold on it too, but I don't know what Mother and Dad would think of opening the house to all these kids. How many are coming?

FIDDLE: Only twelve...six boys and six girls.

ROCKY: Then I don't have enough of these hats. Hey, Fiddle, we can't make all the boys Puritans. Some will have to be Indians. (*Calling*) Frieda, bring me the feather duster, will you, please?

FRIEDA: Ja, I bring it on the chump.

FIDDLE: Maybe all the boys will want to be Indians. (FRIEDA *enters wearing Puritan apron, cap and fichu. She carries some ready-made Indian headdresses which are rolled up to look like a feather duster.*)

FRIEDA: Here is a feather brush. Ach, my gootness, dot turkey bird....Vat a picture he makes a-layin' there in my roaster chust a-drippin' wis juices and filled to bustin' wis rich dressing. And the corn and potatoes and red chelly...ach my! Seems like I could hardly bear to eat 'em so beautiful they look still.

ROCKY: You'll eat 'em all right and so will the kids. Now I'll yank these feathers out of here in a jiffy and we'll have enough headdresses for the six nations.

FIDDLE: We better hurry and set up the card tables before the children come. I don't trust seating them at Mother's new dining room table for fear they'd scratch it. Come on, Frieda, you and I can get things fixed up in no time. Rocky, you clear the stuff off that card table. We'll need it. (ROCKY *removes articles from card table.* FRIEDA *and* FIDDLE *set up several other card tables, making one long table across the stage.*)

FRIEDA: Now I bring the tablecloth. (*Exit.*)

FIDDLE: And the centerpiece. (*Exit.*)

ROCKY (*Trying on first a Puritan hat, then an Indian headdress*): Golly—I can't make up my mind to be Chief Samoset or a Puritan Father. Guess I'd better be a Puritan since I am the host. (*Puts on Puritan hat and square white paper collar. He should be wearing a dark suit.* FRIEDA *and* FIDDLE *reenter with tablecloth and wooden bowls of colorful fruits and vegetables. There should be several ears of corn.*)

FRIEDA: Make to help us, please, with the table, Rocky.

ROCKY: At your service, Mistress Frieda. (*They arrange cloth and* FIDDLE *places centerpiece.*)

FIDDLE: There! It looks like a Thanksgiving party all ready. Here, Rocky, help arrange this corn where it will be most artistic.

ROCKY: First I'm a Puritan, then I'm a waitress, now I'm a decorator! Oh, well — it's all in the day's work. How does that suit you?

FIDDLE: Why, it looks beautiful. Just like a picture book. (*Doorbell rings.*) There they are! Hurry, Frieda. Let them in and take them right upstairs to remove their wraps. (FRIEDA *exits and there are offstage sounds of greetings such*

as: "*Come right in*" *from* FRIEDA *and* "*How do you do*" —
"*Good afternoon,*" *etc., from the children.*)

FIDDLE (*Collecting aprons, caps and fichus*): I'll put these on
the girls as they come in, and you dress up the boys. (ROCKY
*takes up his position on the opposite side of the stage, prepares
to dole out the boys' headgear.* FRIEDA *enters with children.*)

FRIEDA: Mees Fidelity Marston, Master Rocky Marston, allow
me to present your Thanksgiving Day guests. Peter and
Kaatje VanHuysen of Rotterdam.

CHILDREN: How do you do.

FIDDLE: We're so glad you could come, Peter and Kaatje. We
have some paper costumes for you just to give you an idea of
how the people dressed at the first American Thanksgiving
party. Rocky and I will help you to put them on and then you
can help the others.

ROCKY (*Helping* PETER): There! You look like a real
Puritan, Peter.

FIDDLE: And Kaatje makes a perfect Puritan lady. Now who's
next?

FRIEDA: Aaron Moroski from Warsaw and his sister, Betka.
(*Children curtsey.*)

ROCKY: You're my customer, Aaron. I'll make you an Indian
before you can say Squanto.

FIDDLE: And I'll take care of Betka. (*The children help each
other put on the paper costumes so as not to delay the action
of the play.*)

FRIEDA: Michel and Jeanette Beauvais from France. (*Children
curtsey.*)

ROCKY: You won't be the first Frenchman to wear an Indian
costume, Michel.

FIDDLE: Welcome, Jeanette. I think you'll find the dress of a
Puritan maiden most becoming.

FRIEDA: Jan and Maria Corday from Czechoslovakia. (*Curtsey.*)

ROCKY: Hello, Jan. I guess it's your turn to be a Puritan.

FIDDLE: The other girls can help you with your costume, Maria.

FRIEDA: Sonia and Boris Milanovitch from Russia.

ROCKY: I guess a Russian Warrior will make a good Indian Brave. Welcome, Big Chief Boris.

FIDDLE: And here's a cap and apron for you, Sonia. Make yourself at home.

FRIEDA: Tommy and Betsy Higgins from London.

ROCKY: 'Ello, Tommy Atkins. Ow'd you like to be a blarsted Puritan Chappie?

FIDDLE: Rocky's only showing off. He thinks he's the original Britisher. Here's your Puritan outfit, Betsy. Now make yourselves right at home. Rocky and I are going to sit here in the center, and the rest of you sit wherever you please. (*Children take places at table assisted by* FRIEDA. *All remain standing until places are found for them and* FIDDLE *gives them the signal to be seated.*)

FRIEDA (*Standing on one side admiring the group*): Chust like a picture you look: Eenglis, French, Russian, Czecho-Slovakian, Polish, Dutch...all leetle Puritans now...all Americans now same as Fiddle and Rocky. Ach, Ja! 'Tis Thanksgiving like the story books. (*The scene should, indeed, resemble pictures of the First Thanksgiving.*)

FIDDLE: While Frieda is getting ready to serve the dinner, I think it would be nice for Rocky to tell us the story of the first Thanksgiving, and if any of you have any questions, just speak up. We hope we'll know the answers.

ROCKY (*Rising and standing at his place behind the centre of the table*): Well, it was like this. The people who first settled in America left their homes because they were unhappy or because it wasn't safe for them to stay there any longer.

AARON: Were their houses bombed and their mothers and fathers killed?

ROCKY: No, not that exactly; but, you see, these people were a religious folk, and very harsh laws had been passed which prevented them from worshipping God in the way they thought was right.

BETKA: Was there a Ghetto? In Warsaw the Nazis shut all of the Jews up in one narrow section of the city. It was so crowded that hundreds sickened and died, but if they tried to escape, the soldiers shot them. Was it like that for the Puritans?

ROCKY: No, Betka, it wasn't like that; but many of the Puritans were imprisoned or put to death for their religious beliefs....In fact it got so bad that several hundred left their homeland for Holland.

PETER: Holland is a good country...a free country. Didn't the police let them alone in Holland?

ROCKY: Oh, yes, they were allowed to live in peace and safety in Holland...but after a time they had to leave.

KAATJE: Why? Didn't they like Holland?

ROCKY: Yes, yes, they liked it fine; but, you see, Kaatje, these were English people and they loved their country even if the harsh laws had forced them to leave; so when they saw that their children were forgetting the English language and English customs, it made them unhappy; and they thought it best to find a place to live where they could continue their own customs and traditions.

MICHEL: It was like that in Alsace and Lorraine. The French people did not want to speak the German language and follow German customs; they wanted to remain true Frenchmen.

JEANETTE: And it is like that today. The French love their country and their own ways. They do not want to change.

ROCKY: That's right, Jeanette, and they won't change...and

neither did the Puritans. They took a chance in leaving the safety and security of Holland to cross the seas and see what sort of lives they could build for themselves in the new world.

FIDDLE: And it *was* taking a chance, too, because they had no idea what sort of country this was or whether or not they'd ever be able to defend themselves from the Indians.

ROCKY: That first winter was terrible. They had everything imaginable to contend with...illness, blizzards, scanty provisions, an Indian attack...disappointment, grief and despair, but they stuck it out...wouldn't give up.

TOMMY: That's because they were English....We English never know when we're licked.

ROCKY: That's about right, Tommy, and neither did the Puritans. They stuck to their guns and their Bibles and when spring came, they turned to the fields for new life. All summer long they worked, and when autumn came, they had their first real harvest. You can imagine how they felt. Here they were...alive and well after that awful winter, the Indians were growing more friendly every day and they had enough provisions stored away to see them through another winter. No wonder their hearts swelled with gratitude. No wonder that Governor Bradford was moved to set aside a day for a general Thanksgiving.

FIDDLE: And no wonder that the women and children looked forward to that day as a holiday from their long hours of toil and back-breaking work.

ROCKY: So the men went forth into the forests and streams to try their skill at bringing in the choicest provisions for the table and the Puritan women outdid themselves in preparing the foods in the most appetizing ways they knew. And it must have been a success because the feasting and merry-making went on for three whole days...enjoyed by the Indians every bit as much as by the stern-faced Puritans.

FRIEDA: Ach, such a beautiful custom...such a magnificent heritage to pass on to Americans yet unborn.

BORIS: I like best the idea of sharing the good things of the harvest with their neighbors....To share is one of the ideas of Russia, you know.

ROCKY: That's why Fiddle was so disappointed this year, because we were not going to be able to share our Thanksgiving with our loved ones; so then Frieda saved the day by suggesting you as our guests.

BETKA: We are grateful to Frieda and to you, too. It is strange that those others...those first Americans were so much like us. They, too, were refugees. They knew what it is to be thankful for a new home in a strange land. I believe they would like the idea of sharing their Thanksgiving holiday with us.

ROCKY: I know they'd like it, Betka; and we like it, too. After all, that's the one thing all of us have in common today...that feeling of gratitude and thanksgiving because we are all here together in America.

FRIEDA: That touches my sad heart, little friend...I don't know if I feel like crying or singing.

ROCKY: Well, don't cry, for mercy's sake....That would be a terrible ending for your Thanksgiving.

FRIEDA: My Thanksgiving?

ROCKY: But, of course. This is your Thanksgiving...a Thanksgiving for Frieda...that's what Fiddle called it.

FIDDLE (*Rising*): But it's a Thanksgiving for all of us... because we're all giving thanks in our hearts for this great country that gave us such things as Thanksgiving turkeys, and cranberries and football games, and free schools and ice cream cones and all the thousand and one things that make us love America and proud to be Americans. When Father is home, we never sit down to a Thanksgiving dinner without singing a song of Thanksgiving, and even though he isn't at home today, I think that's one more custom we should carry out. (*During the last few speeches,* MR. *and* MRS. MARSTON, TESSIE, *and young* TEXAS *have appeared in the doorway.*)

MR. MARSTON: I second the motion! And I'll lead the song myself.

FIDDLE AND ROCKY: Why...Father! Mother! Tessie! Where did you come from? How did you get here, etc., etc., etc.

MR. MARSTON: I got a chance this morning to fly home and I'm sure glad I grabbed the opportunity. I wouldn't have missed Frieda's Thanksgiving for anything in the world.

FRIEDA: Thank you, sir.

MRS. MARSTON: And I want to offer a special little prayer of thanks to Marie Anderson who volunteered to serve in my place when she found out I was away from my children on Thanksgiving day. I never expected to come home to quite so large a family as this...but I'm glad to see you...every one.

TESSIE: And I'm mighty thankful I met up with Texas here who couldn't stand going to a dance when he found out there was a turkey in the icebox ready to go into the oven. I'm glad I brought him home with me...and I'm proud to introduce him to my kid brother and sister.

TEXAS: Hy'a, Young'uns....I hope you deck me out in a couple of feathers and give me a place at that wonderful looking table.

FIDDLE: We'll sure do that, Texas. You can have the place of honor.

TEXAS (*Bowing*): I'm honored, ma'am.

FRIEDA: You have said it is Thanksgiving for Frieda...then, please, if it is for me....Mr. Marston, sir, will you not please to make like you say...lead in the song of praise and Thanksgiving...and let us choin together...Americans...

efferyone. (MR. MARSTON *stands behind* ROCKY, MRS. MARSTON *takes her place behind* FIDDLE, TEXAS *and* TESSIE *stand at one end of the table and* FRIEDA *at the other. All bow their heads as* MR. MARSTON *leads them in the singing of* "Praise God from Whom All Blessings Flow" *as the curtain falls.*)

THE END

PRODUCTION NOTES

Thanksgiving For Frieda

Characters: 9 male; 10 female.

Playing Time: 30 minutes.

Costumes: In Scene I, all characters are in everyday clothes. Upon her entrance, Fiddle is dressed in a reversible coat and felt hat, and wears a blue sweater and skirt underneath. Frieda wears a maid's uniform. For Scene II the children wear everyday clothes and put the caps, aprons, etc. over their clothes. Rocky wears a dark suit in this scene. Texas is in an army uniform.

Properties: Rolls of white and black crepe paper; football; Indian headdresses; tablecloth; wooden bowl filled with fruit; ears of corn; extra card tables.

Setting: The Marston living room is comfortable and attractive without being luxurious. A couch, several chairs, lamps, end tables, may be placed as desired. There is also a small desk with chair for Mrs. Marston. Scene II is the same as Scene I. A card table has been set up in the center of the room on which are piles of black and white paper, and the hats, aprons, etc., used for Thanksgiving costumes in this scene.

Lighting: None required.

THANKSGIVING BEATS THE DUTCH

Characters

Mrs. Marston, *a busy mother.*
Mr. Marston, *a harassed father.*
Rocky Marston, *the brother.*
Fiddle Marston, *the little sister.*
Aunt Tillie, *from Pennsylvania.*
Aunt Hester, *from Massachusetts.*
Nick Reed, *a G. I.*
Tessie Marston, *the teen-aged daughter.*

Scene: *The living room of the Marston home.*

Time: (Scene 1) *A few days before Thanksgiving.*

(Scene 2) *Thanksgiving morning.*

THANKSGIVING BEATS THE DUTCH

SCENE 1

SETTING: *The living room of the Marston home.*

AT RISE: MRS. MARSTON *is looking over a recipe book.* MR. MARSTON *is absorbed in a magazine.*

MRS. MARSTON: What do you think, Bill, shall we make Grandmother's Thanksgiving pudding for dessert this year or a straight Indian Meal Pudding same as last year?

MR. MARSTON: Uh-huh.

MRS. MARSTON: Grandmother's pudding calls for a quarter of a pound of citron. I wonder if you can still get citron. (*A trifle louder*) Bill, do you think we could get citron at the A. & P.?

MR. MARSTON: Um? What's that?

MRS. MARSTON: I said — I wonder if the A. & P. has any citron?

MR. MARSTON: Ummmm. I shouldn't be surprised.

MRS. MARSTON: The Indian Meal Pudding is easier to make but the children always liked Grandmother's recipe better. Which would you like, Bill?

MR. MARSTON: Uh-huh.

MRS. MARSTON (*Annoyed*): I said — which would you like?

MR. MARSTON: Yeah. Sure. I'd like that fine.

MRS. MARSTON: Bill Marston, you haven't heard a word I've been saying. What on earth are you reading that's so absorbing?

MR. MARSTON: I am not reading anything, actually. I've been holding this magazine in front of my face for the last fifteen minutes but I haven't been able to concentrate for your jabbering.

MRS. MARSTON: Jabbering! I like that! If your Thanksgiving dinner isn't worth a little of your time, it's hardly worth cooking. After all, I'm only trying to please you.

MR. MARSTON: But you do please me, Eleanor. You're a wonderful cook. If you had mush and milk for Thanksgiving dinner, it would be O.K. with me.

MRS. MARSTON: I'd hate to try it. Thank goodness, the children still take an interest in their food. (*Enter* FIDDLE.) Here's Fiddle. Maybe she'll help me decide.

FIDDLE: Decide what? Just bring on your weighty problems and I'll tell you what to do. What's on your mind, Moms?

MRS. MARSTON: Thanksgiving dinner. Shall we have Grandmother's pudding or a straight Indian Meal Pudding like last year?

FIDDLE: How could we have either one with Aunt Hester coming? . She'll have to have pumpkin pie or the world will come to an end.

MRS. MARSTON: But she's not coming, dear. That's why we can relax and have a pudding instead of those everlasting pies.

MR. MARSTON: What's that? (*Laying down magazine*) Did you say something about Hester not coming for Thanksgiving, Eleanor?

MRS. MARSTON: Why yes, dear. It's not her turn. This is Tillie's year. Remember?

MR. MARSTON: It's nothing of the sort. It's Hester's year.

FIDDLE: You're slipping, Moms. Aunt Tillie was here last.

MRS. MARSTON: But I just wrote to Tillie last week...and...

MR. MARSTON: Don't tell me you invited her.

MRS. MARSTON: But certainly I invited her. Your sister Hester was here last Christmas.

MR. MARSTON: And what about the visit we had from Tillie in the summer?

MRS. MARSTON: But that doesn't count. That wasn't a holiday.

MR. MARSTON: Holiday or no holiday, she was here a whole week, and Hester found out about it, so naturally that makes it Hester's turn.

MRS. MARSTON: I never heard of such crazy reasoning. They take turns on holidays...and summer vacation isn't a holiday.

MR. MARSTON: Maybe not, but I heard from Hester today and she's coming.

MRS. MARSTON: Oh, Bill, then we'll have both of them on our hands at one time. Tillie wrote that she's coming too.

FIDDLE: If you ask me, you two are in an awful jam. Boy, oh, boy! This will be something to see. Tillie the Toiler and Hester the Heckler under the same roof.

MR. MARSTON: Fidelity Marston, if you can't show the proper respect for your aunts, you may leave the room.

FIDDLE: Oh, but Daddy, you know they are both perfectly awful and they cramp our style something fierce. Aunt Tillie with her Pennsylvania Dutch accent and her awful clothes, and Aunt Hester with her New England Conscience and all that rigamarole about her family tree. (*Imitating*) Remember, Fidelity, on your father's side, you are a direct descendant of Governor Bradford. The Marstons are one of the oldest families in America. (*Dropping affected voice*) And then Aunt Tillie with her V's like W's and her W's like V's. Oh, boy, oh, boy, oh, boy!

MRS. MARSTON: Hush, Fiddle. Your Aunt Tillie is a very fine person, with or without a family tree. And for that matter the Schneiders came to America in 1731...and that should be enough to satisfy anyone.

MR. MARSTON: Now, Eleanor, let's not make this a family argument. You know perfectly well we can't have Tillie at the same table with Hester.

MRS. MARSTON (*Indignant*): Do you mean to imply your sister is better than mine?

MR. MARSTON (*Groaning*): You know better than that. But we can't have those two old ladies sitting across the table from each other when they don't even speak.

FIDDLE: And the dinner, Moms, think of that! Why, we'd have to have a double-decker. Mashed potatoes for Aunt Tillie, candied sweets for La Belle Hester. Cranberry sauce for Aunt Tillie, cranberry jelly for Aunt Hester. Sauerkraut with the turkey for your sister; fried oysters with the turkey for Pop's sister. Thyme and sage in the turkey stuffing for Aunt Tillie, chestnut dressing for Aunt Hester. Mince pie for one, pumpkin pie for the other. Golly days, we'd kill ourselves cooking. And besides, we can't afford all that stuff for those two old clucks, pardon me, Dad, I should have said those two old dears.

MRS. MARSTON: Yes, I know. You can't tell me a thing about their notions on cookery. It was cooking that caused all the trouble in the first place.

FIDDLE: I never knew that. I thought they were just born hating each other.

MR. MARSTON: Nonsense. Hester was, in her day, a very famous cook, one of the best in New England, in fact.

MRS. MARSTON: Well, you'll have to admit, Bill, Aunt Tillie is no slouch either. Her Schnitz and Knepp and Potato Pancakes and Shoefly Pie are something to dream about.

MR. MARSTON: You win there, Eleanor. And it's just too bad those two had to fall out over a recipe.

MRS. MARSTON: Yes, it seems ridiculous now, but it was tragic to them. You see, Aunt Tillie had a famous old Fastnacht recipe that your Aunt Hester wanted. But Tillie wouldn't give it to her because your Aunt Hester had refused to give her an equally famous recipe for clam chowder. Well, one day when the two of them were visiting here, Aunt Tillie was stirring up some Fastnachts and Hester hid in the back stairway and peeked out through the door to try to get her recipe. Somehow or other Tillie discovered her and there was an awful row. Maybe they could have patched it up, but Tillie called Hester a "dogged old Wonnernose" and that seemed to fix the whole business.

FIDDLE (*Laughing*): A "Wonnernose!" What's that?

MRS. MARSTON: It's a Wonder-Nose...or a nosey person who sticks his nose into other people's business. Anyhow, the two never forgave each other and they haven't spoken since.

ROCKY (*Enters*): Hy'a, all! What's cookin'?

MRS. MARSTON: Don't mention cooking, please.

MR. MARSTON: And take off your hat. No wonder Hester says the children of today have no breeding.

ROCKY: Craminy! Don't tell me Hester De Pester is here.

MR. MARSTON: Rocky! You should be ashamed to call your Aunt Hester names.

ROCKY: I know, but golly, Dad, is she really here?

MRS. MARSTON: No, but she's coming, so you might as well start watching your language right now, and your manners, too. I want you and Fiddle to behave yourselves.

FIDDLE: You'll have to stop calling me Fiddle, Moms. Aunt Hester hates nicknames. I'll have to be Fidelity. And Rocky must be "Cliff." Meet my dear brother, Clifford Bradford Marston.

ROCKY: I'll Clifford Bradford Marston you, Miss Dribble Puss.

MRS. MARSTON: Children! Please! We have enough trouble. Rocky, your Aunt Tillie and your Aunt Hester are both coming for Thanksgiving.

ROCKY: After that there'll be no more need for the atomic bomb. Holy smokes, who got their wires crossed?

MR. MARSTON: I don't know exactly whose fault it is, but we'll have to uncross them right now. Eleanor, you'll have to call Tillie and tell her not to come.

MRS. MARSTON: And what's the matter with your calling Hester and changing her plans?

MR. MARSTON: You know I can't do that. Hester is so sensitive, so easily hurt.

MRS. MARSTON: And what about Tillie? I don't want to hurt her feelings either.

ROCKY: Yeah, but poor Aunt Hester lives all alone. It would be pretty tough to eat alone on Thanksgiving day. At least Aunt Tillie has other people around her.

MRS. MARSTON: If you can count a bunch of other old ladies like herself. An Old Folks Home is no garden spot for Thanksgiving either. She just lives for these visits to our house, she loves you children, and I'm not going to disappoint her.

MR. MARSTON: And that's just how I feel about Hester.

FIDDLE: That's what you call a deadlock. Gee, for once I wish Tessie would come. Maybe she'd have a suggestion.

TESSIE (*Enters*): Did somebody call Tessie? Here I am, and oh, people, I have the most wonderful news.

ROCKY: Then spill it, 'cause everybody else is down in the dumps.

TESSIE: Oh, Mother, remember that perfectly excruciating G. I. I met at the beach? The big handsome one with the brown eyes and the...

ROCKY: And the knock knees. Sure, I remember. He was a lug. What about him?

TESSIE: Quiet, Oaf. Well, Mother, what do you think? He's stationed up here and I just ran into him at the library, and guess what?

ROCKY: You knocked the breath out of him, and no wonder. You're putting on weight, Sis.

TESSIE: Oh, shut up. Nick, that's his name, is coming for Thanksgiving dinner.

ALL: What?

TESSIE: Yes, for dinner. I thought you wouldn't mind. He doesn't know a soul in town and he's as lonely as can be. He was thrilled to come.

MRS. MARSTON: But Tessie, it won't do. You wouldn't want him here with your Aunt Tillie and your Aunt Hester.

TESSIE: Heavenly horrors! Don't tell me they're both coming this year.

MRS. MARSTON: I'm afraid so.

MR. MARSTON: Unless your mother sidetracks Tillie.

MRS. MARSTON: Or unless you cancel Aunt Hester.

FIDDLE: See. (*Shrugging her shoulders*) It's Greek meeting Greek. They're both set...so we're stuck with the two Aunties.

ROCKY: Gosh, I wonder if they'll pull each other's hair out.

TESSIE: Oh, but Mother, I can't disappoint Nick...and yet... Oh, I'll be so embarrassed to have those two fuddy-duddies here, neither one speaking to the other. What will he think of us?

ROCKY: Maybe he has fighting relations, too. It happens in the best of families.

TESSIE: But Nick is different. He's the literary type.

ROCKY: What's that? Does that mean he can read and write?

TESSIE: Oh my, why were brothers ever born? It means he is the bookish type. As a matter of fact he's writing a book of his own.

FIDDLE: Gee, an author? Is he a mystery writer?

ROCKY: Like Ellery Queen?

TESSIE: I don't know. He doesn't talk much about his work.

It's something very important for the army, some sort of research problem, too. Maybe he'll tell us more about it later. But oh, Mother, what shall I do?

MRS. MARSTON: You'll have to decide that for yourself, child. If you can stand it, we can. At least the boy will talk. Maybe that will help to relax the tension.

MR. MARSTON: I'm sure you'll have no cause to be embarrassed by Hester. She'll be polite.

MRS. MARSTON: So will Tillie, but not polite enough to speak first. If Hester meets her half way, they might unbend.

MR. MARSTON: Not in a thousand years. Our best bet is to tell one of them not to come.

FIDDLE: But which one?

MR. AND MRS. MARSTON (*Together*): Tillie. Hester.

TESSIE: Why not call them both off? That would settle the problem.

ROCKY: Aw, heck! Thanksgiving's a time families should be together whether they're mad or not. I say let 'em both come, and we'll see what gives. Maybe it won't be as bad as we think.

FIDDLE: Good for you, Rocky. I second the motion.

MRS. MARSTON: Under the circumstances I don't see what else we could do. What do you say, Bill?

MR. MARSTON: O.K. But it's at your own risk. If we all get indigestion, I'll buy the soda mints.

CURTAIN

* * *

Scene 2

Setting: *The Marston living room on Thanksgiving morning.*

At Rise: Aunt Tillie, *a jolly-looking old lady, somewhat wide in circumference, is seated on a sofa with a dishpan of bread filling on her lap.* Fiddle *is seated on a stool beside her.*

Aunt Tillie: Ach, Fiddle, such a nice house you have here. So bright and warm (*Bouncing up and down*) and this here sofy is wonderful soft like a feather tick.

Fiddle: It's a new one. Dad gave it to Mother last year for Christmas.

Aunt Tillie: Ach yes. Christmas. That's ven your Aunt Hester wisited you last, ain't?

Fiddle: Well, yes, I guess that was the last time Aunt Hester was here.

Aunt Tillie: My, My! That voman looks more like a dill pickle every day she lives.

Fiddle: Oh, Aunt Tillie. (*Laughing*) You're a scream.

Aunt Tillie (*Laughing, too*): More speck she should have still on her old bones. Then she could set better on them hard-backed chairs in that hotel.

Fiddle: Aunt Hester believes in keeping her girlish figure.

Aunt Tillie: And her girlish hair-do, too. Humph! I don't hold with no short hair and permanents...not ven a voman hits her seventies, I don't.

Fiddle: But Aunt Hester's only 69.

Aunt Tillie: Ach, Fiddle, don't be such a dumkopf! 69! So's your Aunt Emmy! How's fer watching a little out wis that bread, Child? Your pieces is too big. Wery, wery fine they must be or it makes not good.

AUNT HESTER (*Entering with her knitting bag. She is a tall, dignified woman, quite thin, and carries herself very straight. She is searching in her bag as she enters*): Oh, dear me, I must have left my glasses upstairs. Do be a good child, Fidelity, and see if you can find them.

FIDDLE: O.K., Aunt Hester. I'll have them in just a sec. (*Almost upsets pan as she rises.*)

AUNT TILLIE: Careful, Fiddle, careful. Don't be so dopplich. (FIDDLE *exits.* AUNT HESTER *seats herself across the room from* AUNT TILLIE *who goes on with her work. There is dead silence.*)

AUNT TILLIE (*Calling*): Eleanor, come see vuncet if this is enough bread. I sink it vill make plenty, still. (*Enter* MRS. MARSTON.)

MRS. MARSTON: Oh, yes, Tillie. That's oodles.

AUNT HESTER: In Massachusetts we always stuff our fowls the day before and have them ready for the oven.

MRS. MARSTON: So do we, Hester, but this is to be baked as a side dish...with thyme and sage. Tillie likes it that way, you know.

AUNT HESTER: Yes, I've heard of folks doing it that way, but personally, I wouldn't care for it.

AUNT TILLIE (*To* MRS. MARSTON): Personally she don't have to eat none of it, so it makes no neffer mind to me.

MRS. MARSTON: How about you coming out in the kitchen, Tillie, and giving me a hand with basting the turkey?

AUNT TILLIE: Sure, sure. Ach, Eleanor, such a wonderful fine sing it is to get back in a kitchen where a body can put on an apron and get to work.

AUNT HESTER (*Very much injured*): I'm sure I'd be willing to help you, Eleanor. After all, I know this big crowd is too much for you.

MRS. MARSTON: Oh, not at all Hester, dear. And I'll call on

you when it comes to making the gravy. There's nobody like you when it comes to gravies.

AUNT HESTER: Oh, Eleanor, you flatter me. It's just that I always mix my flour and water first and then add it very gradually.

AUNT TILLIE: To make gravy what is gravy, the flour must be browned in good hot fat. Otherwise it ain't got no flavor.

AUNT HESTER: Well, well, well. Some folks certainly do intrude their opinions before they are asked.

MRS. MARSTON: Oh, dear! Please, Tillie, do come along with me. (*They exit.* FIDDLE *enters.*)

FIDDLE: Here's your specs, Aunt Hester. My, what a beautiful afghan you're knitting. That must take a lot of time.

AUNT HESTER (*With a deep sigh*): And I have nothing but time on my hands, Fidelity. The days are very long just sitting in a hotel all day. By the way, was your Aunt Tillie here on a visit this summer?

FIDDLE: Yes, she was.

AUNT HESTER: Humph! I heard she stayed a week. Wasn't that a rather long visit?

FIDDLE: Oh, not so long. She seemed to enjoy it.

AUNT HESTER: Doubtless. I notice she is getting very heavy. That's bad for a woman of her years. Often causes high blood pressure. Your Aunt Tillie was always an enormous eater. But I guess she's had to cut down now that she's in her seventies.

FIDDLE: Is Aunt Tillie that old?

AUNT HESTER (*Confidentially*): And then some. But she'll never admit it. Some women are so touchy about their ages. Now take myself, for instance, I don't care a fig who knows I'm 69. I'm proud of it. (MR. MARSTON *enters.*)

MR. MARSTON: Hello there, you two. Where's the rest of my harem?

AUNT HESTER: Out in the kitchen. Eleanor made it very clear that she preferred Tillie to help get the dinner.

MR. MARSTON: Nonsense, Hester. You mustn't be so touchy. Eleanor will be glad for your help.

AUNT HESTER (*Angrily*): Touchy, am I? Don't you call me touchy, William Marston. It's bad enough to be invited to spend my holiday under the same roof with that...that stupid, stubborn woman who won't even speak to me without being called "touchy." The very idea. I have a good notion to go upstairs and pack my things.

MR. MARSTON: Now, now Hester. Control yourself, please. This is Thanksgiving Day...a time we should spend in peace and quiet. Come, now, let's go out in the kitchen together and see how dinner's coming on.

AUNT HESTER: I'll not set foot in that kitchen so long as Tillie Schneider is there.

FIDDLE: Oh, please, Aunt Hester, Aunt Tillie doesn't mean any harm.

AUNT HESTER (*Sniffing into handkerchief*): That's right, side with her. You're all against me, every one of you. I'm not welcome here.

MR. MARSTON: That's silly. Of course, you're welcome. You're my very own sister.

AUNT HESTER: And if you had any respect for me you wouldn't permit me to be insulted.

FIDDLE: But no one insulted you, Aunt Hester. Honest, Dad, Aunt Tillie never said a word to her.

AUNT HESTER: That's just it. She never speaks to me.

FIDDLE: But you don't speak to her, either.

MR. MARSTON: Hush, Fiddle. This is very childish. (*Calling*) Eleanor, come in here, can't you?

MRS. MARSTON (*Entering*): Yes, dear?

MR. MARSTON: Isn't there something Hester can do to help in the kitchen?

MRS. MARSTON: Well, not just now, but later when we start to dish up.

AUNT HESTER (*Crying*): Now you see how it is, William?

AUNT TILLIE (*Entering*): Who's kicking up a rumpus? If it makes trouble for me to be in the kitchen, I can go home still or I can set in my room. I been hearin' every word, and nobody can say Tillie Schneider stays noveres ver she ain't wanted. (*Removing apron and giving it to* ELEANOR) Here, tie this vuncet around that voman and git her out from my sight. She greistles me.

MRS. MARSTON: Tillie, please. You promised me you wouldn't make a fuss.

AUNT TILLIE: Makin' a fuss, am I? Vell, I'll show you vuncet how I could make a fuss if I vasn't a lady.

MRS. MARSTON (*Crying*): Oh, Bill, I knew it would be this way. Oh, dear, this is awful. I'm going upstairs and I don't care who gets the dinner. So there! You can just do the best you can. The turkey's in the oven and from there on, it's up to you. (*Exit* MRS. MARSTON *in tears.*)

MR. MARSTON: Eleanor, please. Eleanor, you can't do this. Come back here, Eleanor. (*He goes after* MRS. MARSTON.)

FIDDLE (*Looks at the two angry women*): Golly, it's no wonder that countries have wars. It would take a whole peace conference to settle this fight. Look, Aunt Tillie, won't you please let bygones be bygones and make up with Aunt Hester?

AUNT HESTER: She called me a "dogged old wonnernose," and I'll never forget it.

AUNT TILLIE: And for why? Because that's chust vat you are...an old vonnernose a-snoopin' into my cookpot to steal my Fastnacht recipe.

AUNT HESTER: Steal? Steal? Why you impudent old woman!

(They are about to fly at each other.)

FIDDLE: Please, please, Aunt Tillie! Aunt Hester! Please.
(TESSIE *enters with* NICK.)

TESSIE: Hello, Fiddle. Where's Mother?

FIDDLE: She — she's upstairs, and I have to see her right away.
(*Exit* FIDDLE.)

TESSIE (*To* NICK): That's my sister, Nick, a screwball if there
ever was one. And this is my Aunt Tillie Schneider and my
Aunt Hester Marston. Aunties, this is Nick Freed. He's
come to have dinner with us.

AUNTS: How do you do.

NICK: I sure am glad to meet Tessie's aunts. Boy, it's wonderful to have a family like this and be together on Thanksgiving day.

TESSIE: Yes, isn't it? If you'll excuse me, Nick, I'll run upstairs and get Mother. Aunt Hester, you'll have to do the
honors. Nick is a writer...maybe a famous one. Aunt
Tillie can tell you some wonderful Pennsylvania Dutch
stories, Nick. Maybe you could use them in your book.
(*Exit.*)

NICK: Oh, I'm not that kind of a writer. You see...well...
it may sound funny...but I write cook books.

AUNTS: Cook books?

NICK: Yes, in a way it sort of embarrasses me, but you see, the
army is interested in collecting regional recipes so that boys
from all over the country will have foods that they are used
to. We want to train our army cooks to be the best chefs in
the whole world. Right now Uncle Sam is overhauling his
cook book, and I'm staying in the Army as one of a staff employed to work on the food survey and help line up popular
recipes from every section in the country.

AUNT HESTER: How very interesting.

AUNT TILLIE: Ach my, I neffer heard of such goings on...a

young sprout like yourself huntin' up recipes. Now vat do you know about the like of that anyhow?

NICK: Oh, I'm not a bad cook, myself, in an amateur way. But since I've been working on this job I'm really interested. Ever since the days of the Puritans, America has been noted for good food, and there's no reason why our famous regional foods can't be made available to the men in our standing armies.

AUNT HESTER: Young man, that's a very sound idea. Now take the New England recipes for instance. Brown bread, corned beef hash, baked beans, fish chowder...

NICK: Oh, boy, fish chowder! You know there aren't any two recipes that are alike. I bet I have skeenteen recipes for clam chowder, for instance, all different.

AUNT HESTER: Well, (*Very proudly*), if I must say so myself ...I make the finest chowder there is...and I'd risk my reputation as a cook on my recipe.

NICK: Golly, maybe this will be the right one. Would you mind giving it to me?

AUNT TILLIE: Ha! Not that vun! Not for all the money in the vorld vould she tell how she makes vis those clams. Sixty years I tried to get that recipe...me her own sister-in-law... and vould she give it me? No.

AUNT HESTER: Pay no attention to this woman, young man. She doesn't know what she's saying. Just because she refuses to give her own recipes away, she thinks everyone else is just like her.

NICK: Are you a cook, too, Mrs....er...

AUNT TILLIE: Schneider is the name, Tillie Schneider. Yes, I can make right smart victuals, if I do say so, as shouldn't. But down Pennsylvania way we make sings different.

NICK: Don't I know it...Smierkase, Hasen-Pfeffer, Scrappel, Sauerbraten, Shupp Noodles, Fastnachts...Oh boy, if I can just run down a really good Fastnacht recipe, I'll be happy.

AUNT HESTER: You've come to the right person, but you'll never get it young man, never.

NICK: You mean you have a recipe, Mrs. Schneider?

AUNT HESTER: Does she? **Mr. Freed, Tillie Schneider makes** the best Fastnachts in the entire United States of America.

AUNT TILLIE: Vy, Hester Marston...that's the first nice sing you said to me in sirty years. (*Bursts into tears.*)

AUNT HESTER: There, there, Tillie. I always did hold you to be the finest cook out of the New England States. I couldn't say less. It's the truth.

AUNT TILLIE: Ach, bless us and save us. It's that good to hear you say so. Set yourself right down here, Mister, and me and Hester vill tell you some recipes vot vill make your mouth water right down on your west.

AUNT HESTER (*Sitting on sofa on the other side of* NICK): Now about this clam chowder. You take a quart and a half of soft shell clams, and separate the stomachs from the necks.

AUNT TILLIE: For Fastnachts you must first make wis a yeast cake and a cup of warm water. Not hot water, mind, but chust so, like you say luke-varm. Then after you soak your yeast cake, you...

AUNT HESTER: You cover the clam necks with water and simmer for three quarters of an hour.

AUNT TILLIE: Then you heat up two cups of milk wis one cup of good rich butter chust out of the churn.

AUNT HESTER: Next you fry three nice big pieces of salt pork with six sliced potatoes and three onions.

AUNT TILLIE: Then add sree cups of vite sugar and the yeast vot you dunked in the varm water.

AUNT HESTER: Then you must very carefully combine — (ROCKY *enters during the exchange of recipes and stands amazed.*)

ROCKY: Say, what goes on here? Where is everybody and

when's dinner ready? There's something burning in the kitchen. I think it's the turkey.

AUNT HESTER: Oh my patience! Quick, Tillie. Let's see what we can do.

AUNT TILLIE: Ai, yai, yai, yai, yai! Hurry, hurry! If the turkey burns, we'll neffer hear the last of it. (*Both exit.*)

NICK: I'm afraid your Aunts and I were so busy talking we forgot all about the dinner.

ROCKY: You mean they were *both* talking?

NICK: Why, sure.

ROCKY: Talking to you or to each other?

NICK: Both — to me and to each other.

ROCKY: Jeepers! Brother, you should run for president. (*Calling*) Hey, everybody...come out...come out wherever you are...the war's over. They've run up the white flag. (MR. *and* MRS. MARSTON, FIDDLE *and* TESSIE *enter.*)

MR. MARSTON: What's all the shouting about?

ROCKY: We really have something to shout about now. Aunt Tillie and Aunt Hester have signed an armistice.

MRS. MARSTON: What are you talking about, Rocky? Where in heaven's name are they?

ROCKY: Out in the kitchen having a conference over the turkey. This fellow here seems to be the original peacemaker.

TESSIE: Oh, Nick, you're wonderful.

NICK: Oh, it was nothing, really, it was just... (*The* AUNTS *enter, smiling broadly and wiping their hands on a dish towel and on an apron.*)

AUNT HESTER: No cause for alarm, Rocky, the bird is doing fine.

AUNT TILLIE: Thanks to your Aunt Hester.

AUNT HESTER: Nothing of the sort, it was your Aunt Tillie who really saved the day.

MRS. MARSTON: Praises be! They've made up.

AUNT HESTER: Made up? What are you talking about, Eleanor? I always did say Tillie was the best cook in 27 counties. And tomorrow morning we're going to stir up a batch of Fastnachts over her recipe, aren't we, Tillie?

AUNT TILLIE: But first I want you should show me how you make wis them clams.

AUNT HESTER: Very well, I will. I'll let you see everything I put in the kettle...you..."you dogged old Wonnernose."

THE END

PRODUCTION NOTES

THANKSGIVING BEATS THE DUTCH

Characters: 3 male; 5 female.

Playing Time: 35 minutes.

Costumes: All of the Marstons wear everyday modern dress. Mrs. Marston wears a housedress with an apron over it. Aunt Tillie may wear a rather drab, longish dress with an apron over it. Aunt Hester is dressed like an old-fashioned New Englander. Nick wears an Army uniform.

Properties: Cook book, magazine, large dishpan, loaf of bread and some bread crumbs in pan, knitting bag, handkerchief, dish towel, aprons.

Setting: A comfortable American living room, furnished with sofa, several easy chairs, end tables, lamps, etc.

ANGEL CHILD

Characters

MRS. REYNOLDS
ANGELA REYNOLDS
JEFF REYNOLDS
ALICE GREY
PATRICIA BOND
MESSENGER BOY

SCENE: *The living room of the Reynolds house.*

TIME: *Early Christmas Eve.*

ANGEL CHILD

SETTING: *The living room of the Reynolds home.*

AT RISE: MRS. REYNOLDS *is struggling to tie up a large package on the davenport.* ANGELA *is mounted on a step-ladder tying balls on a half-trimmed tree. Her twelve-year-old brother is standing a few feet from the tree slinging handfuls of paper icicles in its general direction.*

MRS. REYNOLDS: Come here, somebody, and hold your finger on this string.

ANGELA: Make Jeff do it. I can't come down.

JEFF (*Strolling over to davenport*): O.K., Moms. What's in it?

MRS. REYNOLDS: Never you mind. (*Tying parcel*) There! That's done! Now you two hurry up with that tree and put the finishing touches to it before Ted and Dave arrive.

JEFF (*Thoughtfully*): "Finishing touches—finishing touches." Say, that would make a great slogan, Angie-Pangie. I could use it for the National Funeral Home Contest. *Our finishing touch won't cost you much!* How's that?

ANGELA: Terrible! And if you call me "Angie-Pangie" once more, I'll jump off this ladder and strangle you!

JEFF (*Very carefully arranging some icicles*): Oh, yeah? I hope you remember that crack when you're standing on the Court House steps tonight in Mom's nightgown with that silly halo cocked over one ear. (*Striking what he imagines to be an angelic pose*) You're a good one to talk about "peace and goodwill."

ANGELA (*Patiently superior*): It's not Mom's nightgown, child. It's a celanese voile robe, and the halo positively will not slip this year.

JEFF: Well, then, this will be the first year it hasn't slipped. Honest, last year I thought I'd die. You were the funniest looking angel I ever saw!

ANGELA (*Threateningly*): If I come down this ladder, Jeff Reynolds, you'll be sorry.

JEFF (*In a high, shrill voice*): Now, Angie-Pangie, you wouldn't strike your little brother, would you? Not on Christmas Eve! (ANGELA *descends the ladder in record time and chases "little brother" who ducks behind the sofa screaming "Help!" and "Moms!"*)

MRS. REYNOLDS (*Entering left*): Will you two never grow up? Angela, behave yourself! Jeff, stop acting like an "Our Gang" comedy character! Can't I have a minute's peace in this house even on Christmas Eve? It seems to me, Angela, that you could be of more help when there are a million things to be done. Just look at this room, and Ted bringing Dave Elman home almost any minute!

ANGELA (*Contritely*): I'm sorry, Moms. It's that hateful Jeff tormenting me about this angel business.

JEFF: Aw, what is there to get sore about? I was only kidding, and anyhow, she should be used to it by now. Twelve years' experience wearing wings ought to mellow her some.

ANGELA: That's just it! It's come to be a joke and I'm so sick of dressing up in that halo and wearing those wings, I could die!

JEFF (*Singing the line from the "Prisoner's Song"*): "Oh, if I had the wings of an angel..."

MRS. REYNOLDS: Jeff, stop it! (*To* ANGELA) But, honey, you always look sweet. Your coloring is so lovely.

ANGELA (*Bitterly*): Oh, my coloring! My coloring! I hate

it! That's what got me into this mess! Ever since I was five years old I've been running around in cheesecloth and tinsel every Christmas Eve! Just because I happen to have yellow hair and blue eyes, I always have to be an angel! I never get a chance at a good part where I can really act!

JEFF: You don't need a chance. You're putting on an act all the time.

ANGELA (*Ignoring Jeff*): I swore last year I'd never do it again!

MRS. REYNOLDS: Well, they did ask Alice Grey.

ANGELA (*In disgust*): Yes, and what did little Alice do but get a cold at the last minute! Then they come around to me with a sob story —

JEFF: And say, "Do be an angel" — and you just couldn't refuse.

ANGELA: I'm a chump and they know it.

JEFF: Just a chump off the old block! (*Laughs uproariously.*) Boy! Is that a good one? "Chump off the old block!"

ANGELA (*Crossly*): Oh, shut up! Alice Grey's too delicate to stand out in the cold, but nobody would care if I stood up to my waist in snow and took pneumonia!

JEFF: Why didn't Kate Ramsay do it? She's got baby blue eyes, and (*With a sly wink at his mother*) she's got *naturally* curly hair.

ANGELA: She has not! She gets her permanent at the same place I get mine! Anyhow, she's too fat! Angels must keep slim!

JEFF: Streamlined models, eh?

MRS. REYNOLDS: I heard Mrs. Keller say that Edith had been asked.

ANGELA: Oh, she couldn't be bothered. Too many dates.

MRS. REYNOLDS: Well, Angela, all I can tell you is to be a good sport about it and maybe some day you'll get your reward.

JEFF: Yeah, in forty or fifty years, you can collect your Social Security.

MRS. REYNOLDS (*Looking at her watch*): Heavens! Jeff, hurry up! We'll have to rush if we're going to meet Ted and Dave! You come along with me and stop pestering Angela!

ANGELA: That's the best idea of the century.

MRS. REYNOLDS (*Collecting her things*): Where are my keys and purse? Oh, here they are! Your costume is all ready, dear, on your bed. You had better dress right away because the Director wants you at the Court House by six, and the Bond girls will call for you. And a messenger boy will call for that box on the davenport. It's for Mrs. Hostetter.

ANGELA: Don't worry. I'll be on time. I'm getting out of this house before Dave Elman sees me in that angel suit and (*Advancing on* JEFF *with fire in her eye*) if you dare to say one word, or make any of your awful jokes about angels in front of Dave, or call me "Angie-Pangie," I swear I'll burn every last one of your contest slogans in this house.

JEFF: Aw, Angie-Pa—— Angela, I won't say a word. Honest, I won't. You can trust me. Anyhow, we're the same flesh and blood and there's honor among thieves.

MRS. REYNOLDS (*Ready to leave*): I'll get the car and drive around front. (*Exit right.*)

ANGELA (*Grabbing* JEFF's *coat*): Honest, Jeff, be decent just this once! Dave thinks I'm still an infant.

JEFF: Well, aren't you?

ANGELA: Of course not! And since he has this job in New York, he'll be worse than ever. He'll just kid the life out of me if he finds out I'm still playing angel. Promise you won't tell!

JEFF (*After due deliberation*): O.K. I promise — but I warn you — it will cost you plenty. But buck up, Angie, every family has some skeleton in its closet, only ours happens to be an angel. Say, there's an idea for a slogan! "Angel spray keeps the moths away!" How's that?

ANGELA (*Laughing*) : You monkey! (*Sound of motor horn.*) There's Mother, now get out of here. (*She shoves* JEFF *off right.*)

JEFF (*Yelling gleefully offstage*) : I know a secret! I know a secret!

ANGELA (*Somewhat relieved*) : I wonder if he really will keep his mouth shut. He'd better! (*Phone rings and* ANGELA *answers it.*) Hello, — yes — this is Angela! Oh, hello, Alice! I thought you were sick in bed. (*Pause.*) Oh, your cold's better? Well, I'm glad to hear that! What? Sure, I know about Dave Elman. He's coming home with Ted! Ted's coming down from New Haven and picking him up in New York. (*Doorbell rings.*) Listen, Alice, I'm in a frightful rush, and there's somebody at the door. I'll have to go. (*Doorbell rings again.*) Yes, yes! Well, I just can't talk any longer. I must answer the door. So long! (*Hanging up.*) Plague take that Alice Grey! (*Starting toward door.*) Too sick to be an angel one minute and calling me up the next about Dave Elman! (*Admits* MESSENGER BOY) Here's the box — Mrs. Charles Hostetter — 511 N. Marshall Street. (*Gives him money.*)

MESSENGER BOY : Thanks, ma'am, and Merry Christmas!

ANGELA (*Showing him out*) : Same to you! (*Looking at watch.*) Well, the hour has come. I might as well go put on the war paint and feathers! (ANGELA *exits left. In a second* JEFF *runs in from right. He is carrying a pair of long white stockings.*)

JEFF (*Shouting*) : Hey, Angie! Moms sent me back with a pair of stockings to wear over your arms. She's afraid you'll catch cold! Got 'em at the five and ten! Hey! Where are you?

ANGELA (*Calling*): Upstairs getting ready, and don't you come up here!

JEFF (*Shouting*): She says to be sure and wear a heavy sweater and keep your galoshes on till the last minute! It's cold as blazes! (*Doorbell.*)

ANGELA: Answer the door, Jeff!

JEFF: O.K. (*Throws stockings on davenport. Goes to door right and admits* ALICE GREY.) Oh, hello, Alice! Thought you were sick.

ALICE: I'm better. Where's Angela?

JEFF: Upstairs, putting on her wings. I'll call her. Hey, Angie, Alice Grey's here!

ANGELA: I'll be down in a jiffy!

JEFF: She'll be down in a jiffy. Relax for an hour or two. (*He flops into nearest chair.*)

ALICE (*Pacing up and down*): I do hope she hurries! What time is it?

JEFF: Daylight Saving, Eastern Standard, Central, Mountain, Pacific, or Waltz time? Which will you have?

ALICE: Well, I've no time for my friends' smart-aleck baby brothers! That's one thing certain!

JEFF: Tut! Tut! Tut! A lady should never raise her voice. (ANGELA *enters in full angel regalia.*)

ALICE: Oh, my dear, I didn't expect you to dress so early!

ANGELA: Yes, I promised to be there by six. Jeff, help me with these wings, will you please?

JEFF (*Rising with an air of resignation*): Now I'm supposed to be lady's maid to an angel! (*Bowing elaborately*) And how will madame wear her wings this season — one up and one down, both on the same side, or one front and one back?

ANGELA: Silly! You know how they go! What's up, Alice? What brought you over here on a night like this with that delicate throat of yours?

ALICE: Well, I guess I'm a little late, but it worried me so — disappointing everybody at the last minute — especially you, when I know how you hate all this. So when my cold got better, I thought I'd offer to take my part back.

ANGELA: You mean you'll play the Christmas angel tonight?

ALICE: Sure. After all, you've been a good sport doing it every year, and now that I really am able, you might as well have your evening free.

ANGELA (*In glee*): Alice, do you really mean it? Why, you angel!

JEFF: Not yet, but soon!

ANGELA: Jeff, get me out of this rig! We'll just have time to change! Hurry! (JEFF *removes the wings, and* ANGELA *takes off the halo.*) Here. (*Hands halo to* ALICE.) Put this on! (ALICE *puts on halo and keeps it on for remainder of scene. Phone rings and* ANGELA *reaches for it.*)

ANGELA: Hello! Who? Edith Keller? Oh, hello, Edie. (*In surprise.*) Why, I feel fine, marvellous! (*Pause.*) You what? You want to play the Christmas angel? But I thought you said — Oh, date called off, eh? Well, thank you ever so much, but Alice Grey is here and she offered — Yes, Alice Grey. (*Pause.*) No, I didn't ask her, she just walked in and offered to help me out. — Yes, her cold's better. — O.K. — Thanks for offering. It was sweet of you. So long and Merry Christmas!

JEFF (*Shaking his head and letting out a long whistle*): Something funny! Something funny!

ANGELA: The Christmas spirit must have struck Edie all of a sudden. She offered to take my place tonight.

JEFF (*Sniffing in an exaggerated manner*): Something pretty smelly about all this! Sniff! Sniff! Methinks I smell a rat!

ALICE (*Laughing brightly*): How amusing! Did Edith's date stand her up?

ANGELA: I don't know and I don't care. All I know is that I don't have to be an angel. Come on, Alice, let's go upstairs and change.

JEFF: Just a minute! There's something funny about this, I tell you. I don't trust the motives of these women.

ALICE: Don't be ridiculous!

ANGELA: What do you mean?

JEFF: Did it ever occur to you, my trusting little sister, that these would-be angels might be sheep in wolves' clothing?

ANGELA: Oh, Jeff, talk sense! We're in a hurry!

JEFF: Well, ask yourself — why all this sudden concern about you having a nice Christmas Eve all to yourself? Why? Why? Why?

ANGELA: All right — why?

JEFF (*Shrugging his shoulders*): I don't know. (*Phone rings. JEFF answers. The girls are leaving the room when they hear what JEFF is saying and turn back.*) Yes. This is the Reynolds dump! Who? Mrs. Ramsay! Well for the love of mud! Oh, excuse me, Mrs. Ramsay, I was just surprised. (*Pause.*) Yes, Angie's still here. Do you want to talk to her? Well, I don't know whether she wants anyone to take her place or not. Wait, I'll call her. (*To ANGELA, as he muffles the mouthpiece.*) Psst! It's Mrs. Ramsay. Wants to know if you'd like Kate to take your place on account of she knows your brother and his friend are coming home tonight.

ANGELA (*In surprise*): Well, for heaven's sake! Let me talk to her. (*Takes phone.*) Hello. Yes, Mrs. Ramsay. (*Pause.*) Yes, well, that's very kind of you, I'm sure, but I'm afraid it's too late to make any changes. (*Pause.*) Oh, you did call the Director! What did he say? (*Pause*) Well, to be perfectly frank, Mrs. Ramsay, I don't understand all these kind offers. For twelve years I've been playing angel and now within fifteen minutes, I've had three people offer to do the part. I think I'll just play it myself as usual. Yes, I think so. But thank you for calling. (*As she hangs up*) Maybe next year they'll have two angels and Kate can play both of them!

ALICE: How utterly fantastic that Mrs. Ramsay should call you! I can't imagine poor Kate as an angel!

JEFF (*Confronting* ALICE): No, and I can't imagine *you* as an angel either, Alice Grey. I think you're up to some dirty work.

ALICE (*Indignantly*): Really, Angela, does your little brother go about insulting people all the time? After all, I only came over here to do you a favor.

ANGELA: Did you, Alice? (*Before* ALICE *can answer, an automobile horn sounds offstage.*) Oh, dear me! There are the Bond girls, I'll have to go, or you'll have to go, or somebody — Jeff, go tell them I'll be out in a minute.

JEFF (*Going to door*): She'll be out in a minute. Oh, hello, Pat! Come on in. Angie's not quite ready. (PATRICIA BOND *enters, very much excited over a newspaper she is carrying.*)

PAT (*Eagerly*): Hey, Angela, have you seen the paper? Oh, hello, Alice.

ALICE: Hello.

ANGELA: No, there's been no time around this house to read the news.

PAT (*Putting it into her hands*): Well, look, look! Isn't it wonderful? I'm so thrilled!

JEFF: What? What? Has there been a wreck? Let me see! (ALICE *leaves the group and stands alone by the table.*)

ANGELA (*Reading aloud*): "LOCAL CHRISTMAS PAGEANT TO BE FILMED. FORMER ASHTON YOUTH NEWSREEL CAMERAMAN. The annual Yuletide pageant which Ashton citizens have come to regard as a bit of local tradition will be filmed this year by a cameraman from the Modern Days Newsreel Service. David Elman, a former resident of Ashton, has received as his first assignment as news photographer the job of filming his home town Christmas celebration!"

JEFF: Jumping Jehosophat! That certainly clears up the mystery of the volunteer Angel Department! They took time out to read the paper!

ALICE: You people will never believe me, but I did want to —

JEFF: Skip it, Alice, skip it! I'm afraid your one and only chance to be an angel is gone forever!

ANGELA: Stop it, Jeff! I understand, Alice, but I think I'll be wearing that halo myself! (ALICE *who has forgotten she is wearing the halo snatches it off.*)

ALICE: Here, take the hateful thing! It's always crooked anyhow!

JEFF: Not when it's worn by a "straight" person!

ANGELA: Don't mind him, Alice! Boys are terrible! (*Showing* ALICE *out*) So long, and Merry Christmas!

ALICE (*At door*): I guess I'm not exactly the angel type, Angela. Sorry! Good-bye! (*Exits.*)

JEFF: The nerve of some people!

PAT: None of this makes any sense to me.

ANGELA: Nor to anyone else! Jeff, help me with these wings, and Pat, see if this halo is straight. Read some more of that article, Pat. I'm so excited!

PAT (*Reading*): "One of the most outstanding features of the pageant is the final tableau in which Miss Angela Reynolds has made the part her own by the somewhat unusual feat of playing the role twelve successive years."

JEFF (*Fastening wings*): Gee, Angie, you're famous! But gosh! Now there won't be any point in telling Dave about your angel act!

ANGELA: You wretched boy! Were you going to tell him?

JEFF (*Forgetting himself*): Sure! No, no. (*As* ANGELA *advances toward him.*) No, honest, Angie, I wasn't gonna breathe a word!

PAT (*Laughing*): Save your energy, Angela; besides you'll only knock your halo crooked! Come on, let's hurry!

ANGELA: Do I look right?

JEFF: Just like an angel!

ANGELA (*Giving* JEFF *a friendly pat*): You're sort of an angel yourself at times. Say hello to Ted and Dave when they come, and tell Dave I said these pictures better be good! (*ANGELA and* PAT *dash off.*)

JEFF (*Sinking onto sofa*): Now a man can get some rest! (*Picks up paper*) Boy, oh boy! (*Reading.*) One hundred dollars for this rhyme:

"When Christmas is over
Relax from the strain."

(*Producing a pencil*) Gee! This is a cinch. (*Rereads two lines and adds*)

"Stop playing the angel —
Be human again!"

(*Proudly.*) There! How's that? (*Reads his efforts aloud*)

"When Christmas is over,
Relax from the strain.
Stop playing the angel —
Be human again!"

THE END

PRODUCTION NOTES

Angel Child

Characters: 2 male; 4 female.

Playing Time: 30 minutes.

Costumes: Characters are dressed in everyday clothes. The Messenger Boy is in uniform. Angela's angel costume is long and white and can be made of cheesecloth. There are wings attached at the back. She also wears a halo.

Properties: Large package, string, tree ornaments, wrist watches for Angela and Mrs. Reynolds, pair of long white stockings, newspaper.

Setting: The room is furnished with tables, chairs and a couch, all of which are littered with Christmas wrappings, etc. There is a half-trimmed tree at rear of stage, and in front of it, a stepladder.

Lighting: None required.

HOME FOR CHRISTMAS

Mr. Fairchild
Mrs. Fairchild
Scotty, *a teen-ager.*
Kitty, *a junior high miss.*
Junior, *a kid brother.*
Wayne Crawford

Scene: *The living room of the Fairchild home.*

Time: *A few days before Christmas.*

HOME FOR CHRISTMAS

SETTING: *The living room of the* FAIRCHILD *home, looks like a nursery. A Kiddie Coop, a twin baby carriage and scattered toys give this impression.*

AT RISE: SCOTTY, *the teen-age daughter of the house, is arguing with her mother.*

SCOTTY: Oh, Mother, this is going to be a perfectly dreadful Christmas! Nothing is the way it should be. Wayne and I have had the most horrible fight, and...

MRS. FAIRCHILD: Not again? Tell me something new. You and Wayne Crawford fight twice a day on week days and three times on Sundays.

SCOTTY: But this is different. This time it's serious. He isn't even going to take me to the Evergreen Dance! And it's all on account of Cousin Ruth.

MRS. FAIRCHILD: Don't be silly, dear. Cousin Ruth isn't even here. She's taken the twins into the city for their monthly check up.

SCOTTY: Well, then it's the first day she hasn't been here since this time last month. Oh, Mother, can't we get rid of Cousin Ruth and those twins? They're ruining my life.

MRS. FAIRCHILD: I fail to see how poor Cousin Ruth and two eight-month-old babies could ruin your life.

SCOTTY: That's why Wayne and I quarreled. He's mad because I can never go any place or do anything with him because I've either got to stay home with the twins, or do something for Cousin Ruth. I can't even stay out late any more on week-end nights, because I'll wake up Cousin Ruth when I get home. Oh, Mother, it's simply terrible. He said a lot of mean hateful things about Cousin Ruth and the babies, and of course, I had to stick up for them because they belong to the family, and now he's mad.

MRS. FAIRCHILD: Well, if he feels so strongly on the subject, let him find an apartment for them. They'll leave fast enough if they get a place of their own.

SCOTTY: That's just what I told him, but in the meantime we suffer, while Cousin Ruth sleeps on the living room couch, and the twins and their things are all over the house. And, by the way, what about our annual Christmas Eve party for the gang? Can we go ahead with it?

MRS. FAIRCHILD: Oh, Scotty, you should know better than to ask. Just look at this room. We can hardly squeeze ourselves in here without pushing back the walls. And besides, you can't entertain a bunch of young people in the same house with small children. You know how particular Cousin Ruth is about the twins.

SCOTTY: Oh Cousin Ruth gives me the most colossal pain! The twins this and the twins that! Aren't they ever going to clear out?

MRS. FAIRCHILD: Cousin Ruth is just as eager as you are to move into a place of her own. But you know how impossible it is to get an apartment these days.

SCOTTY: Yes, I know, but my goodness, Mother, is she going to stay here forever? The twins will be in high school by the time she finds an apartment.

MRS. FAIRCHILD: That's probably an overstatement, Scotty, but I'll admit the outlook is a trifle depressing. Remember, I'm just as tired of this arrangement as anyone else, but we'll have to make the best of it. We can't very well turn our own relatives out of house and home, just because you want to

stage a Christmas Eve party. Besides, you're as daffy about
those babies as the rest of us.

SCOTTY: Oh, they're cute enough, but there's a time and a place
for everything and a Christmas Eve party is no place for
eight-month-old twins. (JUNIOR *enters carrying several large
boards and a hammer. He is in fine humor.*)

JUNIOR: Hy'all, folkses! Well, Mom, here's your general
handy man Johnny-on-the-spot. Where do you want the
platform this year?

MRS. FAIRCHILD: Platform? What platform?

JUNIOR: The platform for the Christmas tree.

MRS. FAIRCHILD: Oh, Junior, how can you stand there and talk
about putting up a Christmas tree in this room? Just look
at it.

JUNIOR AND SCOTTY: No Christmas tree?

JUNIOR: Say, what's come over you? How come no Christmas
tree?

SCOTTY: Mother, you can't mean we're not having a tree.

MRS. FAIRCHILD: A table tree, yes. But a big tree with a platform is just out of the question. (KITTY *enters carrying a
large cardboard box that seems quite heavy.*)

KITTY: Oh, there you are, Junior. You always leave me with
the heavy work. I've had to struggle up the cellar steps lug-
ging this box of animals and stuff for the Christmas tree yard,
while brother Junior skips up with nothing heavier than a
few pieces of kindling. I'm glad Christmas comes only once a
year when I have to work with Junior.

JUNIOR: Doesn't look as if it's coming to our house even once
this year.

KITTY: What kind of double talk is that?

MRS. FAIRCHILD: That's Junior's way of breaking the news
that we simply don't have room for a big tree and a Christmas
yard this year.

Scotty: On account of Cousin Ruth and the twins take up all the room.

Kitty: But the twins will adore a tree and a dear little yard.

Mrs. Fairchild: They're too young to adore anything but their food, and your "dear little yard" normally takes up half of the living room. Oh, children, be reasonable and let's make the best of a bad situation. As long as Cousin Ruth and the babies are here, we just can't expect to do things in our usual way.

Kitty: Sure, but gosh! A Christmas tree and a Christmas yard are practically sacred. We just gotta have them.

Mrs. Fairchild: And Cousin Ruth and the babies "just gotta" have a place to stay.

Scotty: So they stay and stay and stay right in our living room. (Mr. Fairchild *enters. He carries a large box and is delighted with himself.*)

Mr. Fairchild: Hello, family. The Old Man's been Christmas shopping and I'm here to tell you it was easier to establish the Anzio Beachhead than it is to secure a foothold on a downtown bus. But wait till you see what I bought!

Mrs. Fairchild: Now don't tell me you can't wait till Christmas to give out the presents. You're worse than the children.

Scotty: Gee, Dad, is it my new portable typewriter?

Junior: Bet it's a movie projector! Is it, Dad?

Kitty: Oh, Pop, did you get me a record player?

Mrs. Fairchild: I'm getting excited too! Is it some new gadget for the car?

Mr. Fairchild (*Undoing package*): Wrong! Wrong! Wrong! But it's something this family has needed for years. I made up my mind while I was in the Service that we'd never spend another Christmas without it...and here it is...the finest money can buy! (*Holds up locomotive*) And I have sixty feet of "O Gauge" track to go with it!

ALL (*With varying emotions*) : An electric train!

MRS. FAIRCHILD: Jim Fairchild, you don't mean you expect to run that electric train in this room?

MR. FAIRCHILD: You catch on quickly, Mrs. F. That's the idea exactly.

JUNIOR: Gee, Dad, that's swell. When do we start?

MR. FAIRCHILD: As soon as the track arrives. I've got a pair of switches and a cross-over so we'll really have a layout here that'll knock 'em cold. How about it, Son?

JUNIOR: Great.

MRS. FAIRCHILD: Oh for pity's sake, Jim, think what you're doing. You can't run an electric train around here in the same room with Cousin Ruth and the twins!

MR. FAIRCHILD: Why not? There's plenty of room.

MRS. FAIRCHILD: This family will drive me crazy! Isn't there anyone else besides me who can see that this room can't serve as a bedroom, a day nursery, a night nursery, a living room, a ballroom, a Christmas barnyard and a model railroad layout? There just isn't the space. Jim, you'll have to put that train away until next year. I'm horribly sorry... but... can't you see the whole thing is impossible with Cousin Ruth and the twins here?

MR. FAIRCHILD: Are you serious? Do you really mean it?

SCOTTY: She means it, and how!

KITTY: Isn't it awful, Dad? Our whole Christmas is going to be ruined on account of this darned old housing shortage.

MRS. FAIRCHILD: Kitty, you should be ashamed. We should all be ashamed to complain about sharing our home with a woman and two children during the Christmas season.

SCOTTY: But they've been here three months.

KITTY: And they're likely to be here three more if they can't find an apartment.

MR. FAIRCHILD: I guess we do sound pretty selfish, but gosh ding it, I've had my heart set on an electric train for years.

Never had one when I was a boy, and I made up my mind I'd have one this year or bust.

MRS. FAIRCHILD: Well, I guess I'm the official killjoy. Scotty's mad because I vetoed her Christmas Eve party, Kitty's injured because I said no Christmas tree yard, Junior's in the dumps because there's no room for the tree and now you look like you lost your last friend because you can't run that train. Oh, Jim, I do wish there were something we could do. Cousin Ruth hates this as much as we do. She'd give anything to be in her own home for Christmas.

MR. FAIRCHILD (*Picking up his train*): I guess I have been acting like a six-year-old...and you're perfectly right, dear, but ye Gods! Can't we find an apartment somewhere for Cousin Ruth and her offsprings?

MRS. FAIRCHILD: I wish we could...but you can imagine how much chance we'd have.

MR. FAIRCHILD: Well, come along, and find me a place in the attic to store this thing. Maybe they'll be out by Easter and we can run it around the Easter nests.

MRS. FAIRCHILD: That's an idea, Jim. We'll have to hope for the best. (MR. *and* MRS. FAIRCHILD *exit*.)

KITTY: It's a darned shame, that's what it is. Pop had his heart set on that train.

SCOTTY: And I had my heart set on that Christmas Eve party.

KITTY: Oh, that's not as important as Dad's train. You can make goo-goo eyes at Wayne Crawford any time.

SCOTTY: Don't be childish, Kitty. And besides, if you must know, Wayne and I have broken off...for keeps...this time.

JUNIOR: Ha! This is how many times you've said goodbye forever!

SCOTTY: This time it's the real McCoy. I'm through with him and I'll never speak to him again...not if he crawled over here on his hands and knees.

KITTY: Now that's something I'd really like to see.

JUNIOR: Stop scrappin' you two and let's think up some way to get Cousin Ruth and the twins into a place of their own by Christmas.

KITTY: Now who has a brain storm? How could we ever find an apartment, when Cousin Ruth has been after every real estate agent in town for weeks!

SCOTTY: Oh, Junior, do you think we could? That would settle everything. I know just how we could decorate this room for my party!

KITTY: Isn't poor old Wayne going to come to this party, I mean if you ever have it?

SCOTTY: Definitely no. I told you I'm off him for life. (*Phone rings.*)

KITTY: I'll get it. (*Goes to phone.*)

JUNIOR: Where's the morning paper? I'm going to look at the ads.

KITTY (*At phone*): Sure, she's here, Wayne. Just a minute. Scotty, it's for you.

SCOTTY: If that's Wayne Crawford, I have nothing to say to him.

KITTY: Oh, be yourself. Come and talk to the poor guy.

SCOTTY: Nothing doing.

KITTY: What'll I tell him?

SCOTTY: Tell him to fly a kite.

KITTY (*In phone*): She says you should go fly a kite....Oh, I don't know what she means, Wayne. Call back later when she's in a better mood. O.K. Goodbye.

JUNIOR (*Looking at paper*): Hey, kids, listen to this. Here's a guy arrested this afternoon for shoplifting. Does that give anybody an idea?

SCOTTY: Sure. It gives me the idea crime doesn't pay.

JUNIOR: Forget that Hunk of Heart-Break you just refused to talk to, and put your mind on more serious business. This fellow that got arrested had to live somewhere, didn't he? Well, it says here he lived at the Brandis Apartments...so what do you say we go after his apartment for Cousin Ruth?

KITTY: I bet by this time five hundred other people have the same idea. I move we advertise.

SCOTTY: Now there's something really original. I bet there are seventy-five ads in this paper right now.

KITTY: But we could make our *ad* different...dynamic... dramatic...something that would hit folks between the eyes.

JUNIOR: And who's going to write such an ad...Orson Welles?

KITTY: Oh, don't be funny. Lots of people write advertisements in rhyme...and we could write something clever...

SCOTTY: Such as...

KITTY: Well such as...let me think...Landlords, wouldn't it be shocking, to have no place to hang your stocking? Mother with two children gay, wants apartment right away. (*Yells of laughter greet this composition.*)

JUNIOR: Boy that's rich! Mother with two children gay! About the time those twins start squalling at four o'clock in the morning, let me know if you still call them gay.

SCOTTY: The thing we should do is offer to swap something for information leading to an apartment rental.

KITTY: What do we have to swap?

JUNIOR: That's the sixty-four dollar question. (*Phone rings.*)

SCOTTY: If that's Wayne again, I won't talk to him.

JUNIOR: Well, I will. (*Goes to phone*) Hello. Yeah. Hello, Wayne. I thought it was you. Yeah, she's here, but as stubborn as a mule. Sure. I'll tell her. (*To* SCOTTY) He says he's got something to tell you.

SCOTTY: I don't want to hear it.

JUNIOR: He says it's something wonderful.

SCOTTY: Nothing he could say would be wonderful to me.

JUNIOR (*To phone*): No soap, Wayne. But give her time. She'll thaw out. You know how women are. O.K. So long. (*Hangs up. Turns to the girls*) From now on, you two can answer your own phone calls. I'm going to concentrate on this apartment situation. Where's that newspaper? (*Gets paper and buries himself in it, paying only slight attention to the following conversation.*)

KITTY: What did you and Wayne fight about this time, Scotty? Is he still burned up about those flowers Dinty Brown sent you?

SCOTTY: I don't want to talk about it.

KITTY: I bet I've guessed it. Wayne's awful jealous of Dinty, and I can't see why. Dinty's an out and out drip.

SCOTTY: So is Wayne.

KITTY: The kids at school told me he's going to ask you to the Evergreen Hop.

SCOTTY: He's already asked me.

KITTY: So you gave him a date, and now Wayne is sore.

SCOTTY: No such thing. I turned him down cold. I'm not going to the old dance at all.

JUNIOR (*Springing to his feet and throwing the newspaper in the air*): Yippee, kids, I got it! I got it! The big idea!

KITTY: He's had a brainstorm.

SCOTTY: Well, let's have it and it better be good.

JUNIOR: This'll kill you at first, but believe me, it's the only way.

SCOTTY: I'd do anything to get an apartment for Cousin Ruth.

JUNIOR: Then there's your chance to prove it. Go dancing with Dinty Brown.

SCOTTY: Are you kidding?

JUNIOR: Not a bit. Go dancing, go skating, go to the movies, go any place the dear boy asks you...from now till Christmas.

SCOTTY: Why, Junior Fairchild, you're out of your mind. I

can't bear Dinty Brown. He's a sawed-off little pest and I hate him.

JUNIOR: But you'll love Dinty Brown with a deep and dog-like devotion from this day forth. Know why?

KITTY: Why?

JUNIOR: Guess where our handsome hero works every night after school and all day on Saturdays.

SCOTTY: I have no idea.

JUNIOR: At the Hathaway Apartments helping his dad.

KITTY: Junior, you're a genius. I catch on. He'd be sure to know the minute there's a vacancy, and if Scotty's extra nice to him, well...Oh, boy! It's in the bag.

SCOTTY: It is not. I'll have nothing to do with such a scheme.

JUNIOR: But, Scotty, his old man's the building superintendent.

SCOTTY: I don't care if he's the whole Housing Bureau. I'm not dating that awful Dinty Brown.

KITTY: But, Scotty...

SCOTTY: You can argue till you're blue in the face! I won't do it.

JUNIOR: O.K. Then, don't. Just sit still and see our Christmas ruined. Babies all over the house! No Christmas tree!

KITTY: No Christmas yard and no Christmas Eve party!

JUNIOR: Dad's first Christmas at home in years and he can't run a train in his own living room, all because his daughter is too selfish to try to get Cousin Ruth an apartment.

SCOTTY: That's not true. I'd do anything...but...

KITTY: Then you will?

SCOTTY: No, I won't. It isn't nice to make a fuss over Dinty and pretend I like him just to get the inside track on an apartment.

JUNIOR: But they do it all the time in the movies. To save the family fortunes, the beautiful heroine always makes some sort of sacrifice.

KITTY: It isn't as if you had to marry him...just have a few dates with the poor boy, that's all.

SCOTTY: Sure, that's all, and have Wayne mad at me for keeps.

JUNIOR: But you're off him for life anyway.

KITTY: Sure, you aren't going to speak to him ever again. He's a closed book.

JUNIOR: And besides, if you really do go around with Dinty for awhile, maybe old Wayne will get plenty jealous.

KITTY: Maybe he needs a little competition.

SCOTTY (*Weakening*): Well, maybe he does.

KITTY: Sure he does. It isn't good for any boy to take a girl for granted.

SCOTTY: Maybe you're right.

JUNIOR: Sure, she's right, for once. And the kids all say Dinty's old man gives him anything he wants.

KITTY: He lets him have his car practically all the time.

JUNIOR: So I bet he'd let a friend of Dinty's have first chance at an apartment.

SCOTTY: But how do we know there'll be a vacancy?

KITTY: There's bound to be one. Lots of people live there who work at the Silk Mill, and they're being transferred all the time.

JUNIOR: There was an apartment just last week. Gee, I'll bet old Dinty could have nabbed that one for us.

KITTY: It's worth a try, Scotty. How about it?

SCOTTY: Oh...all right. I'll go to the Evergreen Dance with him but I won't promise anything else.

KITTY (*Throwing her arms around her*): Oh, that's wonderful, Scotty. You're just like the beautiful big sister in the movies, tossing away her happiness for the sake of the family.

SCOTTY (*Half crying*): But I wouldn't want Wayne to be mad...that is — really mad.

JUNIOR: Oh, he'll get over it.

KITTY: Sure, he will.

JUNIOR (*Getting phone book*): I'll look up Dinty's number so you can call him right away.

KITTY: Before you change your mind.

SCOTTY: Oh, no, I couldn't do that.

JUNIOR: Why not?

SCOTTY: I'd get too nervous on the phone. I'll write him a note.

JUNIOR: Promise? Cross your heart?

SCOTTY: Cross my heart.

KITTY: When?

SCOTTY: Right now and I'll let you read it before I mail it. (*Starts to exit.*) But oh, dear! This is an awful price to pay for an apartment. (*Exit.*)

KITTY: Oh, Junior, do you think it will work?

JUNIOR: It can't miss. Scotty can twist Dinty around her little finger. Dinty can twist his Pop around his little finger, so the first thing we know Cousin Ruth and her terrible twins will be installed in a new home.

KITTY: Oh, it sounds wonderful. Cousin Ruth will be thrilled. That's the only thing she said she wanted for Christmas, a home of her own.

JUNIOR: Well, she'll get it, or I miss my guess. (*Doorbell*)

KITTY (*Starting to door and then coming back*): Good Heavens! It's Wayne Crawford!

JUNIOR: Don't let him in.

KITTY: Too late! He is in. What'll we do? If he sees Scotty now she'll weaken.

JUNIOR: Let me handle this. (WAYNE *enters.*)

WAYNE: Hello, you two. I knocked and walked right in. Where's Scotty?

JUNIOR: Hello, Wayne old man! You're just the boy we want to see.

WAYNE: Hy'a, Junior. Where's Scotty? I want to talk to her.

JUNIOR: Oh, I wouldn't talk to her right now, Wayne. She's in an awful mood.

WAYNE: Where is she?

JUNIOR: In her room, and she better stay there till she calms down.

KITTY: She wants to be alone.

WAYNE: Well, tell her to come down. I'm determined to have things out with her.

KITTY: Oh, I couldn't tell her to come down, Wayne. You know how she is when she's mad. Give her time to cool off.

WAYNE: She's had plenty of time to cool off. Good grief, Scotty and I have had a million fights, but we don't stay mad. I'm ready to make up.

JUNIOR: Yeah, but Scotty isn't, that's just the point.

WAYNE (*Confidently*): She will be when she hears what I have to tell her. Boy, she'll be tickled, she'll go to that Evergreen dance with me like a shot.

JUNIOR: Don't be too sure, old boy.

WAYNE: Want to bet on it?

JUNIOR: It would be like taking candy from a baby because I happen to know Scotty has other plans.

WAYNE (*Alarmed*): Other plans? You mean for the Evergreen Dance?

JUNIOR: Right.

WAYNE: Quit your kidding, Junior. Scotty's going to the dance with me. Oh, sure, we had a fight, and she got plenty sore but everything'll be O.K. if I can just talk to her.

JUNIOR: I tell you, Wayne, it's no go. And for once, I know what I'm talking about.

KITTY: He sure does, Wayne. Honest.

WAYNE: You mean she has another date?

JUNIOR: And how.

WAYNE: Who? Come on, Junior, spill it. Who's the guy?

JUNIOR: Somebody you know.

WAYNE: I'm warning you, Junior Fairchild, if this is a joke, you'll be missing a set of eye teeth.

KITTY: It isn't a joke, Wayne. Scotty's going to the dance with Dinty Brown so you might as well give up and go home!

WAYNE: Dinty Brown! That Parlor Commando! I don't believe it. She'd never walk out on me for him.

JUNIOR: It's true, Wayne. Can't you see it's best for you to go home and let Scotty alone.

WAYNE: Let Scotty alone, nothing! The idea! (*Yelling*) Scotty! Scotty Fairchild, you come right down here! (*Louder*) Scotty, do you hear? Come on down. I've got to talk to you.

SCOTTY (*Entering with note*): My goodness, what's all the racket? Why, Wayne Crawford! Of all the nerve! How did you get in here?

WAYNE: The same way I always come in, by the front door. Say, these kids tell me you're going to the Evergreen Dance with Dinty Brown. Is that true?

SCOTTY: Well...not exactly....In a way...that is....Yes, it's true. I am going with Dinty Brown. So what?

WAYNE: So what? I'll show you so what? You think you can throw me over and go to the Christmas Dance with that miserable Rover Boy, do you? All right, go ahead. Just go ahead and do it.

SCOTTY: That's what I intend to do and who's going to stop me?

WAYNE: Nobody, nobody at all. But you'll be plenty sorry, that's all I have to say.

SCOTTY: Is that a threat?

WAYNE: That's a threat and a promise. Going to that dance with Eager Beaver Brown is going to cost you and your Cousin Ruth the swellest little three-room apartment in town ...so go ahead and enjoy yourself. I hope you have a wonderful time. Goodbye. (*Starts to exit.*)

SCOTTY: Oh, Wayne, Wayne! Wait! Let me explain.

KITTY: Oh, Junior, Junior, grab him. Don't let him get away.

JUNIOR: Hey, Wayne, wait, wait! Don't fly off the handle! Wait a minute. We can explain everything. (*He makes a flying lunge and grabs hold of* WAYNE. *The two girls join in the rush and pull the reluctant* WAYNE *back on the stage.*)

SCOTTY: Oh, Wayne, please believe me. I wasn't going with Dinty Brown because I wanted to. Honest.

KITTY: No, honest, Wayne, we were making her go. It was Junior's idea.

WAYNE: Why you two-timing little monster! Wait till I get my hands on you.

JUNIOR: Now hold your horses, Wayne old boy!

WAYNE: And stop calling me old boy and old man. In fact don't call me anything. Just let me out of here.

SCOTTY: Please, Wayne, I was only going with Dinty to get him to use his influence with his Dad to give Cousin Ruth an apartment.

WAYNE: And I suppose you think *my* influence doesn't count?

KITTY: She didn't know you had any, any influence, I mean.

JUNIOR: Be reasonable, Wayne. She did it for us, her family.

KITTY: It was a great sacrifice...like in the movies.

SCOTTY: And anyhow, I haven't actually told him I'd go.

WAYNE: What do you mean, you haven't told him?

SCOTTY: Here's my note telling him I'd reconsider his invitation. But, of course, if we make up, and if you really and truly do know of an apartment for Cousin Ruth, I'll never send it.

WAYNE: Give me that note.

SCOTTY: With pleasure. Oh, Wayne, I never did want to go with him. Cross my heart and hope to die!

WAYNE: Honest injun? (*Puts note in pocket.*)

SCOTTY: Honest injun.

WAYNE: And you'll go with me after all?

SCOTTY: Sure, I will, if you ask me. You said you'd never ask me. Remember?

WAYNE: Oh, I was mad when I said that. And I'm sorry I was so pig-headed about your Cousin Ruth and the twins.

SCOTTY: Then we've made up?

WAYNE: We sure have. And I feel like a new man.

JUNIOR (*Clearing his throat*): If I could interrupt you two love birds, what about this apartment business?

WAYNE: Simple as ABC. When I got home this afternoon, there was Mother chiming away with Mrs. Hinkle who lives down the street, and when I walked in, she was just moaning to Mother about her wonderful tenants being transferred to New York. She was dead sure she'd never get such a lovely family in her apartment. Boy oh boy, it didn't take me two minutes to sell her on the idea of Cousin Ruth. I've already made a date for her to go look at the apartment tonight, if she gets home in time.

SCOTTY: Oh, Wayne, that's wonderful, Mrs. Hinkle's wonderful, you're wonderful.

KITTY: Wait till I tell the family. (*Runs off stage calling her mother and father to come hear the big news.*)

JUNIOR: My hat's off to you, Wayne, old kid, old kid! You're the best real estate agent in town. Cousin Ruth ought to give you a commission.

WAYNE: I have a good notion to make you eat this note to Dinty Brown, but since it's so close to Christmas I'll stick to peace and good will.

JUNIOR (*Offering his hand*): Put it here, old boy, and let's call it a day. (MR. *and* MRS. FAIRCHILD *enter with* KITTY.)

MRS. FAIRCHILD: Is it really true?

MR. FAIRCHILD: Lead me to this Wonder-Boy-Crawford! (*Shakes hands with* WAYNE) It looks as if you've given

Cousin Ruth and her family a wonderful present, a home for Christmas.

JUNIOR: And he's given us a wonderful Christmas. Now we can have our tree.

KITTY: And the Christmas yard.

SCOTTY: And I can have the gang for a real Christmas Eve party.

MR. FAIRCHILD: And I can run my train around and around and around.

WAYNE (*Looking at* SCOTTY): And I can tear up this letter (*Starts to tear it up...hesitates and looks at it again.*) Ye gods! I almost made a mistake. This isn't Dinty's letter. This is one I picked up in the letter slot as I came in. It's for you, Mrs. Fairchild.

MRS. FAIRCHILD (*Examining letter*) Dear me, it's from my sister Annabel in Cleveland. I guess it's her regular Christmas letter... (*Opening it and scanning it rapidly*) Oh my goodness... (*Collapses on sofa.*) Read it, somebody...I can't.

MR. FAIRCHILD: What's wrong? Is somebody sick? (*Takes letter and reads aloud*) Dear Sis: You'll be surprised to know that Ed has been transferred to San Francisco. He's been out there a month and not an apartment in sight. Our own place here has been sold and we must be out this week. I am writing in desperation. Could you possibly arrange to let me and the children stay with you until after Christmas, or until Ed finds a house? We'll try not to be any trouble...

KITTY: Oh my sainted Aunt!

JUNIOR: Sufferin' cat fish!

MR. FAIRCHILD (*Reading from letter*): I can sleep on the day bed in the living room and the girls could bunk with Kitty and Scotty. As for Henry, maybe he could sleep with Junior.

JUNIOR: That will be cozy!

SCOTTY: Oh, Mother.... What'll we do?

MR. FAIRCHILD: Listen. (*Reading*) I hate to ask you, but you have no idea how awful it is to be crowded out of your own place. If we could just have a home for Christmas...

MRS. FAIRCHILD: A home for Christmas! Oh, the poor dears! We just can't turn them down, can we?

MR. FAIRCHILD: Well, kids, what do you say?

JUNIOR: It's O.K. by me, Pop.

KITTY: Let 'em come, Dad. Christmas is Christmas in this house no matter how many extras sleep in the living room.

SCOTTY: I'm game, too, as long as Wayne sticks by us.

MR. FAIRCHILD: Well, Wayne, it looks as if your real estate deal came through in the nick of time.

WAYNE: This seems to be where I came in, sir... but from what I know of this family, those people couldn't do better than come home for Christmas with the Fairchilds.

THE END

PRODUCTION NOTES

HOME FOR CHRISTMAS

Characters: 3 male; 3 female.

Playing Time: 35 minutes.

Costumes: Everyday modern dress.

Properties: Several large boards, a hammer, large cardboard box, a large box containing an electric train, newspaper, two letters.

Setting: Though this is the living room of an average American home, it should look more like a nursery. A baby's play-yard, a twin baby carriage or two carriages are placed in the room along with regular living room furniture including a couch. Toys are scattered about the room. The impression of a very over-crowded room should be given.

Lighting: None required.

THE MISSING LINC

Characters

MISS GRAY, *an irate librarian.*
PEGGY STONE, *a loyal sister.*
MARTIN STONE, *a writer and Lincoln scholar.*
MARTHA STONE, *an understanding stepmother.*
MR. SAWYER, *an outraged parent.*
FREDDIE SAWYER, *an outraged son.*
LINCOLN STONE, *the Missing "Linc."*

SCENE: *The living room of the Stone family.*

TIME: *The present.*

THE MISSING LINC

SETTING: *Living room of the* STONE *family.*

AT RISE: *A bell is ringing in a loud, insistent manner.* PEGGY, *the seventh-grade daughter of the family, enters on a run to answer the door.*

PEGGY: Oh, dear! I hope that bell hasn't disturbed father.

FATHER (*Off stage*): Can't somebody in this house answer that infernal bell? Martha! Peggy! Where are you? Answer that bell!

PEGGY: Martha's out, Father. I'll get it.

FATHER: And if it's anyone for me....I'm seeing no one this afternoon. No one!

PEGGY: Yes, Father. I understand. (*Goes to door.*) Oh, Miss Gray! I'm so surprised to see you. Please come in. (PEGGY *re-enters with a tall, dignified woman carrying a book that looks as if it had been in a mud puddle instead of on a library shelf.*)

MISS GRAY: Thank you, Peggy. I've come to see your father.

PEGGY: Oh, I'm sorry, Miss Gray, but Father can't see anyone. He's just at a ticklish place in his book right now and we hardly ever see him ourselves. He spends every minute at his typewriter.

MISS GRAY: I am well aware, Peggy, that your Father is a famous Lincoln scholar and a great writer, but he is also a taxpayer and the father of a son, so I must insist upon seeing him.

PEGGY: Oh, but Miss Gray, you don't understand. We never disturb Father when he's working. Why, even when Linc and I were babies, we knew better than to cry when we heard Father's typewriter.

MISS GRAY: It's about your brother that I have come. Just look at this book. (*Holds it in front of* PEGGY, *who draws back in alarm.*) Go ahead. Look at it. I just want you to see the state of this book that your brother returned to the library.

PEGGY: Yes, Miss Gray, I see it. *The Almighty Atom* by John O'Neil. Linc is always reading books on chemistry, and he's read everything he can find on the atomic bomb. He's awfully smart for his age.

MISS GRAY: He might be smart for his age, but he's not smart when it comes to taking care of books. This isn't the first book he has misused like this. What could he possibly do to a book to make it look like this?

PEGGY: Well, er — you see, Miss Gray, Linc is a perfectly awful bookworm. He reads every place and any place he happens to be...and well...he invented a rack to hold a book so he could read in the bathtub...and, well...I guess it must have slipped.

MISS GRAY: That sounds exactly like him. *Organic Chemistry* has a hole in it this big where he spilled sulphuric acid on it and *The Boy Scientist* is warped because he laid it on a radiator.

PEGGY: Oh, that was my fault, Miss Gray. I didn't see it when I turned on the heat in his room. Please don't blame Linc for that.

MISS GRAY: I have no patience with people who are careless with books.

PEGGY: But Linc isn't careless, Miss Gray, he's just unlucky. He's so crazy about reading that he forgets everything else.

MISS GRAY: Then he should be taught how to remember. This book is brand new and it's completely ruined. Your father will have to pay for it.

PEGGY: Oh, my goodness! Miss Gray, you wouldn't tell Father about that book.

MISS GRAY: Why not? That's exactly why I came!

PEGGY: Oh, but Father is so busy and he's so...not exactly cross, but edgy because his book isn't going well. And besides, he doesn't understand Linc sometimes. Oh, Miss Gray, you wouldn't want to see my brother get into trouble, would you?

MISS GRAY: I just want this book replaced.

PEGGY: Well, then, couldn't you let Linc pay for the book himself out of his allowance? He could pay it in installments.

MISS GRAY: He already owes the library four dollars and ninety-two cents which he is paying off in installments. No, Peggy, I must insist on settling this with your father. I told Lincoln that the very next time he damaged one of our books, I would take it up with his father, and I mean to keep my word.

PEGGY: Well, couldn't you come back again, some other day when Father is less upset? You see, he is already cross at Linc because of something that happened this morning, and well...if this breaks on top of everything else, I don't know what he might do. He might even send him away to school. That's what he's threatening to do anyhow.

MISS GRAY: And it might be a very good thing. What that boy needs is discipline.

PEGGY: Oh, but he would hate it! It would just break his heart to leave high school now when he's President of the chemistry club and on the debating team and science editor of the *Weekly*. Oh, please, Miss Gray, don't talk to Father now. If you must talk to somebody, wait till Martha comes home. She's our stepmother. She's good at fixing things up for Linc. Or better yet, I'll pay for the book myself. I'm going to start being a baby-sitter tomorrow and then I'll have lots of money.

Miss Gray: You are a very staunch admirer of your brother, aren't you, Peggy? It's not often that a sister defends her brother so loyally.

Peggy: It's not often a sister has a brother like Linc. Oh, he's wonderful, Miss Gray, and I'd just die if he went away to school. Since mother died, we always stick together on everything.

Miss Gray (*Smiling*): I can see that. Well...for your sake, I'll not go to your father this time. I won't even wait to see your stepmother. But you be sure to tell Lincoln Stone for me that he has till the end of next week to pay his library bill in full.

Peggy: Gee! Thanks, Miss Gray. You're a peach and he'll pay it too, every cent. He has a job after school now, working for Mr. Phipps at the drug store.

Miss Gray: Humph! He'll probably be reading the comic books at the newsstand when he should be waiting on customers. But I've worried you enough, child. After all, you're not responsible for your brother's misdeeds. Now, I'll be off, but don't forget to tell him that the very next time...

Peggy: Yes, I will, Miss Gray, and thanks a million.

Miss Gray: Goodbye. (*Exits*)

Peggy (*Sinking in a chair*): That was a close call.

Mr. Stone (*Entering. He is polishing his glasses. He looks worried. His hair is rumpled and his shirt collar is open*): I thought I heard voices. Who was at the door?

Peggy: Oh, I'm sorry we disturbed you, Father. It was Miss Gray.

Mr. Stone: Miss Gray? Miss Gray? I don't know any Miss Gray.

Peggy: She's our school librarian and she's really awfully nice.

Mr. Stone: Indeed! Has that brother of yours come home yet?

PEGGY: Not yet, Father. Remember he has a job now with Mr. Phipps.

MR. STONE: Oh, yes. I had forgotten. Well, the minute he comes in, I want to see him. Don't forget. The very minute he comes in.

PEGGY: Even if you're working?

MR. STONE: Even if I'm working. Send him in.

PEGGY (*Anxiously*): Is anything wrong?

MR. STONE: Is anything wrong? There's always something wrong where that rapscallion is concerned. I met Miss Harmon, his English teacher, downtown at noon. She showed me a composition he wrote.

PEGGY: Wasn't it all right, Father? Linc does pretty well with compositions. But that Miss Harmon marks awfully hard. She takes off for every little comma and period and if you don't leave a margin...well...she just beats her gums at you something fierce.

MR. STONE (*Horrified*): Margaret Ann Stone! Where did you pick up that coarse, vulgar expression?

PEGGY: What? Beats her gums? Oh, Father, that's nothing. All the kids say it.

MR. STONE: Well no daughter of mine is going to talk like that. It's bad enough that a son of mine should hand in a composition like this. (*Pulls paper from pocket*) Look at it.

PEGGY: *An Atomic Headache*...That's a good title, isn't it?

MR. STONE: I'm not concerned with the title....See what it's written on...the telephone bill!

PEGGY: Oh my goodness! I remember now. Linc got the idea for that composition on the way to school on the bus. There wasn't any paper so I gave him that old receipted telephone bill. It happened to be in my purse. I guess he didn't have time to recopy it.

MR. STONE: It's just another example of his carelessness. I

honestly don't know what will become of your brother if he doesn't soon straighten himself out. He's got his nose in a book and his head in a cloud of chemicals most of the time.

PEGGY: But Father, you like books, too. You even write them.

MR. STONE: It's all right to like books and I'm glad the boy has a brain, but he must learn to pay some attention to the practical side of life. What he needs is the discipline of a good school; and if he gives me much more trouble, I'm packing him off to Norden Academy in spite of you and Martha.

PEGGY: Oh, please, Father. Don't send Linc away now. Martha says he's just at the forgetful age. He'll outgrow it.

MR. STONE: Outgrow it! All that boy outgrows are his pants and shoes. Well, I must get back to the grind. Remember to send him in as soon as he comes home.

PEGGY: Isn't the book going well?

MR. STONE: It isn't going at all. The last three chapters came back again yesterday. I must revise them.

PEGGY: Those old publishers make me sick. They always liked your work before. Why are they so fussy now? Why gee whiz, you know more about Abraham Lincoln than all the history books put together.

MR. STONE: I guess that's the trouble. Maybe I know too many facts. They keep telling me they want more human interest, more atmosphere...more...but you don't understand all this talk.

PEGGY: I understand well enough that you're having trouble. It must be terrible to write pages and pages and pages and then write them all over again.

MR. STONE: And some chapters I've rewritten four and five times. Maybe I've just lost my knack of writing.

PEGGY: Martha says you're tired and working too hard.

MR. STONE (*Smiling*): Oh, Martha babies me almost as much as she babies Linc. (*Doorbell*) Run along and answer the door, Peggy Ann, and if it's anybody for me...I am officially out. (*Starts to exit as* PEGGY *starts to the door; but before either one has left the stage,* MR. SAWYER *enters, pushing his son* FREDERICK *ahead of him.* FREDERICK *is much the worse for wear. His shirt is torn, his clothes are dirty and he has a beautiful black eye. He is also half in tears.* MR. SAWYER *is in a towering rage.*)

MR. SAWYER: I demand to see Mr. Stone at once....At once, do you hear?

PEGGY: I was just coming to answer the door. My father is busy.

MR. SAWYER: I refuse to stand on ceremony. (*Catching sight of* MR. STONE) Oh, there you are, Mr. Stone.

MR. STONE: Your business must be very urgent, sir, if you couldn't wait for my daughter to answer the bell.

MR. SAWYER: Urgent is right. I'm Jim Sawyer and this is my boy, Freddie. I want you to take a good look at him.

PEGGY: He looks as if he's been in a fight.

MR. STONE: And on the losing side, I should say.

MR. SAWYER: Exactly so. And the big bully who made this attack on my boy, Mr. Stone, is your son.

MR. STONE: My son? Lincoln? Are you sure?

PEGGY: Oh my goodness!

MR. SAWYER: Of course, I'm sure. Freddie, speak up and tell Mr. Stone exactly what happened.

FREDDIE (*Sniffling*): Aw, I just went in the drug store after school and...

MR. SAWYER: Go on. Go on.

FREDDIE: And some other boys came in and we started to have some fun and then we got into a little argument and...

MR. STONE: An argument with my son?

FREDDIE: No. With some other boys and then, Linc, the great big old bully, had to butt in. He thinks he owns the place

now just because he works there. Well, then, he starts pushin'
me around and then he slugs me...right in the eye too.

MR. SAWYER: I shall speak to his employer, Mr. Phipps. This
will cost him his job.

PEGGY: Excuse me, Mr. Sawyer, but don't be too sure of that.
It just depends on who those other guys are. (*To* FREDDIE)
Were they Shorty Mullins and Lefty Ryan?

FREDDIE: If they were, so what?

PEGGY: Were they?

FREDDIE: Yeah. Want to make something out of it?

PEGGY: No, but Mr. Phipps will make something out of it.
Those boys and Freddie hang out at that drug store every
night just to make trouble.

FREDDIE: Aw, we do not.

PEGGY: You do so. You push the little kids off the stools at the
soda fountain, upset the chairs, and start a roughhouse. I
heard Mr. Phipps tell them just the other day he'd throw
them out if they started any more trouble. I guess he was
out, so Linc did it for him.

MR. STONE: Maybe this puts a different light on things, Mr.
Sawyer. I am sure you want to be fair, so why not check
with Mr. Phipps? You may use my phone.

MR. SAWYER: No, I'll see him in person and if your daughter's
story is true, I'll have something to say to this fellow.(*Glares
at* FREDDIE.)

FREDDIE: Aw, gee whiz, Pop! She's just lyin' for him 'cause
she's his sister.

MR. SAWYER: Well, Mr. Phipps isn't his sister. He'll tell the
truth. Mr. Stone, I trust you will forgive this intrusion.
I am afraid I was pretty hot under the collar.

MR. STONE: Certainly, sir, and I will question Lincoln when
he comes home. If there has been any bullying, you can rest
assured it won't happen again.

MR. SAWYER: Thank you, sir. (*To* FREDDIE) Now come along, you, and we'll talk to Mr. Phipps.

FREDDIE (*Protesting*): Aw, gee whiz, Pop! (*His father gives him a shove as they exit.*)

PEGGY: This has been a dreadful day for poor Linc.

MR. STONE: Yes, a bad day all around, but in this instance, I am inclined to side with the boy.

PEGGY: I'm glad. Those kids make me sick. They're always picking on somebody and when they picked on Linc they got the wrong boy.

MR. STONE: I wonder why he is so late. It's almost supper time and Martha isn't home either.

MARTHA (*Enters on that line. She wears coat and hat and carries a purse, a suit box and another package*): Speak of the angels and they appear! Here I am. Who was that cross man with the weepy boy I passed on the walk? Friends of ours?

MR. STONE: Not exactly. Just more complaints about Lincoln. It seems he has now gone in for pugilism.

MARTHA: From the looks of his opponent he must be doing all right.

PEGGY: You look as if you've been shopping.

MARTHA: I have. And I want you to see what I bought. (*Opens suit box and holds up a boy's suit*) A present for Linc.

PEGGY: Gee, that's neat! He'll love that.

MR. STONE: But, Martha! A new suit!

MARTHA: Goodness knows he needs one. His clothes are a wreck. Acid holes, ink stains...and he simply ruined his good brown suit last night when he climbed that telephone pole to get the Jones's kitten.

MR. STONE: Martha, you'll have to take that suit back.

MARTHA: Take it back! But it's his birthday present. Have you forgotten the boy's birthday?

MR. STONE: Of course not.   But you can't give him a suit.

MARTHA: Why not?   It's a useful present.

MR. STONE: Because I told Lincoln only this morning that he would have to wear that brown suit just as it was.   He had no business climbing a telephone pole in his best clothes.

MARTHA: But the Joneses asked him to.   The cat was arousing the neighborhood.

MR. STONE: I'm sorry.   But I'm not going back on my word. He is to wear his old suit.

MARTHA (*Putting suit into box and handing it to* PEGGY): Take this upstairs, Peggy, and lay it on my bed.   And while you're up there, you better wrap up the present we bought together last week...the chemistry book.

PEGGY (*Starting to exit*): O.K., Martha.

MARTHA: Really, Martin, you are being most unreasonable.

MR. STONE: Unreasonable!   Can't a man try to enforce a little discipline?   If Lincoln can't learn to take care of his clothes, he'll have to put up with the consequences.

MARTHA: Oh, Martin, I wish you would try to be more understanding.   Linc has his faults but most of his troubles come from perfectly good motives.   (*Phone*)

MR. STONE: I'll get it.   (*In phone*) Hello.   Yes, Martin Stone speaking.   Oh, Mr. Phipps!   Well, what can I do for you? What?   Lincoln?   No, he isn't here.   We thought he was working a bit late.   What?   He left early?   Why, no.   We haven't seen him.   I have no idea where he might be.   I'll have him call you as soon as he comes in.   Isn't in any trouble, is he?   (*Pause*) Oh...the fight.   Yes, we heard about that. Did Mr. Sawyer pay you a visit?   He did, eh?   Well, I'm glad you told him you were pleased.   I'll be sure to tell Linc. Thanks a lot.   Goodbye.   (*Hangs up receiver*) Now where could that boy be? Mr. Phipps says he left the store early. Now there's another example of his thoughtlessness. Late for supper again.

MARTHA: I wonder if he might be over at Jim Blainey's. I've a notion to call.

MR. STONE: And tell him to come home at once. I've plenty to say to him.

MARTHA (*At phone*): 53368, please. (*To* MR. STONE) I do hope he is there. (*At phone*) Hello! Oh, Jim, this is Mrs. Stone. Is Linc there? (*Pause*) He isn't? What? You saw him where? Getting on a Greyhound Bus? Are you sure? Did you talk to him? (*Pause*) Well...all right. No, no, I won't worry. (*Hangs up.*) Not much, I won't worry. What do you think of that, Martin? Do you suppose Linc is running away? Jim saw him get on the westbound bus.

MR. STONE: This is the last straw. Positively the last straw! I told you all along that boy should be away at school where he would learn some discipline.

MARTHA: Discipline! Discipline! Of course, he needs discipline, but he needs more than that. He needs understanding, too. Oh, Martin, your publishers are right. You just don't understand boys.

MR. STONE: What do my publishers have to do with this?

MARTHA: Plenty. (*Handing him package and envelope*) Here are more chapters of your book back for revision. And here is a letter. Read it.

MR. STONE: This is no time for letters.

MARTHA: It's the right time for this one. Go on. Read it.

MR. STONE (*Reading*): My dear Mr. Stone: Your *Boy's Life of Abraham Lincoln* is another fine example of scholarly writing, but it lacks the insight and understanding of boyhood necessary to appeal to young readers. We suggest that you retell the story from the viewpoint of an adolescent boy, injecting more human interest into the narrative and a more sympathetic attitude toward the boy's problems.

MARTHA: Oh, don't you see, Martin, you can't picture Abraham Lincoln as a real live boy because you don't understand what makes a real boy tick. If you don't understand your own fifteen-year-old Lincoln, how could you understand that other fifteen-year-old boy who lived so long ago? After all, boys are boys whether they're making history or just making trouble.

MR. STONE: Maybe you're right, Martha. Maybe I'm a failure as a writer and as a father.

MARTHA: Nonsense! You just have the wrong slant that's all. Try to understand Linc a little better and you'll get closer to the other Lincoln too. Just pretend you're writing about Linc instead of a famous person and you'll get along fine.

MR. STONE: I must say, I fail to see any similarity between them.

MARTHA: Then you must be blind as a bat. You're so busy making Lincoln a great person that you forget he was ever just a boy. I bet his own family and the neighbors didn't think any more of Tom Lincoln's son than they think of ours. To them he was just a long-legged boy and a pesty one at that.

MR. STONE: You act as if I don't love Linc just because I can't see any signs of greatness in him.

MARTHA: That's just because you are his father. I bet Thomas Lincoln was disgusted with that overgrown son of his many a time. (*Reading from manuscript*) Take this for example. "The boy Lincoln was hungry for books. Upon one occasion when rain came in at the chinks of the loft where he slept, and ruined a book he had borrowed from a neighbor, he pulled fodder for two days to pay for it." That sounds very noble in a book, doesn't it? But I'll bet his Dad was mad as hops at his carelessness...just the way you feel when our Linc has an accident with a book or has to pay a library fine.

MR. STONE (*Smiling*) : You should have been a lawyer. I never thought of that. Perhaps I should write a note to Linc's English teacher reminding her that President Lincoln scribbled the Gettysburg address on a torn scrap of wrapping paper. Then maybe she'd be more tolerant of the theme Linc jotted down on the back of the telephone bill.

MARTHA : It's not so far-fetched as you think. What about that fight with the Sawyer boy? Remember chapter ten in your new book?

MR. STONE : Certainly. That's about the fight between young Lincoln and John Johnston. When he cleaned him up, he took on William Grisby, who was something of a bully, and really trimmed him.

MARTHA : Exactly. In a book, that's the way heroes are born, but in real life that's the way a boy gets into trouble.

MR. STONE : I'm not too blind to see your point, Martha, and it's a good one.

MARTHA : And this new suit business is just one more point. In this book you rave about Lincoln's kindness to animals. You even tell about how he dismounted from his horse and waded through mud to rescue a little pig that was stuck under a rail fence. How do you suppose his clothes looked after that good deed?

MR. STONE (*Smiling*) : Considerably worse than Linc's brown suit, I imagine. Yes, Martha. I see your point. I've made the mistake of expecting Linc to be a model boy and I've made my boy Lincoln too much of a model to be human. Maybe that's the trouble with fathers and historians.... Well, perhaps I can improve on both. (*Calling*) Peggy...

PEGGY (*Off stage*) : Yes, Father.

MR. STONE : Bring that new suit down here, right away, please.

PEGGY : O.K., Dad. In a jiffy.

MARTHA : Oh, Martin...I'm so worried and upset about that

boy. Suppose he has run off. Shouldn't we call the police or send out a searching party, or something?

Mr. Stone: Now who's talking nonsense? One minute you give me a pep talk and convince me that Linc and Abe are cut out of the same pattern and the next minute you are talking about the police. I might be a washout in some respects but I have enough confidence in Linc to know that he is not a runaway.

Peggy (*Entering with suit box*): Here it is. What shall I do with it?

Mr. Stone (*Reaching in his pocket*): Just open it and take out the trousers. I have a contribution for his hip pocket. (*Hands her a bill.*) The pockets of a new suit should never be empty, Peggy, and here's a ten spot that will wish him a happy birthday.

Peggy: Gee, Dad, you are generous. I won't have a birthday for six months.

Mr. Stone: Then I'll have six months longer to save up for yours.

Martha: That's wonderful of you, Martin. Now take that upstairs, Peggy, and wrap it in the gift paper. Hurry...(*As Peggy starts to exit with the box, Linc enters. They almost collide in the doorway.*)

Linc: Hey, there! Where's the fire?

Peggy: Oh, dear...Let me go, Linc....I have to wrap this box...

Linc (*Holding her playfully*): Wrap a box? What box? Fee, fo, fi, fum...I smell a birthday present. Am I right?

Martha: Right. The jig's up, Peggy. He's caught us in the act. But run along and fix it up pretty and he can open it at the dinner table. (*Exit Peggy.*)

Mr. Stone: If we ever get to the dinner table. Which reminds me...Where in the world have you been? Martha has been worried sick.

LINC: Worried? What about?

MARTHA: About you, silly. Jim Blainey said he saw you get on a Greyhound bus.

LINC: So he did. The driver's a friend of mine and he gave me a lift out to Glendale.

MR. STONE: Glendale? Why did you traipse way out there before you came home to supper?

LINC (*Embarrassed*): Oh...gee...well...honest, Dad, you always catch up with me in all my dopey mistakes. You see... Mrs. Atkins came in the store and bought a roll of number 126 film. She had no more than left when I discovered I had given her number 112 instead. So there wasn't anything else to do but go out there and make it right.

MARTHA: For mercy's sake! Did you hold our dinner just to go way out to Glendale with a roll of film?

LINC: Why, sure. It was my mistake and 112 wouldn't work in her camera.

MARTHA: But couldn't you have mailed it to her or exchanged it later?

MR. STONE (*Laughing*): You forget, my dear, that boys named *Lincoln* take their store-keeping responsibilities too seriously to let dinner or distance interfere with duty. Let's see now... how far did the young storekeeper, Abraham Lincoln, walk to return a penny change to a customer?

MARTHA: You're making fun of me, Martin Stone.

MR. STONE: Not a bit of it! I'm only proving that for once I do understand.

LINC: Gee, Dad, I was afraid you might be sore because I'm so late. Is the book going better?

MR. STONE: It will go better from tonight on, Son, with your help.

LINC: With my help! Gosh, Dad! History isn't my line. Now if it was chemistry.

MR. STONE: It is chemistry, in a way. I want you to teach me the formula for a harum-scarum, real live American boy and what makes him tick.

PEGGY (*Entering*): I'm hungry. When do we eat?

MARTHA: As soon as you set the table and I fry the chops.

MR. STONE: Sooner than that. Just as soon as we can jump in the car and drive down to the Mayflower Inn. We're dining out tonight in honor of Linc's birthday.

PEGGY: That's swell!

LINC: Thanks a lot, Dad.

MR. STONE: And after dinner, how about going bowling with me, Linc, if the women folks can put in their time at a movie?

LINC: O.K. by me, Dad.

MARTHA: But, Martin, don't you want to work on your book this evening?

MR. STONE: I'll be working on it every minute. I'll be getting better acquainted with my hero. Go on, everybody. Get your hats. I'm hungry. (*Exit*)

PEGGY: Blow me down! Dad's in a wonderful humor. What happened to him, Martha?

LINC: I was afraid old man Sawyer might have him upset about that fight down at the store. But he seems to understand.

MARTHA: I guess he understands us all better than we think. He understands his work too and the great man he is writing about. Yes, Linc, your father is a very understanding man.

PEGGY: He seems changed somehow.

MARTHA: Changed? How?

PEGGY: Oh, I don't know, just changed.

MR. STONE (*At door*): Are you people going to stand there beating your gums all evening or are you going to let me take you out for dinner?

MARTHA (*Moving to door*): Right away, dear.

PEGGY (*To* LINC *in amazement*) : Is he changed?
LINC (*Equally amazed and pleased*) : And how !

THE END

PRODUCTION NOTES

The Missing Linc

Characters: 4 male; 3 female.

Playing Time: 30 minutes.

Costumes: Modern everyday clothes. Mr. Stone does not wear the jacket to his suit. Martha wears a hat and coat when she enters.

Properties: Book; eye-glasses for Mr. Stone; paper for receipted bill; suitbox, containing boy's suit; package containing manuscript; envelope with letter; purse for Martha; paper bill.

Setting: Modern American living room with comfortable furniture. There is a sofa at one side of the stage, with chairs and tables with lamps placed about the room.

Lighting: None required.

MISS LONELYHEART

Characters

MRS. FAIRCHILD, *sympathetic mother.*
JUNIOR, *seventh-grade schemer.*
SCOTTY, *lonely ninth-grader.*
KITTY, *precocious young sister.*

JOE MATHEWS ⎤
SAM FISHER ⎥
             ⎬ *four lonelyhearts.*
BILL MOYER ⎥
PHILIP ROGERS ⎦

SCENE: *The living room of the Fairchild residence.*

TIME: (Scene 1) *A few days before Valentine's Day.*

(Scene 2) *The following Tuesday evening, Valentine's Day.*

MISS LONELYHEART

Scene 1

Setting: *The living room of the Fairchild residence.*

At Rise: Mrs. Fairchild *is reading while* Junior, *aged twelve, and* Kitty, *aged ten, are doing their homework at the living room table.*

Junior: Have a heart, Moms. It's almost 8:30. Can't I please listen to the Gravediggers' Program?

Mother: Have you finished studying that poem for English class?

Junior: Gosh no! "Ode to a Grecian Urn." What's a Grecian urn anyhow?

Kitty (*Brightly*): It seems to me that would depend on the kind of work he was doing. Some Grecians must earn more than others. (Mrs. Fairchild *and* Junior *laugh.*)

Junior: Of all the drips I ever saw, you're the moldiest. u-r-n urn...Not e-a-r-n.

Kitty: Well, why didn't you spell it for me in the first place? How was I to know?

Mother: Never mind, Kitty, your big brother doesn't know either. That's why he asked the question. A Grecian urn happens to be a vase. Now let's drop the subject.

Junior: Yeah. Let's drop it and smash it to smithereens. But to get back to the Gravediggers' Program....

MOTHER: You're not going to get back to the Gravediggers' Program. You're going to get back to that homework. Kitty has been setting you a fine example. She's been working on her geography all evening. (*Rises and picks up one of* KITTY's *papers out of her geography book.*) What country have you been working on, dear?

KITTY (*Trying vainly to rescue her paper*): Oh, that's nothing. That's just...Oh, dear!

MOTHER (*Reading aloud*):
Please be my valentine, Donald Pierce,
Because I love you something fierce!
(*Loud laughter from* JUNIOR.)
Why, Kitty Fairchild! What does this mean? Your whole paper is covered with this drivel!
I'd cross the desert on my knees
If you, my darling, I could please!
(*More laughter from* JUNIOR *and signs of distress from* KITTY.)
I live at Elm Street—29,
So come and be my valentine.

JUNIOR (*In spasms of laughter*): Oh! This is killing me. And you thought she was setting me a good example!

KITTY: Oh shut up! Mother, please don't read any more. Please! Give them back to me. You're not supposed to let anyone else read your valentines.

MOTHER: Don't tell me you are actually going to send these mushy verses to some little boy!

KITTY: Of course. They're for our valentine box at school. Please, Mother, let me finish. I have fifteen more to do.

MOTHER: Fifteen! Gracious Heaven! There are at least five or six on this paper.

KITTY: I know. But there are twenty-one boys in our class, and I'm writing a different valentine for each one.

JUNIOR: Who do you think you are anyway? Dorothy Lamour and Hedy Lamarr combined?

MOTHER: I must say, that's an ambitious program for such a little girl. Now when I was your age I wouldn't have dreamed of sending valentines to twenty-one boys.

KITTY: It was different when you were young. You probably had twenty-one boys all lined up to send valentines to you; but in my case it's different. A girl has to get acquainted somehow. After all, we've lived here only three weeks, and that's not long enough to get any boys to send me valentines. So I just made up my mind, I'd sort of break the ice.

MOTHER: I suppose it is hard for you children. Just about the time you begin to make friends in one school, your father is transferred to another town, and then it's all to be done over again. It's too bad.

JUNIOR: Aw, we get along O.K. And we're not the only ones. A lot of families are moving around these days. We just got to learn how to make friends and influence people, that's all.

MOTHER: I'm glad you can take it in your stride, Junior, and you too, Kitty, even if I don't entirely approve of twenty-one valentines. I only wish Scotty would take a tip from you two youngsters. I have a feeling she's been pretty miserable since we moved here to Adamsford.

JUNIOR: Yeah, she has been sort of droopy lately. Where is she tonight, anyway? Don't tell me she finally got herself a date.

KITTY: No such luck. She went down to the library. Had to look up some school work.

MOTHER: Poor Scotty! She was so popular last year at Cartersville. I know how wretched she must be here. (*Sound of door*)

KITTY: Sh! Here she comes, and she'll be mad as hops if she thinks we've been talking about her. (SCOTTY, *a pretty girl of fifteen, enters. She carries a pile of books and a hankie which she uses frequently, as if she has had a recent attack of tears or hayfever.*)

SCOTTY: Hello, everybody. I'm back.

JUNIOR: So we see.

KITTY: Did you have fun?

SCOTTY (*Bitterly*): How much fun could you have in the Public Library?

MOTHER: What a question, Kitty! Scotty didn't go to the library for fun. It was a case of business—not pleasure.

SCOTTY: A fine chance for pleasure there is in this dump!

JUNIOR: Aw, Adamsford isn't so bad.

MOTHER: Towns are more or less alike, children. It's the people who really matter.

SCOTTY: It's the people I'm complaining about. The people in this town are hateful.

MOTHER: Those are pretty strong words, dear.

SCOTTY: Well, they are! (*Sits on sofa.*) All of them — just perfectly hateful. (*Begins to cry.*) I hate every single one of them, too.

MOTHER (*Sitting down beside her*): Come, dear, tell me what's the matter. You'll feel much better if you just talk about it.

KITTY: That's what I always tell her, but she seems to prefer to cry about it. She cries more now at the age of fifteen than I did at the age of five.

MOTHER: That's enough, Kitty. You just pack up your belongings and go upstairs to bed.

KITTY: Oh, please, Mother, I didn't say anything.

MOTHER: You've had your orders. Now march! I guess your sister has a right to cry without any criticism from you.

JUNIOR: She means it, Sis. You better scram.

KITTY (*Flouncing out*) : Very well, I'll go. But I still think it's sabotage. (*Exit* KITTY.)

MOTHER: Now, Scotty. Let's talk this thing over. What in the world has happened?

SCOTTY (*Between sobs*) : Oh, it's really nothing. It's just that our class is having a Valentine party next Tuesday.

JUNIOR: Craminy! Is that all?

SCOTTY: That's enough to make me miserable, 'cause I don't have a single, solitary soul to go with.

MOTHER: Couldn't you go with some of the girls in your home-room?

SCOTTY: No, they all have dates. At least all the nice ones. And they keep talking about what they're going to wear and what they're going to do. It's awful. There was a crowd of them at the library tonight and one of them even had the nerve to ask me if I was going.

MOTHER: What did you say?

SCOTTY: What could I say? I just pretended I wasn't interested in such small-town stuff.

MOTHER: But, Scotty, that's all wrong. No wonder the girls won't ask you to go places with them if you take an attitude like that. They'll think you are uppity or snobbish.

SCOTTY: I don't care what they think now. I tried to be friendly; but they all have their own gang and they don't seem to take in outsiders.

MOTHER: I know. Girls can be pretty cruel — that is, till you get to know them.

JUNIOR: Fellows aren't that way. I know a lot of good guys.

SCOTTY: I wish I did. But the boys around here are as bad as the girls. They won't take you any place unless they see you at a party or something and how are you going to get to a party, if you don't have somebody to take you in the first place?

MOTHER: I see what you mean. You sort of have to get started. After that, it's easy for any reasonably attractive girl to get some attention.

SCOTTY: Sure, that's it; but how am I going to get started if nobody ever asks me to go any place?

MOTHER: Where is this Valentine party to be held?

SCOTTY: At the school gym, and it's going to be darling. The girls are decorating the whole place with red and white hearts and in the center there's going to be a tremendous paper heart that opens and spills out favors all over the dance floor.

JUNIOR: Good night! Are they gonna have dancing?

SCOTTY: Of course. It's to be a real grown-up party, and they're having punch and everything. Oh, Mother, can't you think of something? I want to go so badly.

MOTHER: Of course, you do, dear. I know just how you feel. Now, listen, Scotty, I do have a suggestion. You might not take to it at first, but —

SCOTTY: Oh, Mother, I'll do anything, simply anything, to get to that Valentine party.

MOTHER: Well, then, dear, consider it settled. You can go with Junior.

SCOTTY (*In horror*): Junior!

JUNIOR: Oh, no. Not me. I'm not goin' to any old dancing party. No, sir, that's out.

MOTHER: Now, Junior, don't argue. There's no reason why you can't take your sister to a Valentine party. After all, you're in the same school.

SCOTTY: But, Mother, Junior's only a seventh-grader. I wouldn't be caught dead with a seventh-grader!

JUNIOR: What do you mean, you wouldn't be caught dead with a seventh-grader? What's the matter with a seventh-grader? They're just as good as those drippy old ninth-graders.

MOTHER: Junior, stop arguing and keep still a minute. You

certainly wouldn't be so mean as to refuse to take your sister
out for one evening.

SCOTTY: But, Mother, I don't want to go with him. He's too
little.

JUNIOR: Who's too little?

SCOTTY: You are. (*Stands up.*) Look at us. Wouldn't we be
a fine-looking couple! They'd all say I was a cradle-snatcher.

JUNIOR: Well, don't have a sunstroke over it, 'cause I'm not
going, and that's flat.

MOTHER: Now don't be so decided, Junior. You'll do as you're
told. Remember, you aren't the head of this household. There
are a few things that parents have a right to expect of their
children.

JUNIOR: Sure, but this isn't one of 'em. Holy Smokes, Mom,
a guy has his pride. What would the other kids say if I
showed up at a dancing party and with my sister, of all
people?

MOTHER: I don't see anything terrible about it. In my day it
was considered good taste for a brother to take his sister to
a dance.

SCOTTY: Honestly, Mother, I'd sooner stay home than go with
Junior.

MOTHER: But don't you see, Scotty? This would get you
started. After the other boys see you at the party and see how
well you dance, then they'll be more likely to invite you to
other parties.

SCOTTY: But on the other hand, they'd all know I was pretty
hard pushed to a dance with my own brother.

JUNIOR: Hey, I resent that. Plenty of worse things could happen to you. I guess when it comes to that, I can dance as
well as those other guys.

MOTHER: Of course you can, dear, and I'm sure after you got
started you'd have a good time. After all, you wouldn't have

to dance together all evening. You'd have a chance to meet other girls and exchange dances.

JUNIOR: But I don't want to dance, not with Scotty or with anybody else. Dancing's sissy. I don't like it. I only went to dancing school in the first place because you made me.

MOTHER: Well, I'm sorry to sound like an autocratic parent, Junior, but I'm afraid this is also a case of *making* you. I think it's really important for Scotty to get to this dance and I don't see any other way out of it except for you to take her.

SCOTTY: But, Mother, I don't want to go with him. I honestly don't.

MOTHER: Let's not argue about it any more tonight. Come on, Scotty, you and I will go upstairs and see if there's any possibility of making over your blue taffeta between now and Tuesday.

SCOTTY: But, Mother...

MOTHER: No more arguments tonight.

JUNIOR: But Mother...

MOTHER: Junior! Not another word. Remember your father comes home tomorrow and there's that little matter of the unexcused absence from school last Thursday afternoon.

JUNIOR: Mother! You wouldn't tell him about that! You said we settled that one out of court.

MOTHER: Did I? Well, we'll talk about it after you've taken Sister to the dance, shall we?

JUNIOR: But, Mother, that's blackmail! That's a criminal offense...that's threatening your own child....

MOTHER: Come on, Scotty, let's go upstairs. (*Exit* MOTHER *and* SCOTTY. JUNIOR, *left alone in the living room, goes into a state of frantic rage. He kicks a rug, seizes his hair in both hands, finally collapses into a chair at the living room table and pounds his fist on the flat surface.*)

JUNIOR: Of all the low-down tricks! And to think my own

mother would threaten me like this! And all for that boy-crazy sister of mine. Good night! Why can't she be like other girls? Every other girl in the ninth grade can get herself a date for this old dance, all except my sister, and I've got to be the goat. Well, I won't do it! And that's that! But on the other hand, if Dad ever finds out about that hooky business...oh, why was I ever born? Why does there have to be such a thing as Valentine's Day anyhow? (*Unconsciously he has picked up one of* KITTY's *poems.*) Valentines —slushy-mushy poems.

"I live at Elm Street — 29,
So come and be my valentine."

Of all the idiotic lame-brained, crackpot...say...wait a minute! By golly, I think I have an idea...."I live at Elm Street —29, So come and be my Valentine." Gee willikins! I believe my dear little sister really has something here. Maybe with a little inspiration and perspiration, I can improve on her original idea. Let me think. (*Takes sheet of paper and chews pencil for a second or two in deep thought.*) Wonder what rhymes with blue. Let me see...true, do, two, through, new, you...That's it, "YOU." (*Writes busily*) There! that should fix everything! Now all I need is a good name, something romantic and lovesick. (*Calling*) Hey! Moms! Where's the evening paper?

MOTHER (*From off stage*): On the radio table, I think.

JUNIOR (*Getting paper*): I'll get a name out of the "Advice to the Lovelorn" column. Here it is. "Blue Eyes." "Brown Eyes." Nope, they won't do. "Anxious." That sounds too middle-aged. "Army-Brat." Ha! She's a brat all right, but we're not army folks. Oh, boy! Here's a good one. "MISS LONELYHEART!" That's a killer-diller. (*Begins to write.*)

MOTHER (*Calling from offstage*): Junior! Come up here a minute, dear. I want you to see something.

JUNIOR: In a minute, Mother, I'm writing something. (*Pause then he chuckles to himself*) Miss Lonelyheart! Oh, Sister Mine, you're gonna get a Valentine! *And how!*

CURTAIN

* * *

SCENE 2

SETTING: *Same as Scene 1, the following Tuesday evening.*

AT RISE: SCOTTY, *dressed for the party, is putting* JUNIOR *through a few practice steps to a jitterbug record.* MRS. FAIRCHILD *looks on with interest, but* KITTY *pretends to be too deeply interested in a book to pay any attention to such foolishness.*

MOTHER: I must say Junior's catching on fine. You'll make a nice-looking couple.

KITTY: A nice-looking couple of dopes, if you ask me.

MOTHER: Nobody did ask you, dear, so just go on with your reading.

KITTY: I'll be glad to. My goodness, I'm thankful I can spend a quiet evening at home and not have to jump around like that wearing myself down to a nub.

SCOTTY (*As she takes off the record*): That wasn't bad, Junior. Now let's try a slow number, just to see if you get the hang of it.

JUNIOR: Aw, skip it, can't you? I'll be worn out before I ever get to the old party.

MOTHER: Now remember, Junior, the whole object of this party is to help Scotty meet some nice boys — help her to get acquainted. So it's up to you to see that she has plenty of partners.

SCOTTY: Oh, Mother, you sound as if he'll have to drag the boys over to me by main force.

JUNIOR: I'll do the best I can, but I won't promise too much in the way of results.

MOTHER: That's something anyhow. I'm glad to see you're changing your attitude about this party.

JUNIOR: Oh, well, maybe it won't be so bad. Maybe something'll happen that I won't have to go...er...or...I mean...

SCOTTY: What do you mean?

MOTHER: That's a strange way to talk. Just what are you hinting at?

JUNIOR: Oh, nothing...nothing at all. Lots of things happen to make people change their plans sometimes.

MOTHER: Like what for instance?

JUNIOR: Oh, like...like...Well, I don't know exactly...like getting company or having a bad storm....But honestly I didn't mean anything special. I guess it was just wishful thinking. (*Starts victrola.*) Come on, Sis, let's cut a rug. Bet you can't do this one. (*Does an elaborate jitterbug step. Doorbell rings.*)

KITTY: That's probably for me. I'll go.

JUNIOR: No...no. Stay right where you are. I'll go. It might be for me. You never can tell. (*Dashes out.*)

KITTY: That boy slays me...he honestly does.

MOTHER: Scotty, you better get your coat and bag. It's time you were getting started.

SCOTTY: Oh, Mother, do you honestly think it will turn out all right? Junior is so...Oh, I don't know...so sort of unpredictable. You just can't ever tell what he's likely to do.

JUNIOR (*Loudly offstage*) : Why, Joe Mathews! Of all people!
    Where did you come from?   Am I ever glad to see you!
    Come in...Come in.   I want you to meet the folks.   (JUNIOR
    *enters with a tall, nice-looking boy whom he introduces with
    great enthusiasm.*) Mother, this is a friend of mine, Joe
    Mathews.
MOTHER : How do you do?
JOE : Good evening!
JUNIOR : The bookworm on the sofa is my kid sister, Kitty, and
    the glamour girl over there is my other sister, Scotty.
JOE : How do you do.
KITTY (*Primly*) : How do you do.
SCOTTY : Hello, Joe, I think I've seen you from a distance in
    assembly.
JUNIOR : Sure.   Joe goes to our school, but he's new in town so
    I guess that's why you've never met each other.   In fact, that's
    why he dropped in tonight.   He doesn't know very many
    people here and this being Valentine Day, he's sort of looking
    for something to do or...er...some place to go!   Isn't that
    about right, Joe?
JOE (*A bit embarrassed*) : Er...why...yes...that's about
    right.
MOTHER : Well, you are certainly welcome.   Is your father
    working here, Joe?
JOE : Yes, ma'am.   We moved here from Illinois and it's sort
    of hard to get acquainted.   At least I've found it that way.
SCOTTY : So have I.   All the kids at school seem to have their
    own gang.
JUNIOR : I was just gonna mention there's a dance up at school
    tonight, maybe...
MOTHER (*Firmly*) : *Junior!*
SCOTTY : *Junior!*
JUNIOR : Well...I was just gonna mention it!   (*Doorbell*) Gee

whiz! The doorbell. Excuse me, folks. I'm the doortender tonight. (*Exits.*)

MOTHER: Sit down, Joe, and let's get acquainted. What course are you taking at school?

JOE (*Sits*): I'm one of those scientific bugs...interested in chemicals and all that stuff.

SCOTTY: I like that too, but Daddy had a notion I should take Latin so I'm in a Classical section.

JUNIOR (*Loudly offstage*): Well...well...well! Good old Sam Fisher! You're a sight for sore eyes. Come right in and meet the family. (*Enters with another boy, a big, broad-shouldered lad, shy and a trifle awkward.*) Mother, this is a friend of mine, Sam Fisher. He's a new guy in town, too. Sam, these are my two sisters, Kitty and Scotty, and maybe you have already met Joe Mathews. (*All acknowledge introductions.*) Sam just couldn't imagine spending Valentine evening alone, so he dropped in to see us. Wasn't that swell?

MOTHER: Yes, indeed. Sit down, Sam. How long have you been living in Adamsford?

SAM: Only about two weeks. We came from Tennessee and the folks up hereabouts aren't very friendly-like. 'Pears like they give a body the cold shoulder.

SCOTTY: I'll say they do. I feel as if I had been packed in dry ice ever since we moved here.

SAM: Same here, Miss, er...uh...

SCOTTY: Oh, just call me Scotty. I think I've seen you several times in the library.

SAM: You sure have. And I've seen you too, but gosh...well, I've been sort of scared to speak to strangers since we came up here. I don't know what's got into me.

JOE: I know the feeling. You'd like to talk only your tongue seems to be paralyzed. (*All laugh.*)

MOTHER: Well now that you are beginning to know each other your tongues will loosen up in no time.

JUNIOR: Yeah, and do you know somethin'? There's nothing like a good dance band to loosen you up all over. I hear they're havin' the Sunlight Serenaders up at school tonight to play for the Valentine dance. Now those fellows are right on the beam. I'm not so keen on dancing myself, but you older kids who go in for that sort of thing shouldn't miss out on that Valentine party.

KITTY: My goodness, Junior, you're anything but "subtile." You make your hints as broad as a barn door.

MOTHER: Kitty! Don't interrupt.

KITTY: My goodness, I wasn't interrupting, but anybody with half an eye could see what Junior's up to.

MOTHER: Kitty, that will do.

SCOTTY: Do either of you boys have any little sisters at home?

JOE: Oh, sure. I got two of 'em. One's just about her age too.

KITTY: Sure. I know her. Ellen Mathews; she's in my room.

SCOTTY: Well, isn't that just ducky? (*Doorbell.*)

MOTHER: Honestly, I've never seen the equal of the way that doorbell has been ringing tonight! Junior, I guess you'll have to answer it again.

JUNIOR: With pleasure. (*Exits.*)

SAM: I'll say one thing for your brother, Scotty, he sure is a lot more anxious to run to the door and do little things like that around the house than my brother is.

KITTY: Well, don't think he's always like this!

MOTHER: No, I must agree Junior seems on his extra special behavior tonight.

SCOTTY: For which let us all be thankful. (*Laughs*)

KITTY: Mother, don't you think it's a little queer that Junior is suddenly crashing through with so many friends? Listen, there he goes again. Who is it this time?

JUNIOR (*Offstage*): Hello, there, Bill Moyer. Where have you been keeping yourself? Can you imagine this? Popping in here on Valentine night just as big as life. You're lucky to find us all at home. Come right in and meet the folks. (*Enters with another rather shy ninth-grade boy.*) Mother, here's a fellow I want you to meet. Bill Moyer, and take it from me, he's one of the best.

MOTHER: I'm always glad to meet a friend of Junior's.

BILL: How do you do, Mrs. Fairchild.

JUNIOR: And this is Kitty, and my sister, Scotty.

GIRLS: How do you do.

JUNIOR: And that's old Sam Fisher over there and Joe Mathews holding down the sofa. I always wanted you guys to know each other. (*Boys acknowledge introduction.*)

SCOTTY: I believe we're in the same English class, aren't we?

BILL: I guess we are. We only moved here three days ago, and I have hardly had time to look around and see who's who and what's what.

KITTY: Three days! Then how in the world did you ever get to know Junior?

JUNIOR: Oh, that's easy, my girl. Your big brother gets around plenty fast. After all I couldn't have an old friend like Bill here sitting at home all by himself on Valentine night and especially when there's a dance on up at school.

KITTY: There it is again, Mother, that dance business.

MOTHER: Be quiet, Kitty.

BILL: Do you like to dance, Junior?

JUNIOR: Who? Me? Heck, no, but dancing's a fine thing for those who like it, especially for the ninth-graders. They seem to get a big kick out of it. The dance begins a little after eight, but you could drop in any time you wanted to.

SCOTTY: Junior, can't you see that nobody wants to talk about that dance.

JUNIOR: But I thought that you...well, my goodness, how was I to know you changed your mind? (*Phone*)

KITTY: I'll answer it. Junior's too busy tending to the doorbell to be bothered with the telephone too.

MOTHER: Yes, this has been a busy household this evening.

KITTY: Hello...Yes...Yes, this is 29 Elm Street. Who? Who did you say? I'm sorry...I thought you said Miss Lonelyheart....What? You *did* say Miss Lonelyheart? Oh, (*Laugh*) there must be some mistake. Somebody has been kidding you. There's nobody here by that name.

JUNIOR (*Showing extreme alarm*): Here, here, Kitty, let me take that call. I think that's for me.

KITTY: Don't be silly. It's somebody calling Miss Lonelyheart. That couldn't possibly be you.   (*To phone*) No, excuse me, please, I was just talking to my brother. No, you must have the wrong number. I'm sorry, goodbye. (*Hangs up.*)

JUNIOR: Why wouldn't you give me that phone?

KITTY: Because it didn't concern you. Gee...that was funny. Some fellow asked if this was twenty-nine Elm Street and when I said, "yes," he wanted to know if Miss Lonelyheart lived here. (*All laugh but boys look uncomfortable, especially* JUNIOR.)

MOTHER: Isn't that silly? I wonder what he could have meant or whom he was looking for.

KITTY: But the funniest part was that he had our correct address. Say, Junior, why did you want to take that call? What do you know about this?

JUNIOR: Why—er—nothing. Not a thing. (*Doorbell*)

MOTHER: This is getting mighty mysterious. I think I'll go to the door myself this time.

JUNIOR: Oh, no, Mother, please. You just sit still. It's probably...

KITTY: Probably another one of your unexpected friends.

JUNIOR: And what is so funny about that? Can't a fellow have a few friends?

SCOTTY: Of course, but I must say I never knew you had so many.

JUNIOR (*Defiantly*): Well, I have, see. And as a matter of fact, I *was* expecting someone else. (*A boy suddenly appears in the doorway. He carries his hat in one hand, a folded newspaper in the other.*)

JUNIOR (*Weakly*): See, what did I tell you?

MOTHER: And just who is this, Junior?

JUNIOR: Well, I—er—uh—for the moment I just can't think of his name...

PHILIP: My name is Philip Rogers, and I do hope you will excuse me for bursting in on you like this. I rang but no one answered and as the door was ajar, I just thought I'd step in.

MOTHER: That's quite all right, young man. Are you a friend of Junior's by any chance?

JUNIOR: Oh, yes, sure we're friends.

PHILIP: Why, er, no, I'm sorry, but I am afraid I don't know you. Maybe you have me confused with somebody else. People tell me I have one of those faces that come in large numbers. You see, I just came to see about the advertisement.

SCOTTY: Advertisement? What advertisement?

MOTHER: Oh, dear me. He's come to see about the bicycle we had advertised last week.

JUNIOR: Sure. That's it. Well, I'm awfully sorry, old man, but that's sold. Sold it last Wednesday...or was it Thursday, Moms?

PHILIP: Oh, no, it wasn't the bicycle. It was the Valentine ad.

SCOTTY AND MOTHER: Valentine ad?

MOTHER: What in the world are you talking about?

JUNIOR: Gee whiz, Mother. I just remembered. I have a book I must return to the library tonight. It's overdue. I'll be right back.

MOTHER: Oh, no you don't. No library for you, young man.
You stay right here till we solve this little mystery.

KITTY: Looks to me like it might turn out to be a murder mystery with Junior as the victim.

SCOTTY: Oh, this is terrible. Mother, I think Junior has been up to something dreadful.

PHILIP: Oh, I don't think it's dreadful. In fact it's the most exciting thing that's happened to me since I came to Adamsford four weeks ago. I take it you are Miss Lonelyheart.

SCOTTY: Miss Lonelyheart? I don't understand this at all. My name is Scotty Fairchild.

PHILIP: Gosh, that's a lovely name. Of course, I knew your real name wouldn't be Miss Lonelyheart, but it does have a lovely sound and it looks well in print.

MOTHER: In print? Young man, you're driving me crazy. I command you to stop this beating around the bush and explain yourself.

PHILIP (*Handing her the paper*): I'm not beating around the bush, Mrs. Fairchild. I'm just trying to tell you that I saw your daughter's ad in the paper and dropped in to see what was cooking, as the fellows say. See—there it is in the Lovelorn Column, the first one.

MOTHER (*Reading*:"Attention all Newcomers to the Ninth-Grade of Stanford High —

If you're a stranger in this town,
And all the girls have turned you down,
If you are sad and feeling blue
'Cause no one ever talks to you,
Just come to Elm Street, twenty-nine,
And I will be your Valentine.

> Signed,
> Miss Lonelyheart."

(MOTHER *stands in stricken silence.* KITTY *laughs and* SCOTTY *begins to cry.*)

SCOTTY: Oh, this is terrible. I'll die of humiliation. Oh, Junior, how could you do such a thing?

MOTHER: Harold Maddison Fairchild, did you put this dreadful piece in the paper?

JUNIOR: Oh my goodness! I'll have to tell the whole business. Sure, I put it in the paper, but it was a good deed, not a criminal offense.

MOTHER: Your Father will be the judge of that, young man.

JUNIOR: But, Mother, please. After all, we have company. Lots of it.

MOTHER: Yes, and I am sure that we owe all of them an apology. (*To boys*) I am sure neither my daughter nor myself can be held responsible for this piece of outlandish foolishness.

JOE: Oh, don't feel so bad about it, Mrs. Fairchild. This is the first home I've visited since my folks moved here. After all, it's been a lot of fun.

SCOTTY (*Still crying*): Yes, fun at my expense.

SAM: Oh, no, Scotty. Don't take it like that. We're all in the same boat. Why, I was so gol-darned lonesome last night I'd have advertised in six papers if I had only had brains enough to think of it.

JUNIOR: Thanks, Pal.

BILL: And me too. This moving around has been getting me down. Why, I haven't been to any parties or had any dates for ages, and when I saw that ad in this evening's paper, it looked to me like a first-class Valentine adventure.

PHILIP: That's the way it struck me, too. I even went so far as to get the telephone number of this address, but I didn't get any satisfaction over the phone. I guess maybe your maid answered.

KITTY: Maid nothing. That was me. I mean "I." All I said was that we didn't have any Miss Lonelyheart.

SCOTTY: But we did. I'll admit I've been a flat failure at making friends in this town. That's why Mother was making Junior take me to the dance tonight.

JUNIOR: Sure. I only did what I did in self-defense.

KITTY (*Laughing*): You know, Mother, I think it was pretty smart of Junior. He got Scottie acquainted with a lot of nice boys without going to the old dance at all—and he used my poem. That part about "Elm Street twenty-nine" was from one of the valentines I wrote.

MOTHER: This whole Valentine business has given me a headache. Junior, I don't know what to say to you. You're a disgrace to the family.

JOE: Maybe he's just a good publicity man. Have a heart, Mrs. Fairchild, let us stay here and spend the evening, won't you?

SAM: We won't promise to be quiet but we won't break any of the furniture or anything like that.

BILL: Golly, Mrs. Fairchild, you'll be our fairy godmother if you'll let us stay. After all, it's no crime to answer an advertisement....

KITTY: And they could go to the dance, after all.

SCOTTY: Don't mention that awful dance again. I'd rather have a party here at home.

MOTHER: A party? With four boys and one girl? That looks to me like a one-sided affair.

KITTY: Gee, it's a wonder to me Junior didn't think of that. Didn't you advertise for any girls, Junior?

JUNIOR: No, I just figured that the first guy who answered the ad could take Sis to the dance, and I'd get rid of the rest of the applicants. That's why I was so anxious to meet every one of them in the hall, so I could get their names and steer them in here before they could say anything incriminating.

I sorta had a hunch Mother and Scotty wouldn't think much of the advertising idea.

MOTHER: You were right about that. But since you boys have put up such a plea, I don't have the heart to turn you out without some kind of party. If you can think of some other girls to invite, I guess Kitty and I could rustle some refreshments and you could play the victrola and dance to your hearts' content.

SCOTTY: Oh, Mother, that would be marvelous!

JOE: I know a girl in our home-room who has just moved to town. Her name is Esther Ryan.

JUNIOR: Sure, I know her too. She lives on Emerson Street. Let me call her up.

MOTHER: I've had enough of your promotion tactics for one evening, Junior. From now on, you keep out of things. I'll call up Mrs. Ryan and explain that we are having a little party at our house for some of the young people who have just moved to town. Maybe she'll let Esther come.

SCOTTY: That's a swell idea. I can think of a couple of new girls in my own section. I guess if I hadn't been so selfish I would have realized they were as lonely and homesick as I've been.

PHILIP: We new guys better stick together.

JUNIOR: You might organize a Lonelyheart Club.

SCOTTY: No more Lonelyhearts after tonight. We have a gang of our own now.

MOTHER: Well, how about taking your gang down to the game room while I do some phoning?

SAM: Gee, Mrs. Fairchild, you're swell to let us stay.

BOYS: I'll say she is! (*The whole gang exits singing, "For she's a jolly good fellow." KITTY and JUNIOR follow at the end of the line, but MRS. FAIRCHILD sees JUNIOR in time to call him back.*)

MOTHER: Junior, you come back here.

JUNIOR: Aw, gee, Moms, have a heart. After all, this is Valentine's Day.

MOTHER: Honestly, Junior, I don't know whether to kick you or kiss you; you are the limit.

JUNIOR: Aw, well...I guess I was taking a chance, but after all, we can't have an Old Maid in the family.

MOTHER (*Laughing*): She's hardly an old maid at 15, Junior. Oh, dear, I wonder how I'll live through it, when *you* begin to take an interest in girls.

JUNIOR: Nix on that stuff, Moms. After tonight, there's only one valentine for me, and *you are it*. (*He grabs his* MOTHER *around the waist and swings her around in a dizzy whirl as she keeps screaming, "Junior, Junior, let me go! Junior, do you hear me?" Quick curtain.*)

THE END

PRODUCTION NOTES

Miss Lonelyheart

Characters: 5 male; 3 female.

Playing Time: 45 minutes.

Costumes: The characters are dressed in everyday, modern clothes. For Scene 2 Scotty wears a blue taffeta.

Properties: Books, paper, pencil, newspaper, hankie, victrola and records, telephone.

Setting: A typical American living room in which there a number of chairs, lounge and a straight-backed sofa, a few end tables, lamps, etc., etc. On one of these tables is a victrola and a pile of records. Against the wall is a desk. At right is door leading into reception hall. At left is door leading to rest of house. There is a table visible in the reception hall on which is a telephone.

Lighting: None required.

THE WASHINGTONS SLEPT HERE

Characters

MARTHA WASHINGTON, *his wife.*
GEORGE WASHINGTON, *a G. I. university student.*
MRS. VAN HOLDEN, *Hostess of Randolph House.*
NANCY CAMERON, *Junior Hostess.*
SARALEE BATES, *Junior Hostess.*
MR. GARFIELD, *a philanthropist.*
LITTLE BUTCH
VISITORS

SCENE: *The reception room of Randolph House.*

TIME: *Washington's Birthday.*

THE WASHINGTONS SLEPT HERE

SETTING: *The reception room of Randolph House, historical shrine at Greenville, a small town which prides itself on historical associations. Randolph House, famous for being visited by George and Martha Washington, is open to the public.*

AT RISE: SARALEE BATES *and* NANCY CAMERON, *high school girls, are serving as hostesses. They are wearing Colonial costumes.* SARALEE *is examining the Guest Book.* NANCY *is adjusting her cap before a mirror.*

NANCY: I so wish Dick could see me in this lace cap. It's ever so much more becoming than my old red kerchief. But Dick won't even poke his nose inside Randolph House. Afraid of catching something historical, he says.

SARALEE: Well, we don't need Dick to swell our quota of visitors. Seventy-five paid admissions this afternoon, and we've had thirty-seven this evening. If only we could keep that up every day, no one would need to worry about closing Randolph House. But it isn't every day you get a hundred and twelve people to pay a quarter to see the house where George and Martha Washington visited, and look at the chairs they sat in, and the dishes they used, and the beds they slept in. People just aren't that patriotic.

NANCY: How can you say such a thing? Not patriotic! Patriotism these days means more than historical pilgrimages. Most people are too busy to travel.

SARALEE: Why, Nancy, you sound as if you don't think Randolph House is important.

NANCY: Sure, I think it is important. If I didn't think so, I wouldn't be giving up an evening's fun to serve here as a hostess. But I'm not a fanatic on the subject, like Mrs. Van Holden, for instance. She can't see anything else except Randolph House. I honestly think she'll pass out if Mr. Garfield doesn't come across with his big contribution this year...a contribution that will take care of this place for another season.

SARALEE: She's sure working hard enough on it. Nothing stops her...not even this hostess business. You'd think she'd be dead tired from running up and down the steps showing people around, but will she turn those sight-seers over to you or me? Not a chance. She nabs every one of them, as soon as he sets foot inside the door.

NANCY: Well, business is dying down now. Not many more people will come tonight...not in this downpour. And we close in less than an hour.

SARALEE: Here comes Mrs. Van Holden with her party. She's going strong. (MRS. VAN HOLDEN *enters with party of sight-seers consisting of three women and a child.*)

MRS. VAN HOLDEN: I do hope you've enjoyed your visit to Randolph House, and that you'll come again soon. We strive to preserve the spirit of the old place as well as the actual furnishings, and hospitality was always the first law of this house. So do come again.

1ST LADY: Thank you very much. It's been perfectly delightful.

CHILD: Mamma, did George Washington really sleep in that big high bed with all those ruffles?

MRS. VAN HOLDEN: Indeed, he did, child. Many a good night's rest he enjoyed here. The General and Mrs. Washington were frequent guests of the Randolphs.

MOTHER: You can write about this trip, Clara, for your next composition in school.

Mrs. Van Holden: A lovely idea! I always say there's nothing so educational for children as trips to our national shrines. Maybe your little girl would like one of our folders. There's a fine picture of the Washington Guest Room.

Mother: Oh that would be fine.

2nd Lady: I'd like one, too, please. (*Accepting folder*) Thank you very much. What charming hostesses you have here.

Mrs. Van Holden: Yes, these dear girls have been very helpful to me all day. Our high school girls take a big interest in Randolph House and have volunteered their services for our Washington celebration. And now, you really must register in our Guest Book. (*As guests register, phone rings. Saralee answers.*)

Saralee: Yes...yes. Mrs. Van Holden is right here. Just a minute, I'll call her. What? A message? Certainly. I'll be glad to give it to her. Very well. Goodbye.

Saralee (*To Mrs. Van Holden*): That was Mr. Lane from the Historical Society. They'd like you to come over right away. Mr. Garfield is meeting with the committee.

Mrs. Van Holden: Mr. Garfield! Dear me! They must have called an emergency meeting. I wonder what's happening. I'll go at once. You girls can take care of everything, I am sure. I'll get my wraps. Excuse me, please. (*Exit Mrs. Van Holden.*)

Nancy (*To guests who are registering*): It's too bad you had such disagreeable weather for your trip.

2nd Lady: Oh, it was worth it, I'm sure.

1st Lady: I think it's wonderful to have a house like this in your town with all these historical relics. It must be an inspiration to everyone.

Nancy: Yes, we're all proud of Randolph House.

Saralee: Be sure to stop again the next time you are in town.

Mother: I'm sure we'd enjoy a dozen trips here. Goodnight,

girls. Come, dear (*To child*), get your umbrella. (*Chorus of goodbyes as visitors exit*)

MRS. VAN HOLDEN (*Re-enters wearing cape over her costume*): Well, girls, this meeting tonight should tell the tale. No doubt Mr. Garfield has made up his mind about his contribution. Let's hope it's a generous one.

SARALEE: We'll keep our fingers crossed for luck, Mrs. Van Holden.

MRS. VAN HOLDEN: It would be too, too dreadful if we should have to close Randolph House. I simply can't think of such a thing.

NANCY: It won't close, Mrs. Van Holden. Mr. Garfield always comes across at the last minute.

MRS. VAN HOLDEN: That is true. He has never failed us yet. Well, I must hurry. Take good care of everything, girls, and be sure all the doors are locked when you leave. Tomorrow's Saturday, so maybe you'll open up in the morning.

NANCY: Sure, we will. We'll take the key home and be here at nine-thirty sharp.

MRS. VAN HOLDEN: I don't know what I should do without you. Well, goodnight. I don't imagine you'll have any more visitors. (MRS. VAN HOLDEN *exits*.)

SARALEE: She's really a dear, but she does have herself worked into a frenzy about Mr. Garfield's contribution.

NANCY: I hope we do have some more visitors. It will be deadly just sitting here looking at each other till nine o'clock.

SARALEE (*Yawning*): I'm so sleepy, I'd like to go right upstairs and take a nap on that big canopied bed.

NANCY: Shades of Mrs. Van Holden! She'd slay you in cold blood if she ever caught you on the General's bed. (*Doorbell*)

NANCY: There! Customers! I'll go. (*She goes toward door*.)

SARALEE: All right. You play hostess and let them in. But I get to take them through the house. I haven't had a chance to say my guide speech once today.

NANCY (*At door*): Welcome to Randolph House. Oh, do come in. It's simply pouring. (*A man and his wife enter. The man carries two suitcases. The wife pushes a baby carriage.*)

GEORGE (*Mopping his face*): Whew! It feels good to get inside out of this downpour.

WIFE: Indeed it does. We're nearly drowned.

SARALEE (*With a curtsey*): Welcome to Randolph House. Let me put your umbrellas in the rack. Wouldn't you like to take off your coats before you start on the tour?

GEORGE: Thank you. (*Helps wife with coat and removes his own. Hands them to* NANCY *who takes them off stage.*)

WIFE: It's lovely here. So pleasant and cheerful, and warm. (*Sneezes*) Oh excuse me. I seem to be catching cold.

SARALEE: That's too bad. I hope you like the house. Will you register now or when we come back?

WIFE: Oh, I guess I won't be able to go through the house. I'll stay here with the baby while George makes the rounds. He is more interested in historical things.

NANCY(*Re-entering*): Nonsense! Both of you should see the house, now that you are here. I'll be glad to stay with the baby. (*Looking in coach*) He's a darling, and the way he's sleeping, he'll never miss you.

GEORGE: That would be fine. I know my wife would enjoy it. She loves antique furniture.

WIFE: I'll admit I'd like to go, and if you're sure the baby won't be any trouble, I'll go. (*Sneezes*)

NANCY: Of course, he won't be any trouble. I'll wheel him over by the desk where I can keep my eye on him. Saralee will show you around.

SARALEE: Just come this way. May I ask where you folks are from?

GEORGE: We're from North Dakota, and I've always wanted to

see these historical places I've read so much about. That's one reason I selected this University to finish my degree.

SARALEE: Oh, you're a University student.

WIFE: Make that plural. I signed up for two courses myself. But we're out of luck in finding a place to stay. This town is running over with G.I.'s and their families pursuing education. Do you girls happen to know of a room? We've just about run our legs off and can't find one for love or money.

NANCY: I'll see what I can do while Saralee steers you around and delivers her lecture.

BOTH: Thanks a million.

SARALEE (*As she exits with the man and his wife*): The house was built in 1700 and is the oldest stone house in the state. In 1743 the left wing was added when the house was purchased by George Kendall Randolph...

NANCY (*Wheeling baby coach close to desk*): There, now, little man, you can stay here as snug as a bug in a rug till your Mommie and Daddy come back, and in the meantime I'll see about getting a room for you. (*Goes to telephone and dials, repeating number aloud*) 2-3-7-8...Hello...Aunt Grace? This is Nancy. Have you rented your spare room yet? Oh, dear! I'm sorry. There's a young couple over here at Randolph House who have been looking all over town for a room. Could you tell me of any other place? Oh, yes... Mrs. Spencer. I didn't think of her. I'll call right away. Do you happen to know her number? 3-9-5-7. Thanks a lot, Aunt Grace. I'll try her. (*Hangs up. To baby*) Well, well, Old Timer, we'll just have to try again. Better luck this time. How about it? (*Dials*) 3-9-5-7...Hello, is this Mrs. Spencer? This is Nancy Cameron. Aunt Grace suggested I call you about a room for a veteran and his wife. They're over here at Randolph House and they've just tried every place to get a room. What? Oh, dear me! Can you beat

that! If only I had called a few minutes sooner. Yes, I know
they would have loved it. Well, could you tell me some other
place? Who? Oh...Mrs. Wilson on Locust Street, No, I
don't know her, but I'll call. Thanks very much, Mrs. Spencer,
and I'm surely sorry they can't come over to your place. Goodbye. Well, here we go again, Junior. My goodness, you'll
be sleeping on a park bench if I don't do better than this. Now
where's that phone book? Ah, here we are...Wilson...
Locust Street...5896... (*Dialing*) Keep your fingers
crossed, Baby, maybe we'll have good luck. Hello. May I
speak to Mrs. Wilson, please. Yes....Oh, hello, Mrs. Wilson.
This is Nancy Cameron calling from Randolph House. I'm
trying to locate a room for a young couple for the night. Do
you happen to have anything? You do? Oh, that's marvelous. They'll be so pleased. I'll send them right over. What?
Oh...Well, yes...they do have a baby...but...Oh, but
Mrs. Wilson, he's a darling...and he's just a little baby...
not a bit of trouble. (*Beginning to get angry*) He does *not*
cry. He's been here quite a while and he's as good as gold.
Not a sound out of him. But, please, Mrs. Wilson, couldn't
you make an exception just for tonight? These people have
looked every place and it's such a miserable night. Surely
you wouldn't want them to take this baby out in the rain
again. If you'd only...What's that? Mrs. Wilson...Can
you beat it? She hung up on me! Why, the old meanie!
(*To baby*) Never you mind, Sweetie Pie, I'll get you a room
if it takes all night. The very idea of that hateful Mrs. Wilson
refusing to rent a room on account of you. She makes me
good and mad. Now let me think. There must be somebody
else...Oh, yes...Mrs. Nelson....I'll try her. (*Leafing
through phone book*) Nelson, Nelson, Nelson....Here we
are...7394. (*Dials*) 7-3-9-4. Maybe this will be our lucky
number. Oh, dear, why don't they answer? Hello...Hello

...yes....Oh, yes...Mrs. Nelson, this is Nancy Cameron.
Do you have any rooms for rent? What? You don't rent
rooms any more on account of not being able to get help?
Oh, dear! Well, couldn't you take a young couple and a baby
for just one night? Oh, I'm sure they wouldn't be any
trouble. Well, yes, of course, they're strangers. No, no, I
don't know very much about them, but I can see they're nice
people. They're from North Dakota. (*Laugh*) Oh, well, I
know that's no guarantee of their honesty, but really, they're
very nice. After all, the man was in the service and...Oh,
very well, if that's the way you feel about it. I'm sorry I
bothered you. Goodbye. (*Hangs up*.) Oh, mercy me! This
is terrible! Surely there must be one vacant room in this
town. (*Wife re-enters. She is still sneezing at intervals*)

WIFE: How's the baby? Still sleeping?

NANCY: Yes, he's sound asleep. I wasn't expecting you back
so soon. Saralee must have rushed you through.

WIFE: Oh, no. She and George are still upstairs. I was just
too tired to walk another step...even in the interests of
history. (*Sits down*)

NANCY: I don't blame you. I'm beginning to see what you're
up against trying to get a room in this town.

WIFE: Didn't you have any luck either?

NANCY: Not a thing. I called four places but they all said...

WIFE: I can guess. Just rented their last one or won't take any
people with children.

NANCY: That's the story.

WIFE: I'm so tired and discouraged, I could cry. But I don't
want to worry George.

NANCY: It's a dirty shame. Maybe Saralee can think of a
place.

WIFE: I hope so, though I don't want to bother you girls with
our problem.

NANCY: We're only too glad to help if we can. Here comes Saralee now.

SARALEE (*Re-enters with man*): And now we're back to our starting place. And this time, you must sign the Guest Book. How did you like your tour?

GEORGE: Oh, swell. And thanks a lot for the lecture. It was interesting. You see, I have a very special interest in George Washington. He and I have a lot in common, as you will discover when I sign this book. (*Signs*) There!

SARALEE: Well, I declare! Is your name really and truly George Washington?

GEORGE: It sure is...and believe me, I've taken plenty of razzing in my time on account of it. We call the baby Jim... Butch for short, so he won't go through life being kidded about his name.

NANCY: But aren't you proud of it?

MARTHA: Of course he is, in a way. But it wasn't enough for his parents to name him *George Washington*...he had to marry a girl named *Martha*.

SARALEE: So you're really George and Martha Washington. My goodness, Nancy, we're forgetting our manners. We owe them a special curtsey or something.

NANCY (*As the man's wife sneezes*): A cup of tea would do them a lot more good; and what they need most of all is a place to stay tonight.

SARALEE: Didn't you find a room?

NANCY: There isn't a vacant room in this town.

GEORGE: Good grief! Well, honey, here we go again. You and Butchie and I back to the big parade.

MARTHA (*Sneezing*): At least we're a lot warmer and drier than we were when we first came in here. (*Rises*)

GEORGE: Thanks for everything, girls. Now how much do we owe you for the grand tour?

SARALEE: Oh, nothing.   The hospitality of Randolph House is free to University students.

NANCY (*Eagerly*) : Say that again, Pal.

SARALEE: The hospitality of Randolph House is free to University students.   That's what it says in the rule book.

NANCY: Of course, it's what it says in the rule book...and doesn't it give you the most marvelous idea?

SARALEE: You mean...

NANCY: Exactly.   I mean just what you think I mean if the hospitality of Randolph House is free...

SARALEE: And *hospitality* means *shelter* and *shelter* certainly means a roof over your head and a bed to sleep in...

NANCY: And what a bed!   Sir, did you ever sleep in a feather bed?

GEORGE: What are you talking about?

SARALEE: After all, who has a better right to the Washington Guest Room than his namesake?

MARTHA: The famous Washington room?   Oh, we could never stay there.

GEORGE: Sure, we could.   The girls are right.   No one can dispute the fact that we really are George and Martha Washington.

SARALEE: And there's even a trundle bed for little Butch.

MARTHA: But won't you girls get into trouble?

NANCY: No one will ever know a thing about it.   We have the key to the house and we've promised to be on duty tomorrow at nine-thirty.   We'll just come a little earlier and get you out of here before anyone's the wiser.

SARALEE: Everything has been aired, and the bed is all made up with clean sheets.   Nancy and I will bring another pair tomorrow and change them till we get a chance to have yours laundered again.

GEORGE: Don't worry, Martha.   It will be all right, and it will be fun, too. Just think, some day little Butch can boast of the night he spent in the Washington Guest Room.

MARTHA: All right, if you think it won't get these girls into trouble. But suppose we're caught.

GEORGE: What if we are! We're not criminals. We won't hurt anything. (*Picks up suitcases*) Lead on, my friend, the Washingtons follow.

SARALEE (*With a low curtsey*): Right this way, sir. (SARALEE and GEORGE *exit*.)

NANCY: You can leave the baby coach here till morning.

MARTHA (*Picking up baby out of coach*): Come on, Butchie, you are going to sleep in a historic spot tonight, and you'll probably not appreciate it. (*To* NANCY) Goodnight, my dear, and thank you so much for all your kindness.

NANCY: You're very welcome. I do hope you'll be comfortable.

MARTHA: I'm sure we will be. Goodnight. (*Starts to exit*.)

NANCY: Tell Saralee to hurry down and help me close up.

MARTHA (*As she exits*): I'll tell her.

NANCY: What an evening! I'm glad it's closing time. (*Straightens desk and closes Guest Book*.) "George and Martha Washington, North Dakota." Mrs. Van Holden will appreciate that. (SARALEE *enters. She carries two capes*.)

SARALEE: Oh, Nancy, do you really think we can get away with this?

NANCY: Sure. Why not? It's after nine now, so we're safe from any more visitors. No one will come poking around here till nine-thirty tomorrow morning. It's foolproof, and besides, we did the right thing. We couldn't turn those people out in the rain. All this talk about hospitality and tradition and then to do a thing like that to a veteran and his family. No siree....We did the right thing. Come on, let's go home.

SARALEE: I checked the doors when I took our friends through the house. Everything is okay.

NANCY: Then let's go.

SARALEE: Here's your cape. (*Girls put on their capes.*) I'll turn out the lights. (*Turns out lights. There is the offstage sound of footsteps.*)

SARALEE: Nancy, did you hear that?

NANCY: Yes. (*Stage whisper*) Someone's coming up the front steps. Quick...look out the front door. You'll be able to see who it is from the street lamp.

SARALEE: Merciful Heavens! It's Mrs. Van Holden and Mr. Garfield! What shall we do?

NANCY: We can't let them in.

SARALEE: We won't need to. Mr. Garfield has a key. Quick... turn on the lights. We don't want to act as if we're hiding here in the dark.

NANCY: Okay. Let them in. We'll have to keep them from getting upstairs. (*Lights go on.* SARALEE *opens door.* MRS. VAN HOLDEN *and* MR. GARFIELD *enter.*)

SARALEE: We were just leaving. You almost scared the wits out of us.

MRS. VAN HOLDEN: Oh, I'm sorry. I thought you girls would probably be leaving on the stroke of nine.

NANCY: Oh, yes...well...we were sort of held up.

MR. GARFIELD: Did you have a lot of visitors?

NANCY: Oh, not very many.

SARALEE: Just two or three.

MRS. VAN HOLDEN: Well, now you can run along. Mr. Garfield and I want to talk business.

NANCY (*Hesitating*): Oh...but...well, we don't mean to butt in, but maybe you'd like us to stay a while.

SARALEE: Perhaps we could make you a cup of tea. It's so cold and wet outside.

GARFIELD: No thank you, girls, but it's kind of you to offer. (*Goes to put umbrella in stand. Sees other umbrellas.*) Sakes alive! You must have had some absent-minded professors here tonight. How could anyone forget their umbrellas on a night like this?

NANCY (*Laughing feebly*) : Isn't that silly? I wonder who it could have been. (SARALEE *sees baby coach beside desk. She tries to shove it out of sight.*)

SARALEE (*Giggling*) : People do forget the strangest things.

NANCY (*Also seeing baby coach*) : Yes, don't they? I've known people to go off and leave their pocketbooks, and handbags... once...I even knew someone who went off and forgot a baby coach.

MRS. VAN HOLDEN : You girls seem nervous. Did anything happen to frighten you?

NANCY : Oh, no...No indeed. Everything has been very quiet.

MRS. VAN HOLDEN : Well, I'm glad to hear it. I never thought either of you was the nervous type. Well, thank you very much, girls, for all you've done. Good night.

GIRLS : Good-night. (*Not moving from baby coach which they are trying to conceal.*)

NANCY : Is it still raining?

SARALEE : I did hope it would stop before we had to go home.

MR. GARFIELD : It's still pouring. Do you have far to go?

MRS. VAN HOLDEN : Only a square. That's why we're so fortunate to have these girls as hostesses. You see, Mr. Garfield, how much Randolph House means to these young people that they are willing to give their time to working here.

MR. GARFIELD : I understand, Mrs. Van Holden. That is not my reason for withdrawing my contribution this year. It's just that...

NANCY : Oh, Mr. Garfield! You're not withdrawing your contribution, are you?

MR. GARFIELD : Dear me! I hadn't intended to say that. It just slipped out. Excuse me, Mrs. Van Holden, I didn't mean to discuss this with anyone else.

SARALEE: But, Mr. Garfield, we can't keep Randolph House open without your support.

MR. GARFIELD: Yes, yes....I know, and no one regrets that any more than I do...but it's just that I feel I should use that money in some other way... (*Sound of a baby crying*) Bless my soul! What's that?

SARALEE: What's what?

NANCY: I didn't hear a thing.

MRS. VAN HOLDEN: Well, I did. It sounded exactly like a baby crying. But of course, that's impossible.

NANCY: And how!

SARALEE: As we were saying, Mr. Garfield, the whole town takes pride in this place and appreciates what you do for it. (*Crying stops.*)

MR. GARFIELD: I understand. But don't you people realize that our government needs money for more important things right now.

MRS. VAN HOLDEN: But this is a matter of history, Mr. Garfield.

MR. GARFIELD: But right now, with so many people starving... (*Baby cries.*) Bless my soul! There's that noise again. There must be a baby in this house.

MRS. VAN HOLDEN: Nonsense! How could there be?

NANCY: It must be the water pipes or something.

MR. GARFIELD: Young woman, I can distinguish between the cry of a baby and a water pipe and I say that's a baby. I'm going to investigate. I'm going upstairs.

GIRLS (*Dashing forward forgetting about concealing baby coach*): Oh, no. Please don't. Don't go upstairs.

MRS. VAN HOLDEN (*Seeing baby coach*): Girls, girls! What's that? Behind you? (*Points accusingly at baby coach.*)

GIRLS: Oh dear! We're sunk. (*Baby cries louder.*)

MR. GARFIELD: I told you there's a baby in this house and I mean to find it.

MRS. VAN HOLDEN: Girls! What is the meaning of this? I demand an explanation. (*George enters. He is wearing a bathrobe and carries a baby's bottle.*)

GEORGE: Gosh! I'm glad you girls are still here. I forgot to ask you if there was a place we could heat Butchie's milk. (*Suddenly sees* MRS. VAN HOLDEN *and* MR. GARFIELD. *Almost collapses on desk.*) Ye gods! I didn't know you had company.

MRS. VAN HOLDEN: And neither did we know that there were guests in Randolph House. Girls, I am ashamed of you. I trusted you. I left this house in your care...and you have betrayed my confidence. Who is this man?

NANCY: You'll never believe us if we tell you, Mrs. Van Holden.

MRS. VAN HOLDEN: I insist on an explanation. Young man, what is your name and what are you doing in this house?

MR. GARFIELD: This is a matter for the police.

SARALEE: Oh, no...it's not. It's all our fault. But it isn't anything for the police . We haven't broken any laws. If you just promise to believe us, we'll explain everything.

MR. GARFIELD: You'll explain anyhow. We'll soon find out if you're telling the truth. For the second time, young man, what is your name?

GEORGE: George Washington, at your service, sir.

MR. GARFIELD: Don't be impertinent.

MRS. VAN HOLDEN: This is no time for jokes.

SARALEE (*Getting Guest Book*): But he's not joking. Honest, he isn't. See...here....That's his real name...and his wife's name is Martha and the baby is Little Butch...er...James.

MRS. VAN HOLDEN: I think I'll have to sit down.

MR. GARFIELD: This is the most preposterous thing I ever heard of. (*As baby cries louder*) Can't someone stop that baby from screaming its head off?

GEORGE: Yes, sir, I can if I can just heat this milk and take it upstairs so Martha can feed him.

MR. GARFIELD: And where, may I ask, are this Martha and that screaming infant?

SARALEE: Upstairs in the Washington Guest Room.

MRS. VAN HOLDEN (*Fairly screaming*): The Washington Guest Room! Never in my life have I heard of anything so disgraceful! Mr. Garfield, call the police. Get these people out of this house at once. This very minute.

GEORGE: You won't have to do anything so drastic, Ma'am. We'll get out. And don't blame these girls. They only did what they thought was their patriotic duty.

MR. GARFIELD: What does patriotic duty have to do with it?

GEORGE: If you'd just keep calm, I believe I could explain it. My name really is George Washington and my wife's name is really Martha. We've been looking all over town for a room and there's none to be had. These young ladies were kind enough to offer us the hospitality of this house...a house which once sheltered another American soldier and his wife. That's all there is to it. I'm sorry we've intruded and I'll get my wife and child out of here as quickly as I can. But I'd still like to warm this bottle of milk.

MR. GARFIELD: Well, I'll be jiminied!

NANCY: Oh, Mrs. Van Holden, it wasn't so terrible, really. They're such nice people and they just had to have a room.

SARALEE: Please forgive us...and forgive them, too. I suppose we never should have done it...but the rule book does say...Hospitality of Randolph House is free to University people.

MRS. VAN HOLDEN: Young man, give me that baby's bottle and follow me. I'll show you where to heat it. Mr. Garfield, you talk things over, but I don't think we'll need the police.

MR. GARFIELD: I'm sure we won't. Mr. Washington, I beg

your pardon. (*Shakes hands with* GEORGE.) And as to you young ladies, you took a lot on yourselves by making such a decision and I am here to stand back of it. This house has stood for hospitality ever since it was built, and I guess it's too old to change now. (GEORGE'S WIFE *enters.*)

WIFE: You won't need to hurry with that milk, George. The baby cried himself to sleep. Oh my goodness!

MR. GARFIELD: Don't be alarmed, my dear. I suppose you are Mistress Martha Washington.

GEORGE: Yes, sir. This is my wife. Martha, this gentleman's name is Mr. Garfield...and it looks as if he is going to let us stay here for the night.

MRS. VAN HOLDEN (*Entering*): That milk will be warm in a few minutes. (*To* WIFE) Welcome to Randolph House, George and Martha. That's our customary greeting to strangers and this time we really mean it.

MR. GARFIELD: I'm beginning to think this is a lucky night for Randolph House. Mrs. Van Holden and I have just been discussing the possibility of closing the place. I could see no point in spending money on an empty and useless house. Now I can see that it is neither empty nor useless. There must be other young couples and their families who would appreciate the hospitality of this house.

MARTHA: Oh, there are so many, Mr. Garfield. It's heart-breaking to spend hours and hours looking for a place to stay.

MRS. VAN HOLDEN: It's a wonder none of us thought of it before. I'll never forget what you said about this house sheltering another American soldier and his wife. That is the kind of monument General Washington would have appreciated most.

MR. GARFIELD: And that is the kind of memorial he shall have. Tomorrow morning, Mrs. Van Holden, you will receive my check for twice the customary amount.

MRS. VAN HOLDEN: Thank you, Mr. Garfield. You're a real American.

MR. GARFIELD: But only on one condition, mind you. That these two young ladies be employed as regular Junior Hostesses. They know the real meaning of hospitality.

NANCY: Thank you, sir. You can count on us.

SARALEE: We'll be on duty whenever you need us.

MR. GARFIELD: Then I'll need both of you here tomorrow morning at nine-thirty to help lay plans for transforming Randolph House into the sort of place that offers real hospitality to our veterans and their families.

MARTHA: Oh, that's wonderful, Mr. Garfield. I wish we could help too.

MRS. VAN HOLDEN: You have already helped, my dear, just by staying here tonight. I think you and your husband are the most distinguished guests this house has known since the days of that other George and Martha.

GEORGE: Thank you, Mrs. Van Holden. (*Baby cries.*)

MRS. VAN HOLDEN (*As she exits*): My gracious! The milk.

MR. GARFIELD: One of the first things we'll have to do is to get out a new folder for Randolph House.

MRS. VAN HOLDEN (*Entering with baby's bottle*): And this time be sure to include this information.... The Washingtons slept here. (*The* WASHINGTONS *bow to the rest of the cast who return the salute as the curtains close.*)

THE END

PRODUCTION NOTES

The Washingtons Slept Here

Characters: 2 male; 4 female; extras.

Playing Time: 30 minutes.

Costumes: Nancy and Saralee are in Colonial costumes. And all other characters are dressed in everyday clothes.

Properties: Baby carriage, two suitcases, baby doll, two capes, umbrellas for Mr. and Mrs. Washington and Mr. Garfield, baby's bottle.

Setting: The furnishings include a desk, several chairs, a table with a Guest Book and folders, and an umbrella stand full of wet umbrellas. Pictures of George and Martha Washington hang in a conspicuous place.

Lighting: The scene can be made very attractive by using period furniture and lighting the stage with candles.

NOTHING TO WEAR

Characters

PHILIP JOHNSON ⎫
HILDA JOHNSON ⎬ *soft-hearted parents.*
RUTH JOHNSON, *the oldest daughter.*
ELLEN JOHNSON, *the teen-ager.*
JERRY JOHNSON, *college freshman.*
MRS. PALMER, *Sunday school superintendent.*

SCENE: *The Johnsons' living room.*

TIME: *The day before Easter.*

NOTHING TO WEAR

SETTING: *The Johnsons' living room.*

AT RISE: MRS. JOHNSON *is modeling her new Easter suit and hat for her husband's appreciative eye. On the table is an open suit box containing* MR. JOHNSON'S *new suit and draped over a chair is his overcoat.*

MRS. JOHNSON: Now tell me the truth, Phil. Do you really like it?

MR. JOHNSON: Like it? I'll say I do. It's a knockout.

MRS. JOHNSON (*Anxiously*): And you don't think this hat is a little too...

MR. JOHNSON: A little too what?

MRS. JOHNSON: A little too youthful.

MR. JOHNSON: Nonsense, Hilda. You're hardly the age to be wearing one of those little black bonnets such as my grandmother used to wear. Besides, there's no such thing as age when it comes to ladies' hats.

MRS. JOHNSON: I guess you're right! But this does make me feel awfully frivolous.

MR. JOHNSON: That's just how an Easter bonnet should make you feel. Yes, ma'am, Mrs. Johnson, you look mighty nifty in the whole outfit.

MRS. JOHNSON: I can hardly believe it. Everything new from heels to head. Shoes, stockings, suit, gloves, bag, hat...even this lovely fur neckpiece. I feel more like Cinderella than anyone else.

MR. JOHNSON: You deserve every bit of it, my dear. As they

391

say in the song, "I'll be the proudest fellow in the Easter Parade" when we step out together tomorrow.

MRS. JOHNSON: You'll look pretty smart yourself, if I'm any judge. (*Holding overcoat for him*) Here, try this on again so I can admire you. (*As* MR. JOHNSON *puts on coat*) There! It really does have a beautiful fit across the shoulders. (*Taking his arm and striking a pose*) Maybe we should have our pictures taken, bride and groom style.

MR. JOHNSON: I'm game. To hear all this fuss we're making over these new clothes, anybody would think we never had anything new.

MRS. JOHNSON: Well, it's been a long, long time, I can tell you. I don't believe we've had a complete set of glad-rags like this since the children were little.

MR. JOHNSON: By the time we outfitted Jerry and got Ruthie and Ellen fixed up our budget was always plumb busted. Well, this year it's our turn and I must say we've done all right by ourselves.

MRS. JOHNSON: And the children are as pleased as we are. Ruth bought me some perfume and Ellen gave me a new hanky. I thought it was sweet of them.

MR. JOHNSON: They're pretty good kids.

MRS. JOHNSON: Ellen decided she'd have her old suit cleaned and pressed this year. She's taken a sudden interest in saving money. Ruth has bought her entire spring outfit herself, although she says she isn't going to wear a stitch of it until Ralph comes back from California.

MR. JOHNSON: Then she'll be celebrating Easter around July or August.

MRS. JOHNSON: I wouldn't be surprised. Although he might cut his trip short.

MR. JOHNSON: Well, I might as well remove my finery and go down to the station to meet Jerry. He's due on the 4:15.

MRS. JOHNSON: I hope the train's on time. I can hardly wait to see him. I'll bet he's grown since he was home for Christmas vacation. Are you taking the car?

MR. JOHNSON: No, I'll walk. I need the exercise. If he's loaded down with baggage we'll taxi back.

MRS. JOHNSON: I better shed my fine feathers too in favor of something more practical. Jerry will probably want something to eat as soon as he arrives. You can just leave your new overcoat here, Phil. I'll take them upstairs when I go up. (*As* PHIL *exits*) And don't forget your Easter date with your best girl.

MR. JOHNSON: Not a chance. Not a chance. (*Exit.*)

MRS. JOHNSON (*Looking at herself in mirror*): I wish there were a mirror in this house that would be big enough to give me the whole effect at one time. Oh, dear! I wonder if this hat isn't on the silly side after all? (RUTH *enters in a flurry of excitement. She is wearing a coat which conceals the rest of her costume. This is necessary for a quick change which must be made later and can be affected by removal of the coat.*)

RUTH: Oh, Mother! Mother! You'll never guess what's happened! (*She grabs her mother in a violent hug.*)

MRS. JOHNSON: Oh my goodness! Ruth, be careful! You almost knocked the breath out of me. Watch out for my new suit. Look out for my new hat! You'll ruin the veil! What on earth has come over you?

RUTH: It's Ralph! He's home. Oh, Mother, I'm so excited. Isn't it simply **super**?

MRS. JOHNSON: Ralph? Home? Are you sure? When did you hear?

RUTH: He called me at the office just a few minutes ago. I stopped everything and ran. Mr. Jenkins said it would be all right. Oh, Mother, he wants me to drive up to Spring City and meet his family. Do you think I can make it in time for dinner?

MRS. JOHNSON: Of course you can make it. Dad's gone to meet Jerry but he didn't take the car. Let's not waste any time. I'll help you dress. Aren't you glad you have everything ready? I suppose you'll be wearing your new outfit? (RUTH *stops dead as a sudden thought strikes her.*)

RUTH: Mother! How perfectly awful! My hat!

MRS. JOHNSON: Your hat? What about it?

RUTH: I have none. I can't possibly wear that old brown felt and my spring hat from last year is green. It would look fierce with that blue suit. That lovely blue one I ordered from Miss DeLaine won't be in for another week at least. Oh dear! I never dreamed Ralph would get here for Easter. Now I just can't wear my new suit at all.

MRS. JOHNSON: Sure you can.

RUTH: Not without a hat!

MRS. JOHNSON: Of course not... *with a hat.*

RUTH: Where would I get one at this late date?

MRS. JOHNSON (*Removing her own hat*): What's the matter with this little number? It will match your suit perfectly.

RUTH: Oh, I couldn't take yours.

MRS. JOHNSON: Why not? It's too young for me anyhow. Try it on. (*Puts hat on* RUTH.) It looks sweet on you. (*Pushes her to mirror.*) There, see for yourself.

RUTH (*Admiring herself*): Oh, Mother, it's simply adorable. I love it...but...

MRS. JOHNSON: It's perfect. What more do you want? Now, come along. We have no time for arguments.

RUTH (*Still protesting about the hat as they exit*): But, Mother, it isn't fair to take your new hat before you even get a chance to wear it yourself. I feel like a selfish pig. Really, Mother...I shouldn't do it...

MRS. JOHNSON: Nonsense. Go get dressed. (*They exit. There is a short pause and then* JERRY *enters. He carries a traveling bag.*)

JERRY: Hy'a, everybody. Surprise! Surprise! (*Looks around and sees no one in the room*) This is a fine welcome when the wandering boy comes home from school ahead of schedule. I thought they'd all be on deck to meet me. (*As he sets down his suitcase he sees the new overcoat and the suit box.*) Aha! Looks as if they've been doing some Easter shopping for their son and heir. (*Reads the clothing store label from the box*) Hmmmm Gregory Brothers! Some class! This must be my reward for being a good boy. Well, I guess I'll have to have a look-see and find out if it's the latest model. (*Opens suit box and takes out coat which should be a fairly sporty tweed or plaid*) Oh boy! Some class! Pretty sporty number! Guess I'll try it on. (*Tries on the coat to the suit and finds it a good fit*) Very neat, I'd say! Very neat indeed! In fact, I might say the Old Man has pretty good taste. Takes after me in that respect. Like son, like father, I always say. (*Holds up trousers to measure the length*) Just my size. Won't even have to have 'em altered. (*Sees overcoat*) Say, they have gone all out for their wayward boy! An overcoat too. (*Slips on the overcoat.*) This is really swell. Gosh! I really do have a couple of swell parents. When Elaine sees me in this outfit she'll be so dazzled she'll forget I didn't send her an orchid. Golly! I'll have to dash upstairs and put on the whole works. Then I can give the folks a real surprise when I descend upon them at supper. (*Picks up his own bag, and the suit box.*) I'll go up the back stairs so I won't run into any of the family if they should be home. Now that I've gone this far, I might as well make it a complete surprise. (*As* JERRY *exits from one side of the stage,* RUTH *and* MRS. JOHNSON *enter from the other. Ruth is wearing her new suit and her mother's hat. She carries a small overnight bag.*

MRS. JOHNSON *carries the fur neckpiece which she was wearing at the beginning of the play.*)

MRS. JOHNSON: Now, listen to me, Ruth, and don't argue. I want you to wear this neckpiece. It's just what that suit needs to give it an air.

RUTH: Oh, Mother, you're hopeless! Didn't anybody ever warn you about spoiling your children?

MRS. JOHNSON: It's too late now. If they're spoiled, they're spoiled. But you're going to wear this neckpiece just the same. I know you want to look your best for Ralph.

RUTH: Maybe I'll look so wonderful, he won't even know me.

MRS. JOHNSON: Small danger of that. Now, there...(*As* RUTH *puts on the neckpiece*) That's perfect. I must say you look pretty as a picture, even if you are my child. Now, do be careful, dear. The traffic will be heavy.

RUTH: I will, Mother. And you've been wonderful. When Jerry comes, tell him I said hello and I'll see him tomorrow.

MRS. JOHNSON: I'll go out to the garage with you and back the car out. That starter has been acting up lately. You might have trouble.

RUTH: I'll keep my fingers crossed. I wouldn't want anything to hold me up now. (*Exit* RUTH *and her mother as* JERRY *enters from opposite side. He is fully arrayed in his father's clothes.*)

JERRY: Still no family! Well, I guess I'll have to contact the girl friend! (*At phone*) 7-9-6-3 Please. (*Pause*) Hello, Sweetness! (*Pause*) Oh, excuse me! Hello, Mrs. Craley. Yes, this is Jerry. How did you guess? Yes, I just got home a few minutes ago. Is Elaine around there any place? Yes, I would like to talk to her. Thanks a lot. (*Pause*) Hy'a, there, beautiful! Sure...sure...I'm fine. I just got in. Got a ride all the way from State. How's for comin' over? When? Right now. When do you think? I'm a sight for your gorgeous blue eyes. Wait till you get a load of the new outfit the family bought me. I guess they thought I rated a coming-home present. O.K. No, I won't stay long...just long enough to date you up for tonight. What do you mean... you got another date? You can't do that to a College Freshman. Well...we'll settle that when I come over. I'll give it my personal attention. So long...I'll be right over... 'Bye. (*Hangs up and starts to exit.*) Huh! When she sees this razzle-dazzle outfit, she'll give me top billing for the rest of the vacation. I feel like an advertisement of what the well-dressed lad-about-town is wearing. (*Starts to exit, then pauses.*) Maybe I should leave a note for my missing parents. Nope! Serves 'em right for missing me. I'll drop in on 'em at supper time. (*Exit.*)

MRS. JOHNSON (*Re-enters*) : Well, I must say my Easter outfit is somewhat depleted. Phil will probably be disgusted but my dark blue felt will have to do and the rest of me looks all right. He'll understand. I'll take his things upstairs and change before supper. (*Discovers that the overcoat and suit are gone.*) Well, for heaven's sake! Where are they? I'm positive he left them right there. I certainly didn't take them upstairs when I went to help Ruth. And he went straight out the front door... (ELLEN *enters carrying a long bag from the Dry Cleaner's.*)

ELLEN: Hello, Mother! I just got my suit from the Jiff-Job-Cleaners.

MRS. JOHNSON (*In disappointment*) : Oh, Ellen! What in the world made you take your suit there? I thought you'd leave it at our regular Press-Right Place in the Square.

ELLEN: I should pay a dollar and a quarter when the Jiffy Job does it for sixty-nine cents! Nothing doing. Little Ellen's watching her pennies from now on. I want to have some real dough when our class goes to Washington next month.

MRS. JOHNSON: But...Ellen...that Jiffy Job place...

ELLEN (*Opening bag and taking out suit*): Just look how nice and clean it is! It looks just as good as any of my dresses that were cleaned at the other place. And just think... this was only sixty-nine cents!

MRS. JOHNSON: It's a fine idea to try to save money, Ellen, but sometimes it pays to spend a little more and get better quality. After all, we get what we pay for.

ELLEN: Well...I just thought I'd try the Jiffy Cleaners. Doris Decker told me about them. She says they're swell.

MRS. JOHNSON: Maybe so...but...

ELLEN: But what?

MRS. JOHNSON: I hate to mention it, dear, but doesn't your suit look smaller to you? I know you think I am a regular Calamity Jane but it looks to me as if it had shrunk.

ELLEN: Oh, how awful! If it should shrink even the least bit, I'll never be able to wear it. It fit me like the paper on the wall last year. Oh, my gosh! I'd better try on the coat. (*Tries on coat which is hopelessly small. The sleeves are ridiculously short and it won't meet in the front.*

MRS. JOHNSON: Oh, Ellen, you poor child! It's miles too little.

ELLEN (*In tears*): They've ruined it, that's what they've done. Oh, Mother, what'll I do? Now I don't have a single decent thing to wear tomorrow. Not a thing! And the Collins girls invited me out to their house after church. They always look like a picture out of a fashion magazine.

MRS. JOHNSON: Don't cry, dear. We'll figure out something.

ELLEN: Can't you let out a few darts here and there to give me some extra room?

MRS. JOHNSON: It would take more than a dart to fix this coat. Take it off, dear, and forget about it until after Easter. Then you can try on the skirt and I'll see if I can rip the seams and let down the hem. Maybe I can make you a bolero jacket out of the coat.

ELLEN: But what about tomorrow? Oh, Mother, Bill Collins will be home from college, and I always did have a yen for that boy. He never noticed me last year but I thought this year maybe I could make an impression on him. Now I don't have a chance. Oh, Mother, he's strictly fatal. All the girls are out of their minds about him.

MRS. JOHNSON: And does that include you?

ELLEN: It sure does. I thought I could get him to the point of asking me to the Monday Hop but I'll never stand a chance now.

MRS. JOHNSON: While there's life there's hope. (*Takes off her jacket.*) Here, try this. You always did look better in blue than any other color.

ELLEN: But, Mother, this is your brand new suit. You were going to wear it to church tomorrow.

MRS. JOHNSON: I can go to church just as well in my old gray suit. Gray is always good for spring.

ELLEN: You should know. You've been wearing it every spring since I can remember.

MRS. JOHNSON: Oh, it's not that bad. Now come along, and try on the rest of the outfit. You might as well take the shoes and gloves. They won't be much good to me now. We'll have to hurry. Jerry will be arriving any minute and you know how it is when he's in the house. (*Exit.* MR. JOHNSON *enters shortly after* ELLEN *and* MRS. JOHNSON *leave the stage. He is in a bad humor.*)

MR. JOHNSON: I never knew it to fail! When a train is on time the person you've gone to meet isn't on it. (*Calling*) Hilda! Hilda! Where are you? (*Crosses stage and calls louder.*) Hilda, are you upstairs?

MRS. JOHNSON (*Off stage*): Is that you, Phil? Did Jerry come?

MR. JOHNSON: No. He wasn't on the train. I thought you

might have had some word from him? Any wire or phone call?

Mrs. Johnson: Not a thing. Maybe you'd better phone the school.

Mr. Johnson: Phone the school nothing! I'll not spend money to find that he was just fiddling around and missed the train. (*To himself*) Confound that boy! He's always late for everything. I wonder if he did change his plans at the last minute. Maybe there's something in the late afternoon mail. (*Calling*) Hilda, did you see if there was any mail?

Mrs. Johnson: No, I didn't. I don't know if the postman stopped or not. Better look in the box.

Mr. Johnson (*Exits quickly and re-enters with letter.*): Here it is...a letter from State. Looks official too. Maybe he's in some sort of trouble and can't come home for the holidays. (*Reads letter. His face brightens.*) Well, I'll be doggoned! A chip off the old block. (*Calling*) Hilda, come on down here. I just got a letter from the Dean.

Mrs. Johnson (*Enters wearing a housecoat*): A letter from the Dean! Oh, my goodness! Has Jerry been expelled?

Mr. Johnson: Nothing of the sort! He's made the Dean's list! Here, read it for yourself.

Mrs. Johnson (*Reading letter*): Oh, Phil! Isn't that wonderful! Of course, I always knew Jerry was smart, but I've been so worried that he wouldn't apply himself. He must have been studying hard to rate marks like these.

Mr. Johnson: That's really something to make the Dean's list this early in his Freshman year. And he's never peeped about what kind of grades he's been getting.

Mrs. Johnson: It seems to be the style to act as stupid as possible. I had no idea he was making a record like this for himself. Oh, Phil, aren't you proud of him?

Mr. Johnson: Proud? I can feel myself beaming from ear to

ear. I can hardly wait to show him this letter. Which reminds me...where do you suppose he is?

MRS. JOHNSON: When is the next train?

MR. JOHNSON: Sometime around six, I believe. We'll wait till then, and if he doesn't arrive, I'll phone the school. By Jove! My son on the Dean's list! I guess we Johnsons are pretty smart guys!

ELLEN (*Entering in her mother's suit*): I'll say we Johnsons are pretty smart guys! How do I look?

MR. JOHNSON: Ellen Johnson! That's your mother's suit. You march right upstairs and take it off. I'm not having any clothes snatching in this house.

ELLEN: But, Daddy...

MRS. JOHNSON: Easy, Phil. We've had a catastrophe. Ellen's suit was ruined at the cleaner's and she simply must have something to wear tomorrow.

MR. JOHNSON: Let her wear Ruth's new suit. She's not wearing yours.

MRS. JOHNSON: Ruth's new suit is another story, dear. She's gone up to Spring City to meet Ralph and his parents.

MR. JOHNSON: Ralph? When did he get home?

MRS. JOHNSON: Just this afternoon and Ruth was all in a dither. She wanted to wear her new suit...and was all upset because her blue hat hadn't come so...

MR. JOHNSON: Don't tell me. I can guess the rest. Your new hat is on its way to Spring City.

MRS. JOHNSON: I'm afraid you're right. After all, Phil, clothes mean so much to young girls.

MR. JOHNSON: And what about you? You were tickled pink with that new outfit!

ELLEN: That's what I told her, Daddy. I honestly didn't want to take it. But it does look neat, doesn't it?

Mr. Johnson: Of course it does, but not half as neat as it looked on your mother. I don't like it. I don't like it at all.

Mrs. Johnson: Oh, Phil, you'd have done the same thing yourself. Ellen, run upstairs and take off the suit. You'll have to help me with supper. Hang it in your closet and be sure you hang the skirt straight so it doesn't wrinkle.

Ellen: O.K., Moms. (*Exit.*)

Mrs. Johnson: Don't fuss with her, Phil. She's invited out tomorrow and she wants to make an impression on some boy.

Mr. Johnson: So what? You and I were going to make an impression on each other. You talked me into getting that whole new suit and overcoat...so we could step out together in style. Now I'll be all dressed up and you'll have to wear your old clothes. It's a shame.

Mrs. Johnson: I know...but ...well...after all...I guess parents are just a bunch of softies.

Mr. Johnson: Not me...I'd like to see myself handing over my clothes before I even wear them myself. That's the way you mothers spoil kids. (*At this point in the conversation* Jerry *enters in all the splendor of his father's new suit and overcoat.*)

Jerry: Hy'a there, Old Timers! I'd just about given you up for lost!

Mrs. Johnson: Jerry!

Mr. Johnson: Well, I'll be doggoned! Where did you come from? (*There is a burst of greetings all around.*)

Mrs. Johnson: Oh, Jerry, we were beginning to worry about you!

Mr. Johnson: Did you miss the train?

Jerry: Train? No train for me. I had better luck hitch-hiking. I got here a long time ago but no one was home so I skipped over to see Elaine...but first I got myself dressed up in the new outfit. Thanks a million, Dad. It was swell of you. I was wondering all the way home what I'd wear tomorrow. My clothes are a sad sight.

MRS. JOHNSON: Your clothes?

MR. JOHNSON: What on earth are you babbling about? (*Suddenly realizing that* JERRY *is wearing his suit*) Say...what goes on here?

MRS. JOHNSON: Jerry Johnson, where did you get those clothes?

JERRY: Gee whiz! I just got done thanking you for them. Golly, I sure got a surprise when I walked in here and saw this whole lay-out. I knew right away they were for me. This is the kind of stuff I always go for...and trust you and Dad to remember. They just fit too. (*As he turns around to show off the fit,* MRS. JOHNSON *starts to protest to her husband, but he silences her with a look and gesture.*)

MRS. JOHNSON: Phil...tell him he's...

MR. JOHNSON: Sh! Hilda...(*Clearing his throat*) You look fine, Jerry. You surely do fill out that coat.

JERRY: How did you know my exact size? I've grown a lot since you saw me at Christmas.

MR. JOHNSON: Well...I tried them on before I bought them. Apparently, we wear the same size now.

MRS. JOHNSON: Phil, aren't you going to tell him?

JERRY: Tell me what?

MR. JOHNSON: Your mother wants me to tell you why we went in for such an extravagant Easter present. Did you know you make the Dean's list?

JERRY: The Dean's list? Holy Jumpin'! Gee whiz! (*Sits down quickly.*) Are you kidding?

MR. JOHNSON: Not a bit of it. The letter came today. And we're mighty proud of you, son.

MRS. JOHNSON: We certainly are, dear. You deserve a lot of credit.

JERRY: Well, thanks...but golly...well...I'm as surprised as you are. That trigonometry had me sunk for a while but I must have made out better than I thought. And I sure made out O.K. with you. These clothes are a sensation...a real knock-out.

MRS. JOHNSON: I agree with you. (*With a look at* MR. JOHNSON.)

JERRY: But I'm afraid they must have set you back plenty. Are you sure the family budget can stand all this?

MR. JOHNSON: Oh, I guess so. Your mother was just telling me as you came in that parents are just a bunch of softies at heart.

JERRY: I guess you're right...but I like 'em that way. Say, where's the rest of the family?

MRS. JOHNSON: Ruth's gone to meet Ralph and his family at Spring City.

JERRY: Gee, that's great. I had no idea he'd be home so soon. I bet she's in a tailspin.

MRS. JOHNSON: They'll be back tomorrow. Ellen is upstairs.

JERRY: I'll have to dash up and see her. (*Yelling to* ELLEN) Look out above...I'm coming up...(*Exit.*)

MRS. JOHNSON: Philip Johnson, I could wring your neck. The very idea of giving your whole new outfit to that boy!

MR. JOHNSON: Oh, Hilda, for heaven's sake. How could I tell him it wasn't for him when he thought we had bought him an Easter present? Besides, a boy doesn't get on the Dean's list every day in the year. This was a special occasion.

MRS. JOHNSON: Softie!

MR. JOHNSON: Softie yourself! (*They both laugh.*)

MRS. JOHNSON: We're a fine pair, we are. I don't know which is the worse.

MR. JOHNSON: Well, he did look like a million dollars, didn't he?

Mrs. Johnson: You and I will look like the poor relations when we go to church tomorrow morning.

Mr. Johnson: For once I can understand how you women feel when you moan about having nothing to wear.

Mrs. Johnson: And for once it's pretty near the truth. That gray suit of mine is on its last legs.

Mr. Johnson: Well...this suit has certainly seen its best days.

Mrs. Johnson: Oh well...nobody will look at us anyhow. (*Doorbell*) Now who in the world could that be? You answer the door, dear.... I'll slip up the back stairs and change into something more presentable.

Mrs. Palmer (*Off stage*): Yoo-hoo! Anybody home? (*Enters carrying an extra large suit box.*) Oh, there you are! The front door was open, so I just walked right in.

Mrs. Johnson: Oh, good afternoon, Mrs. Palmer.

Mr. Johnson: How do you do, Mrs. Palmer. Won't you sit down?

Mrs. Palmer: Oh, no, thanks. I just came from the church. We've been having the most awful time with the Easter Party for the Primary Department. Practically everything has gone wrong. I've been working over there all afternoon. The jelly beans were late in arriving and the grass for the baskets never came till after three o'clock.

Mrs. Johnson: Oh, that's too bad. I can imagine things were pretty hectic.

Mr. Johnson: But I guess you have everything under control by now.

Mrs. Palmer: That's just where you're wrong. Haven't you heard about Mr. and Mrs. Morse?

Mrs. Johnson: Why, no. Is anything wrong?

Mrs. Palmer: They've been quarantined. One of the children has scarlet fever.

Mr. Johnson: That's bad.

MRS. PALMER: Bad? It's terrific. They were going to be Papa and Mamma Rabbit at the Easter party. I just knew we had to do something right away, so the minute I heard it, I just grabbed up the costumes and tore right over here to ask you and Mrs. Johnson. (*Opening suit box*)

MRS. JOHNSON: To ask us what?

MRS. PALMER: To ask you to take their places. You're just about their size...and I know how interested you are...

MR. JOHNSON: Oh, no, no, Mrs. Palmer...we couldn't possibly. (MRS. PALMER *takes out a white flannel Bunny suit and holds it up to the protesting* MR. JOHNSON.)

MRS. PALMER: See...it would just fit. And the mask is too cute for anything.

MRS. JOHNSON (*Starting to laugh*): Oh, Mrs. Palmer, I don't see how we could possibly do it for you. I'd like to help you out but...

MRS. PALMER: Then I'll count on you. Honestly, it's just terrible to get anybody to help these days...and I knew you could wear the suits.

MR. JOHNSON: But we can't...that is...well...we just can't. Hilda, tell her we can't...

MRS. JOHNSON: Well...Oh, Phil, maybe we could help. We used to play Papa and Mamma Rabbit years ago when the children were little.

MRS. PALMER: That's sweet of you, Mrs. Johnson. I always said you and Mr. Johnson were the most cooperative parents in the church. Aren't the costumes adorable?

MRS. JOHNSON: They *are* cute. Well, Phil, I'm game if you are. What do you say?

MR. JOHNSON: What do I say? Why put it on me?

MRS. PALMER: Oh you will say yes, won't you, Mr. Johnson? Please?

MR. JOHNSON: Well...Oh, my gosh...what else can I say?

All right. I'll do it.

MRS. PALMER: Oh, that's perfectly wonderful. Just come over to the Sunday school room about eight-thirty. You'll make much better Rabbits than the Morses.

MR. JOHNSON: I'm afraid you flatter us.

MRS. PALMER: No, indeed. I mean every word of it. Well, I must fly. But thanks a million. I'll try to help you out sometime.

MRS. JOHNSON: I'm sure you will, Mrs. Palmer.

MRS. PALMER: Don't forget. Eight-thirty sharp...in costume.

MR. JOHNSON (*Moaning*): In costume!

MRS. JOHNSON: You can count on us.

MRS. PALMER: Well, thanks again...and good-bye. (MRS. PALMER *exits as* MRS. JOHNSON *walks to door with her.*)

MRS. JOHNSON: Good-bye, Mrs. Palmer.

MR. JOHNSON (*Holding up his Bunny suit in disgust*): So now I wind up in the Easter Parade as the Papa Rabbit!

MRS. JOHNSON (*Laughing*): Oh, Phil...we'll have new Easter outfits after all. (*Holds her costume up to her.*)

MR. JOHNSON (*Laughing*): And how! Well, at least now we both have something to wear. (*The curtain closes with the* JOHNSONS *laughing as they try on their Easter Bunny masks.*)

THE END

PRODUCTION NOTES

Nothing To Wear

Characters: 2 male; 4 female.

Playing Time: 35 minutes.

Costumes: Everyday modern clothes. At the opening of the play, Mrs. Johnson is dressed in a new outfit — blue suit, blue hat with veil, fur neckpiece, etc. She later changes into a housecoat. At her entrance, Ruth wears a coat under which she wears her new suit. During the action of the play, Jerry changes his clothes for the new suit and overcoat intended for his father. Ellen later changes into her mother's suit.

Properties: Suit box containing new suit, new overcoat, Mrs. Johnson's shoes and gloves, traveling bag, overnight bag, cleaner's paper bag containing suit which must be too small for Ellen, letter, extra large suit box, white flannel Bunny suits, Easter bunny masks.

Setting: A modern American living room. The room is comfortably furnished with easy chairs, occasional tables and lamps, a sofa, etc.

Lighting: None required.

A SURPRISE FOR MOTHER

Characters

MR. FOGEL, *a photographer.*
MISS BLAKE, *his assistant.*
BARBARA STANDISH, *the sixteen-year-old.*
RITA *and* RICKY, *the junior high twins.*
MR. STANDISH, *with an allergy for photos.*
MRS. STANDISH, *who gets the surprise.*

SCENE: *A photographer's studio.*

TIME: *A few days before Mother's Day.*

A SURPRISE FOR MOTHER

SETTING: *A photographer's studio.*

AT RISE: *Sixteen-year-old* BARBARA STANDISH *is posing for her photograph in* MR. FOGEL'S *studio. Wearing a toothpaste smile, she is seated center stage on an imitation marble bench.* MR. FOGEL *is constantly appearing and disappearing amid the folds of black cloth which conceal his tripod-mounted camera.* MISS BLAKE *busies herself adjusting* BARBARA'S *dress, tilting her head, smoothing her hair, and arranging the various screens and lights.*

MISS BLAKE: Now tilt your head a trifle, Miss Standish. Just a little more to the right. Not too far. Now a bit to the left. Hold it. How's that, Mr. Fogel?

MR. FOGEL (*From under the black cloth*): A little higher, please.

BARBARA: Are my hands all right? I do hope the lace on my hankie shows. It's Mother's best one and she'll get a laugh out of seeing it in the picture.

MISS BLAKE: Mr. Fogel uses only the most expensive equipment, and this camera has a very powerful lens. It won't miss a trick.

BARBARA: Well, it can miss the freckles on my nose and I'll not complain.

MISS BLAKE: Now just look straight ahead, smile your prettiest, and I think we'll have a lovely picture. Don't you agree, Mr. Fogel?

MR. FOGEL (*Crawling out from under the curtain*): Yes, yes, yes, indeed. Now don't move, Miss. (*Holds camera bulb in*

411

his right hand and raises his left to catch BARBARA'S *eye.*)
Look right at my hand. Steady now —

BARBARA: Oh, dear me! I believe I'm going to sneeze.

MISS BLAKE: Oh, please, please! Not just now. Wait! (*Runs to* BARBARA *and presses her finger against her upper lip.*)
Hold your breath till I count ten. (*Counts.*) There! Is everything under control?

BARBARA: I — I think so. Yes, I'm sure. Thanks a lot. (*Smiles.*) I'm ready.

MR. FOGEL: Eyes this way. That's it. Good! Steady, now. 1-2-3-4-5. There. That's it.

MISS BLAKE: Shall we try a profile now?

MR. FOGEL: Yes, I think that would be fine. (*Crawls under the curtain.*)

BARBARA: I'm afraid my nose turns up too much for a side view.

MISS BLAKE: Not at all. And your hair is a nice length for a profile. Now — tilt your chin a bit higher. That's it....
A little more. There. How do you like that, Mr. Fogel?

MR. FOGEL (*From under the curtain*): Lower the chin.

BARBARA (*Dropping her chin almost to her chest:*) This way?

MISS BLAKE: No, no. That's too much. (*Raising* BARBARA'S *chin with her hand.*) Say when, Mr. Fogel.

MR. FOGEL: There. Stop. That's just right. (*Crawls out.*)
Now hold that, young lady.

BARBARA: I feel as if I'm getting a stiff neck. Better hurry.

MR. FOGEL: Move that screen a bit to the right, Miss Blake.

MISS BLAKE (*Moving screen*): This will throw a lovely shadow on her neck.

BARBARA (*Giggling*): I hope Mother doesn't mistake it for dirt.

MR. FOGEL: There! That's perfect. Steady, now. (*Hand on bulb*) Here we go. 1-2-3-4-5. There. We're all finished.

BARBARA: What a relief!

MISS BLAKE: Was it as bad as all that?

BARBARA: Oh, it wasn't so terrible. But I had forgotten what an ordeal this picture-taking business really is. You see, I haven't had mine taken since I was five. Oh, I've had lots of snapshots, but somehow Mother and Dad never seemed to think my face was worth spending any money on.

MISS BLAKE: Well, I'm sure your young man will not agree with that.

BARBARA: What young man?

MISS BLAKE: Why the young man who gets this picture. Aren't you having it made for someone pretty special?

BARBARA: I'll say I am. But it's not a young man. It's Mother. And will she be surprised!

MISS BLAKE: Oh, I see — a Mother's Day gift?

MR. FOGEL: And a very wise choice, my dear, a very wise choice.

BARBARA: That's what I thought. You see our whole family is camera-shy. Mother has been trying for years to lure one of us into a photographer's studio, but we always escaped in time. But this year — oh, I don't know, I just thought I'd break down and surprise her. I haven't told a living soul either. Dad and the twins would faint if they knew. But there's something about Mother's Day that makes you want to put yourself out a bit.

MISS BLAKE: I certainly hope you will be pleased with the proofs.

BARBARA: I'm dying to see them. When will they be ready?

MR. FOGEL: Not for a day or two. Maybe Wednesday.

BARBARA: That will be fine. I'll stop on my way home from school.

MR. FOGEL: We'll have them ready for you. I'll take these plates down now. (*Exits.*)

MISS BLAKE: We have some very nice frames too, Miss Standish.

BARBARA: I'd love to see them, but I guess I'll have to take mine in a folder. It's kept me busy squeezing my allowance this far. I'll never be able to afford a frame.

MISS BLAKE: I'm sure we could find one to fit your pocketbook.

BARBARA: I'll go and change, and then I'll have a look at them. It would be nice to see myself in a frame, and Mother might like it for her desk.

MISS BLAKE: I'll get them ready for you to look at when you've finished dressing. (BARBARA *exits left.*) Poor child! Spending all her money on a Mother's Day gift! (*Looking in desk*). Now where did I put those cheap frames?

MR. FOGEL (*Re-entering*): Did you sell the young lady a frame, Miss Blake?

MISS BLAKE: I'm going to show her some before she leaves.

MR. FOGEL: Be sure to show her that five-ninety-eight number in silver with the antique finish.

MISS BLAKE: Five ninety-eight! One-fifty is more her speed.

MR. FOGEL: But she'll want the best for Mother's Day.

MISS BLAKE: Mother's Day! Mother's Day! Just another day for the merchants to ring up more sales. That kid can't afford the picture itself to say nothing of a five-ninety-eight frame.

MR. FOGEL: It's your business to make her think she can afford it. Tell her nothing's too good for her mother and she'll buy it right off.

MISS BLAKE: Why, Mr. Fogel! I'd be ashamed!

MR. FOGEL (*Shrugging his shoulders*): Business is business. You got to learn how to give a sales talk, Miss Blake.

MISS BLAKE: Well, maybe I could sell her a two-dollar frame.

MR. FOGEL: I'm sure you could, if you put your mind on it. And by the way, Miss Blake, what are you going to give *your* mother for Mother's Day?

Miss Blake: Nothing.

Mr. Fogel: What? No candy? No flowers? No pretty hankies? No perfume?

Miss Blake: No, sir. Nothing. I don't believe in Mother's Day. I just think it's a scheme to sell more merchandise to the public.

Mr. Fogel: You better not let anyone hear you say you don't believe in Mother's Day, Miss Blake. You might just as well say you don't believe in Christmas or birthdays.

Miss Blake: I guess it does sound terrible, but I'll give my mother presents some other time. (*Bell rings offstage.*)

Mr. Fogel: There's the bell. Business is picking up. (*Steps to right entrance.*) Right this way, Miss. What can we do for you (Rita Standish *enters. She is a very business-like seventh-grader.*)

Rita: I want to know how much it will cost to have a picture taken.

Mr. Fogel: Well now, that just depends. Suppose you sit down here and talk it over with Miss Blake. I have some things to 'tend to downstairs. When you come to a decision, just call me and we'll take care of you right away.

Rita: Thank you very much. (Mr. Fogel *exits left.*)

Miss Blake (*Sitting at desk and offering* Rita *a chair*): Now, what did you have in mind?

Rita: Oh, just a picture — a picture of me, of course. You see, I want it for a surprise for my mother, for Mother's Day. I don't have much money — just a dollar seventy-five to be exact, but if that isn't enough maybe I can get some more by the end of the week. The Kelleys always go out Friday nights and I can take care of their baby for fifty cents.

Miss Blake: But if we wait till the week-end, I'm afraid we won't have your picture finished in time. I think we can give you a very nice photograph in a neat folder for your price.

Did you want more than one?

RITA: Oh, no! One is plenty. Mother is the only person in the world who'd want one. Ricky would kill himself laughing if I'd offer him one and —

MISS BLAKE: Who's Ricky, if I may ask?

RITA: Ricky Standish — he's my twin brother.

MISS BLAKE: So your name is Standish.

RITA: Yes, isn't it awful? I sometimes wish either Miles Standish or I had never been born on account of the way I'm always being teased about it. But that's my name all right.

MISS BLAKE: So you're planning this surprise for your mother all by yourself?

RITA: Yes, you see I've always given Mother something dumb for Mother's Day and this year — well, I'd like to give her something special. So when I saw that "ad" in the paper (*Pointing to sign on desk*), why, it sort of gave me an idea.

MISS BLAKE: Doesn't anyone else in your family know?

RITA: I should say not. If you'd live in our house for a while, you'd learn to keep a secret. I'm not telling a soul till I spring that big surprise next Sunday. Ricky would think I was trying to be a movie star or something and Barbara — Well, she's got all the looks in the family, so she could never understand why anybody would want my picture — except maybe for a comic valentine.

MISS BLAKE: Don't you want us to take your picture right away?

RITA: The sooner the better before I lose my nerve.

MISS BLAKE: Oh, it won't require any amount of nerve. You'll want to take off your coat and hat and fix your hair a bit. I'll show you to a dressing room where you can make yourself beautiful, and we'll call you when we're ready.

RITA: Thank you very much, but there's not a whole lot I can do about making myself beautiful.

MISS BLAKE: You'll do very nicely as you are, but you'll feel better if you take time to primp a bit. This way, dear. (*She steers* RITA *off left just as* BARBARA *comes on right.*)

BARBARA (*Fumbling in her purse*): I do hope I can find a frame to fit my budget or make my budget fit the frame. I'd hate to ask Mother for money to help pay for her present, and Dad — I don't know about Dad.

MISS BLAKE (*Re-entering*): Now let's see what we can find in the way of frames. (*Opening desk drawer*) Here's a lovely one for five-ninety-eight.

BARBARA: It might just as well be a hundred and ninety-eight.

MISS BLAKE: It's really a lovely little frame for the money.

BARBARA: It is very pretty, but isn't there something less expensive?

MISS BLAKE: Oh, yes, we have them at all prices. Here is one for three-seventy-five.

BARBARA: That's still out of my class. Is there nothing around a dollar?

MISS BLAKE: No, but we have one for a dollar and a half.

MR. FOGEL (*Entering*): Oh, my dear Miss Blake, Miss Standish wouldn't want *that* frame! Why, it would spoil the whole effect. That beautiful dress she was wearing demands quality in a frame. Otherwise the whole thing will look cheap.

BARBARA: Oh, I wouldn't want it to look cheap.

MR. FOGEL: Of course not. Did you show her the silver frame, Miss Blake?

MISS BLAKE: Yes, I did but she —

MR. FOGEL: Now this is just the thing, Miss Standish. Did I hear you say the picture is for your mother?

BARBARA: Yes, it is, but five-ninety-eight —

MR. FOGEL: Five-ninety-eight — that's a real bargain. And it's absolutely perfect for your picture. Your mother would surely be delighted with such a gift.

BARBARA: Oh, she'd love it but — well — I just don't have five dollars and ninety-eight cents.

MR. FOGEL: Is this the last of this number we have in stock, Miss Blake?

MISS BLAKE: I believe it is, sir.

MR. FOGEL: Well, I know how it is with young ladies who are trying to buy something nice for their mothers. They want the best, and we can't blame them. Tell you what I'll do. I'll let you have this for five dollars straight.

BARBARA: You will? Oh, that's wonderful, Mr. Fogel! You hold it for me, and I'll run down to Daddy's office and see if he'll lend me the money. I'll be back before closing time. Will you hold it for me?

MR. FOGEL: Sure I will. And don't hurry. We'll keep it for you.

BARBARA: Thanks a million. I'll be right back. (BARBARA *exits right.*)

MR. FOGEL: See that, Miss Blake? That's salesmanship.

MISS BLAKE: That's what *you* call it. Oh, my goodness, I almost forgot! We have another member of the Standish family in there. Little Rita Standish has decided to surprise her mother, too. She has exactly one dollar and seventy-five cents, so please don't bring up the question of frames. And don't tell her that her sister was just here. This is a family secret.

MR. FOGEL: All right, Miss Blake. Bring the little lady in and we'll take her picture — and her dollar seventy-five.

MISS BLAKE (*Calling off left*): We're ready, Miss Standish.

RITA (*Enters left*): Gosh, that's the first time anybody called me Miss Standish. For a minute I couldn't think who you meant.

MR. FOGEL: So you're our next customer.

RITA: Next patient is what I feel like. You sound just like my dentist when he calls "next."

MISS BLAKE: Oh, you'll enjoy this a lot more than a visit to the dentist.

RITA: I'm not so sure. I feel nervous....

MR. FOGEL (*Disappearing under curtain*): Nothing to be nervous about here, young lady. This is a perfectly painless ordeal.

MISS BLAKE: Would you like the full figure or just the head and shoulders?

RITA: Does full figure cost more?

MISS BLAKE: Oh, no, they are the same price.

RITA: Then I'd like all of me. Mother's used to seeing me all in one piece. Besides these are my first long stockings and I'm wearing a pair of Barbie's open-toed shoes so I'd like to get everything in.

MISS BLAKE (*Placing her center stage. She poses* RITA *with her hand on a chair*): There. How's that?

RITA: Terrible. I feel as if I'm going to recite or be shot.

MISS BLAKE: You're safe enough from both those evils, thank goodness. Now just relax and smile.

RITA: Oh, must I smile?

MISS BLAKE: Don't you want to?

RITA: Not unless it's absolutely necessary. Dad says I look exactly like my Great-Aunt Abigail when I smile, and she has three double chins.

MISS BLAKE: Then I should say your Dad was exaggerating just the least bit.

RITA: I think so, too, but I'd better stay on the safe side and look intelligent.

MISS BLAKE: All right. Just stand still and look straight ahead. Are you ready, Mr. Fogel?

MR. FOGEL (*Coming out from under the cloth*): Ready and waiting. If the young lady will watch my hand, we'll be finished in a jiffy. (*Holding bulb*) Ready — 1-2-3-4-5. That does the trick. Would you like to try another pose?

RITA: Oh, no, thank you! This one is plenty. I'd look the same, no matter how many you'd take. When will it be finished?

MISS BLAKE: We'll have the proof ready for you on Wednesday.

RITA: That will be fine. Shall I pay for it now?

MR. FOGEL: Don't you want to wait for the finished product?

RITA: I'd rather pay now before I spend the money for something else.

MISS BLAKE: Do you want me to keep it for you?

RITA: It would be a load off my mind. Mother says money slips through my fingers like melted butter.

MR. FOGEL: I'm sure she'll approve of this purchase. Would you like to look at some frames?

MISS BLAKE: I don't think she'd be interested, Mr. Fogel. And if she is, we can talk about it when she comes for her proofs.

MR. FOGEL: Very well. Do we have any other appointments for this afternoon?

MISS BLAKE: No, not a one. Perhaps you can work on those other plates. (*Desk 'phone rings.*)

RITA: I guess I'll be on my way. See you Wednesday.

MISS BLAKE: One minute, please. I'll want you to sign the order slip. (*Answering 'phone*) Hello — Fogel's Studio — Yes. This afternoon? One moment, please. Why, yes, I believe we can take you. What is the name, please? What? Standish? S-t-a-n-d-i-s-h? Mr. Peter Standish? Very well, sir. We'll expect you in half an hour. Mr. Fogel can take care of you. Thank you very much, Mr. Standish. Good-bye.

RITA: Mr. Standish! Why, that's my daddy. Is he coming here?

MISS BLAKE: It looks that way.

RITA: What on earth would he be doing here?

MISS BLAKE: Maybe he is planning a surprise for your mother, too.

RITA (*Laughing*) If he is, that will be the biggest surprise of Mother's life. She can never get him near a camera. He says he's allergic to them. Claims he breaks out in a rash if he gets too close to one.

MISS BLAKE: Then he's due for a bad case of measles at four o'clock.

RITA: I'd better get out of here. He won't want to see me, and I won't want to see him. Where's that paper you want me to sign?

MISS BLAKE (*Doorbell rings*): Right here. You sign on the dotted line. Excuse me, please. Someone has just come in. (*Exit* MISS BLAKE. *As* RITA *is signing, we can hear* MISS BLAKE *talking to the new customer in the next room.*)

MISS BLAKE: Good afternoon.

RICKY: How do you do — I mean — Good afternoon. Is this where you get your pictures taken?

RITA (*Registering excitement as she recognizes her brother's voice*): Why, that's Ricky!

MISS BLAKE: Yes, it is.

RICKY: Could you take mine?

MISS BLAKE: Are you in a hurry?

RICKY: Yes, kind of. I'd like to be taken right now.

MISS BLAKE: One minute, please. I'll find out. (*Re-enters.*) Business is certainly brisk.

RITA: Say, do you know who that is?

MISS BLAKE: It's a little boy, but I didn't ask him his name.

RITA: You don't need to ask. I'll tell you. That's my brother Ricky. What does he want?

MISS BLAKE: He wants his picture taken — right away, too. I'm just going to call Mr. Fogel.

RITA: I wouldn't miss this for a circus. Do you mind if I wait? I mean, in the dressing-room? I'll be as quiet as a mouse. He'll never know I'm there.

Miss Blake: I'm sure I don't mind, and I don't think the young gentleman will be needing the dressing room. He seems to be in costume.

Rita: In costume? I don't understand.

Miss Blake: He's wearing a baseball suit, and he's brought his bat with him. Now you get out of here if you want to wait. We'll have to rush to finish him before your father gets here.

Rita: This is a riot! Don't you dare tell him I've been here.

Miss Blake: You can trust me with all your family secrets. (*Calling*) Mr. Fogel! Can you come here a minute, please? (Rita *exits as* Mr. Fogel *enters.*) Believe it or not, we have two more Standishes. One at four o'clock and one right now in the waiting-room. Can we manage?

Mr. Fogel: I think so, if they're not too fussy.

Miss Blake: This is the masculine side of the house, so there won't be much primping.

Mr. Fogel: O.K. I'll get ready for them. (*Disappears under camera cloth.*)

Miss Blake (*At doorway*): You can come in now. Mr. Fogel will be ready in a few minutes. (*Enter* Ricky *in full baseball uniform carrying a bat.*)

Ricky: Will it take long?

Miss Blake: Only a few minutes. What is the name, please?

Ricky: Richard Standish. Ricky for short.

Miss Blake: What size picture would you like?

Ricky: Oh, I dunno. Whatever size you're giving away for these soap coupons. (*Digs in his pocket and produces a handful of paper coupons.*)

Miss Blake: Soap coupons? What do you mean?

Ricky: Just what it says here on the wrapper — "Free Portrait Photo for twenty-four Rosy-Glo Soap Wrappers."

Miss Blake: But I don't understand.

Ricky: I sold two dozen cakes of that soap and got the people to save me the wrappers just so I could have this picture taken for Mother for Mother's Day present.

MISS BLAKE: There must be some mistake. Mr. Fogel, you'd better have a look at this.

MR. FOGEL (*Emerging*): What's all this about soap wrappers?

MISS BLAKE (*Handing him the wrappers*): This young man has made a collection of these and offers them in exchange for his photograph.

RICKY: Just like it says on the wrapper. Free for 24, and I got 24.

MR. FOGEL: There must be some mistake, my boy. They're not good here.

RICKY: You mean I can't get my picture taken with these?

MR. FOGEL: I'm afraid not, sonny.

RICKY: After selling all that soap, I still can't get a picture.

MISS BLAKE: It does seem too bad.

RICKY: Too bad? It's a gyp, that's what it is. And that picture was for my Mom. Now I won't have any Mother's Day present for her.

MISS BLAKE: Perhaps Mr. Fogel could make some special arrangement with you. (*Very sweetly*) Couldn't you, MR. FOGEL?

MR. FOGEL: I don't see what arrangements I could make.

MISS BLAKE: Well, I do. I tell you what, Ricky, you go in the other room and wait a few minutes. I think Mr. Fogel might be able to use those coupons after all.

RICKY: Gosh, I sure hope so. I don't want to give Mom bath salts again this year. She has a whole cupboard full now. (*Exit.*)

MISS BLAKE: We can't disappoint that little boy. After all, we have done a pretty good business with the Standish family today. Please, Mr. Fogel, take Ricky's picture. You can collect the money out of my salary, if you wish.

Mr. Fogel: But I thought you had no time for Mother's Day, Miss Blake.

Miss Blake: Maybe I haven't. But I can't bear to see him disappointed, after he worked so hard to sell all that soap. Please, Mr. Fogel, have a heart!

Mr. Fogel: What do you mean, "Have a heart"? I've got a perfectly good heart, even if it is a little soft in spots. Bring in your little Babe Ruth and we'll see if he breaks the camera. (*Goes under camera cloth.*)

Miss Blake: That's sweet of you, Mr. Fogel. Thanks a lot. (*Calling*) Come on back, Ricky. Mr. Fogel says it's a deal. He'll take the coupons.

Ricky: Golly! What a relief! Thanks, Mister. Say, where did he go?

Miss Blake: He's fixing the camera. Now you stand right over there and get into whatever position you think will be most effective.

Ricky (*Assuming a batting posture*): How's this?

Miss Blake: Fine. Can you hold still?

Ricky: Sure. Just tell me when you're ready.

Mr. Fogel (*Holding up his hand*): Ready. Don't move a muscle. 1-2-3-4-5. There. Now you are preserved for the future.

Ricky: Phew! I'm sure glad. Mom will like this picture, I know. You see she missed seeing me play, the day I made a home run for the Swamp Cats, so this is a real souvenir.

Mr. Fogel: It ought to be a success.

Miss Blake: Come around Wednesday afternoon for your proof.

Ricky: What's that?

Mr.. Fogel: That's your unfinished picture. Sort of a sample. (*Exit.*)

Ricky: Okel-dokel. I'll be seeing you.

Miss Blake: Before you go, just sign here. This is your official order blank. (*As* Ricky *signs, the outside doorbell rings and before* Miss Blake *can answer it,* Barbara *enters.*)

Barbara: Oh, Miss Blake, I hurried over to tell you I can't find Dad anywhere! He's not at the office and — Why, for Heaven's sake! Ricky Standish! What are you doing here?

Ricky: What's it look like? I'm signing my name.

Barbara: But why? And why are you downtown in that horrid baseball suit? Mother would have a fit.

Ricky: She would not. I wore it specially for her, and she'll like it. So there!

Barbara (*Looking over his shoulder*): An order blank? Ricky, don't tell me you've had your picture taken.

Ricky: I'm not telling you — you're telling me.

Barbara: But did you, honest, Ricky?

Ricky: What if I did? Can't a guy get his picture taken without telling the whole world?

Barbara: Ricky, this is a joke on both of us. I had mine taken, too.

Ricky: You did?

Barbara: I sure did. It's a surprise for Mother's Day.

Ricky: Now it'll be a double surprise. Won't Rita be sore when she finds it out? She'll wish she had thought of it, too.

Rita (*Entering from dressing room*): So you two think you're pretty smart, don't you? Well, just ask Miss Blake whose picture Mr. Fogel took right before you came in.

Both: You mean — you, too?

Rita (*Laughing*): Me, too. Now it's a triple surprise.

Barbara: Poor Mother. Last year she got nothing but bath salts, and this year it's all pictures.

Rita: And that's not the worst. Guess who's coming at four. Show 'em your appointment book, Miss Blake.

MISS BLAKE (*Showing book*): None other than Mr. Peter Standish.

BARBARA: Not Dad!

RICKY: This is a family reunion.

BARBARA: If Dad's coming here, I'll try to melt him down for that five dollars.

RITA: If we all wait we can ride home with him.

RICKY: If I know Pop, he won't want us for an audience. He'll get all fussed up.

RITA: You're right, Ricky. (*Doorbell*) Let's scram. There he is!

BARBARA: Back to the dressing room, kids. Quick, make it snappy.

MISS BLAKE (*At door*): This way, please, Mr. Standish.

MR. STANDISH: I hope I haven't kept you waiting.

MISS BLAKE: Not at all. Our last customer just left. Mr. Fogel should be here in a minute. I'll ring for him. (*Presses buzzer on desk.*)

MR. STANDISH (*Pointing to sign on desk*): That advertising should bring you plenty of customers. Gosh! I was stuck for an idea of what to give my wife for Mother's Day till I saw your ad in the paper. Then, thinks I, that's the very thing. Emily, that's my wife, is the darndest person for family sentiment I ever saw. And when Jim, that's our oldest boy, left for college last fall, she just couldn't get over the fact that we didn't have a recent picture of him, and he didn't have any of us. So here I am ready for the great sacrifice. I'll have two made — one for Mother's Day, and I'll save the other one for Jim on Father's Day.

MISS BLAKE: That's a lovely idea, Mr. Standish. (*Presses buzzer.*) I wonder what can be keeping Mr. Fogel. Oh, here he is now!

MR. FOGEL: Good afternoon, sir. Sorry to keep you waiting.

I'm afraid we have complications. There's been a little mistake. It seems we have scheduled someone else for four o'clock.

MISS BLAKE: But I don't understand. There's no one listed in the book.

MR. FOGEL: Indeed, it is most embarrassing. But I just met the janitor on the stairs, and he told me about it. It seems he was in here this noon while the studio was officially closed, and the 'phone rang. Pete never likes to see us lose any business, so he answered. It was a lady asking for a four o'clock appointment. Pete glanced at our book, saw the hour was free and signed her up. Only he forgot to enter her name in the book.

MISS BLAKE: That surely is a mixup. Did he get the lady's name at all?

MR. FOGEL: Yes, it's a Mrs. Peter Standish.

MR. STANDISH: Holy Smokes!

MISS BLAKE: Mrs. Standish!

MR. STANDISH: I must get out of here.

MR. FOGEL: What's up?

MISS BLAKE: Don't you understand? This is Mr. Standish. He came to surprise his wife. Now it looks as if the surprise is going to come off too soon. (*Doorbell rings.*) Oh, dear! That must be Mrs. Standish now.

MR. STANDISH: Couldn't I wait somewhere till she goes away? Isn't there a dressing room?

MR. FOGEL: Sure. Right this way.

MISS BLAKE: No, no. He can't go in there.

MR. FOGEL: Why not?

MISS BLAKE: Because it's full of children. His children!

MR. STANDISH: *My* children! Why, what does this mean? Why did they come here?

MISS BLAKE: For the very same reason that you did, Mr.

Standish. Apparently this picture-taking idea is an epidemic in your family.

MR. STANDISH: But my wife! She'll find out and our surprise will be ruined.

MR. FOGEL: Maybe you better retreat to the dressing-room after all and seek refuge with the others. Miss Blake, you talk with Mrs. Standish while I show this gentleman to our little hide-out. (*Exit* MISS BLAKE *right as the two men go left.*)

MR. STANDISH: Yes, yes. My goodness! This *is* a surprise.

MISS BLAKE (*Re-enters immediately with* MRS. STANDISH, *who carries a small dressing case*): We've had a busy day, Mrs. Standish. Everybody seems possessed with the idea to have pictures made for Mother's Day.

MRS. STANDISH: And I'm no exception. I decided this year to give my family gifts on Mother's Day. They are always so good to me that I figured I'd surprise each of them with my photograph.

MISS BLAKE: Then you'll want a half dozen, I suppose.

MRS. STANDISH: How did you guess? There are four children and I couldn't forget Mr. Standish. That makes five, and I'll use the sixth one for my own mother.

MISS BLAKE: Six surprises is a big order.

MRS. STANDISH: Now if you'll just show me the way to the dressing-room I'll change into something more attractive.

MISS BLAKE: Oh — er — well — yes, but — well, I'm sorry, but you'll have to excuse us. The dressing room is in use right now. (*With cries of "Surprise! Surprise!" The children and* MR. STANDISH *rush on stage,* MR. FOGEL *in their midst.* MRS. STANDISH *is flabbergasted and keeps saying, "What on earth? How in the world? What does this mean?" Everyone talks at once. Finally* RICKY *gets the floor.*)

RICKY: We have too many surprise packages in this family, Mom.

RITA: We've all had our pictures taken.

BARBARA: All but poor Dad and he hasn't had a chance.

MR. STANDISH: But it's my turn, now. What do you say, Emily, that we make this a family affair and have a group picture taken of the whole outfit?

MRS. STANDISH: I'd say that was the best Mother's Day present in the whole world. And we can send one to Jim.

BARBARA: It sure will be a saving on frames.

MR. FOGEL: I have some beauties for family groups.

MISS BLAKE: I think I can arrange you so you'll make a beautiful picture.

MR. FOGEL: I'll get everything set. (*Dives under the black cloth.*)

MISS BLAKE: Now, Mrs. Standish, since you are the center of interest, we'll put you here and group the others around you. (*Arranges family in attractive grouping.*)

MOTHER: I feel like a queen, surrounded by her faithful subjects.

MR. STANDISH: I feel more like one of the three Stooges.

RITA: There must be safety in numbers. I'm not a bit scared now.

BARBARA: Somebody better look to see if Mr. Fogel has died under that blackout curtain.

MR. FOGEL (*Emerging*): You'll find me a pretty lively corpse. Now let's make this the grand finale. 1-2-3-4-5. Presto! The job is done.

MISS BLAKE: You all looked beautiful and nobody moved.

FATHER: Is it safe to move now?

MR. FOGEL: Company — dismissed! Now about your proofs—

CHILDREN: We know — they'll be ready on Wednesday.

MRS. STANDISH: I'm afraid we've been an awful lot of trouble.

MR. FOGEL: Not at all. I wish all families were like yours.

RICKY: Not a chance, Mister. There's only one Mom and Pop like ours.

RITA: Good-bye, everybody. See you on Wednesday and those pictures better be good.

BARBARA: And I'll come along and pick out a really expensive frame, now that Dad is going to foot the bill. (*All exit laughing and calling, "Good-bye."*)

MISS BLAKE: You know, Mr. Fogel, that was fun, wasn't it, working with that family. They were all so sincere. They really and truly wanted to please their mother and do something special for her.

MR. FOGEL: Sure thing. She appreciated it too. She's a lucky woman to have such a thoughtful bunch of kids and a husband who believes in Mother's Day.

MISS BLAKE: You know, there's something I'd like to ask you, but I'm afraid you'll laugh.

MR. FOGEL: No, I won't. Honest! Go ahead.

MISS BLAKE: Remember that speech I made a while ago about not believing in Mother's Day?

MR. FOGEL: Yeah, I remember.

MISS BLAKE: Well, I've changed my mind. I think it's a sweet idea, and I want to send *my* mother something too. She lives a thousand miles from here, but I'd like her to know I'm thinking of her.

MR. FOGEL: Why, that's great. I still don't see anything to laugh at.

MISS BLAKE: I'm coming to that part now. If you're not too tired, would you mind taking my picture? I think she'd like that best of all.

MR. FOGEL: Laugh? Why, I should say not. I'll take your picture right away...on one condition.

MISS BLAKE: And what's that?

MR. FOGEL: On condition that as soon as we're finished, you'll take mine. After all, I have a mother too — and though you might not agree with her — my face is *her* idea of beauty.

MISS BLAKE (*Laughing*): Why, Mr. Fogel, this is going to be fun. You take me and I'll take you. —

MR. FOGEL: And no knife could cut our Mother's Day Greeting in two. (*Both laugh.*) How's that for poetry?

MISS BLAKE: You're a better photographer than a poet.

MR. FOGEL: Now get ready while I do my disappearing act. (*Goes under the curtain.* MISS BLAKE *settles herself center stage for picture.*)

MISS BLAKE: When we're finished with this, no one can say we don't practice what we preach.

MR. FOGEL: You're right, Miss Blake. (*As he comes out from under curtain*) And now if you'll tilt your head a little higher, no, a little lower, a bit to the right, just a trifle to the left. (*Curtains close as* MISS BLAKE *tries to follow all these directions.*)

THE END

PRODUCTION NOTES

A Surprise For Mother

Characters: 3 male; 4 female.

Playing Time: 40 minutes.

Costumes: Mr. Fogel may wear a smock or regular business suit. Mr. Standish wears a business suit. Barbara wears a dressy party dress. Miss Blake is clothed in a simple black work dress. Ricky appears in a baseball suit and carries a bat. Rita may wear a simple frock.

Properties: Telephone; appointment book; a tripod on which there is supposedly mounted a camera covered with a large black cloth; slips of paper; pencil, frames; rubber bulb attached to camera; pieces of paper for coupons for Ricky; small dressing case; purse for Barbara.

Setting: A typical photographer's studio. There is a camera or what may pass for one at one side. In the center is an imitation marble bench on which customers sit when having their pictures taken. Behind this are a few screens. The camera is covered with a black cloth. On a desk right stage are a telephone, appointment book, and sign reading, "Give Your Mother Your Picture on Mother's Day." There is a chair in front of the desk and a chair or two around the room. There is also a buzzer which can be rung from the desk.

Lighting: None required.